THE STUDENT'S TECHNOLOGY OF BREADMAKING AND FLOUR CONFECTIONERY

THE STUDENT'S TECHNOLOGY OF

Breadmaking and Flour Confectionery

by

WILFRED JAMES FANCE

F. Inst. B.B.

Head of Bakery Department
1964
Rush Green College
of Further Education,
Romford, Essex

President, Institute of British Bakers
1954–5

Member of
Education Committee
National Board for Bakery Education
1952–9

Member of
Advisory Committee for Bakery Subjects
City and Guilds of London Institute
1950-1967

Chairman
Association of Bakery Teachers
1964–66

ROUTLEDGE AND KEGAN PAUL

London, Henley and Boston

First published 1960
by Routledge & Kegan Paul Ltd
39 Store Street, London WC1E 7DD and
Broadway House, Newtown Road, Henley-on-Thames, Oxon RG9 1EN
and 9 Park Street, Boston, Mass. 02108, USA
Second edition (revised) 1966
Reprinted 1969, 1972, 1976 and 1978
Reprinted and First Published
as a Paperback in 1981
Printed in Great Britain by
St Edmundsbury Press
Bury St Edmunds, Suffolk

ISBN 0 7100 1363 9 (c)
ISBN 0 7100 9046 3 (p)

THIS BOOK IS DEDICATED
TO THE MEMORY OF

CHARLES H. R. JARVIS, F.S.S.

Late Secretary—National Board for Bakery Education and the National Joint Apprenticeship Council for the Baking Industry. One of the Architects of Present-day Bakery Education

CONTENTS

FIGURES

PART ONE: Breadmaking and Fermented Goods

PART TWO: **Flour Confectionery**

PLATES

PART ONE: **Breadmaking and Fermented Goods**

PART TWO: **Flour Confectionery**

ACKNOWLEDGEMENTS

ANY new textbook must rest on the sum total of knowledge at the time of writing. Knowledge is culled from many sources, from books and publications; from lecturers and demonstrators; from personal endeavour and hard experience when the results of trial and error etch themselves sharply on the memory.

My introduction to the delights and mysteries of baking was in my father's little bakery, where as an apprentice I learned to mix cake batters by hand and to develop my strength in the making of hand-made doughs, to fire and scuffle a side-flue oven and to set and draw bread with a peel. It was my father who instilled into his sons the value of systematic thought and the application of it to creative work. I acknowledge the value of the hard training given by my father and his help and wisdom.

A series of articles written by myself under the heading 'Bakery Classroom' received the accolade of publication in the *Bakers' Review* and it was the Editor, Ronald Sheppard, who suggested that I might follow his example and become an author, for he and his colleague, Edward Newton, had just had published *The Story of Bread.* I join them with this book and would thank Mr. Sheppard for permission to use the articles, for the loan of many photographs and for the courteous help that he has always extended to me.

During the fret and strain of writing and compilation, the wonderful kindness and co-operation that I have received from individuals and firms have acted as a balm and made all effort seem well worth while.

My thanks to Dr. A. J. Amos, B.Sc., F.R.I.C., for his help and advice on the subject of Physical Methods of Dough Testing and for his permission to make a précis of a series of articles on the subject published in *The Baker*. For permission to use the articles, I must thank the Editor, Peter Macnab, F.Inst.B.B. (Hon.); also for his kindness in reading part of the typescript of this book and for the loan of many photographs.

I have to thank that great fountain-head of bakery knowledge, the late W. E. Spencer, M.B.E., F.Inst.B.B., not only for his assistance in compiling this volume, but also for the advice and assistance given so freely over many years. To A. T. Corless, F.Inst.B.B., A.R.S.H., of the National Bakery School, London, for permission to use charts and for data on the subject of Hygiene and Freda Redfearn, B.Sc., M.Inst. Biology, South-East Essex Technical College, for assistance on the subject of Nutrition, I extend my thanks.

To my friend and colleague of the Commerce Department of the South-East Essex Technical College, Iorwerth Williams., M.Sc., my thanks for his assistance with economic geography and for his map of the Wheatlands of the World, and to Paul Gough, of John Renshaw & Co., Ltd., Mitcham, for the use of the very fine photograph (Plate XXX) and for his vetting of the subject-matter on Almonds and Almond Products. I should also like to thank my daughter Margery, for her patient reading of the typescript and for her advice on the use of the English language.

One would have to use panegyrics to try and record the great assistance given by firms and their specialist staffs in the compilation of this volume. I must thank Baker Perkins Ltd., Peterborough; Cox Ovenbuilders, Ltd., Leamington Spa and G. & R. Gilbert Ltd., Wallington, for the provision of data and photographs of ovens. I must also extend thanks to Robinson Ltd., Rochdale, and Henry Simon Ltd., Stockport, for their ready help with photographs of dough-testing apparatus and graphs of dough tests. I acknowledge also the kind assistance of Advita Ltd., London; the Director and the specialist staff of the Service Bakery of Craigmillar & British Creameries Ltd., London; Thomas Hedley & Co. Ltd., Newcastle-upon-Tyne, for their kind permission to use data from their publication *Freezing and Storage of Baked Products*, and to J. B. H. Thomas, F.Inst.B.B., of Thomas Hedley, for his ready assistance; to E. E. F. Colam, of the Milk Marketing Board, and to S. Hume, F.Inst.B.B., of Polak & Schwarz Ltd., London, for his assistance on the subject of Food Colours and Flavours.

Finally my thanks to the many persons who have, at one time or another, made contributions, directly or indirectly, to the store of knowledge, without which this volume could not have been written.

W. J. FANCE

Barking,
Essex

FOREWORD

by Lt. Col. E. J. Neal, M.B.E., F.Inst.B.B.

MR. W. J. Fance is a teacher with many years' experience of the baking industry. In his book he has produced a work which should be of great assistance to hundreds of students who are hoping to make a career in the baking industry.

In one volume he has covered comprehensively the making of both bread and flour confectionery. The result is a textbook which is certain to provide essential reading for the bakers of the future.

There is a great need for well-trained young people to enter the baking industry, and I am convinced that this well-illustrated and informative book will be of the utmost value both to those who are receiving their training in our various bakery schools, as well as to apprentices.

As Secretary of the National Board for Bakery Education I am delighted to commend *The Student's Technology of Breadmaking and Flour Confectionery* to all those young people, as well as to those master bakers and their staffs who would welcome a first-rate book of reference dealing with all aspects of their craft.

INTRODUCTION

THIS is a technical age. More and more is it becoming necessary not only to be a good craftsman, but also a good technician. The old system of learning by trial and error and long painstaking practice has largely passed. The path is shorter now; the bakery schools, textbooks, trade journals and bulletins, together with the very fine work of the British Baking Industries Research Association and other research and demonstration services, all make it easier for the ambitious bakery student to get to the top of his chosen profession.

Although the path to knowledge is easier, there is no excuse for complacency; with the passage of the years new materials and techniques have been introduced, and a much wider compass of knowledge is required to meet the new conditions.

The craftsman today has to know not only how to use his hands; the background to his knowledge must be such that he will know why he does certain things and for what purpose. There is a satisfaction in this knowledge, because it gives a fillip to the creative urge in man. Knowledge of the sources and processing of raw materials; the interactions during manipulation and baking, give a greater awareness of the possibilities inherent in creative work. Because of this knowledge, each task becomes an object of research and the hands and brain become attuned to a greater accuracy. The habit of thinking and reaching conclusions is wholly satisfying and makes for happiness not only as an individual, but as knowledge is extended, as a citizen. A new sense of responsibility is born and the dignity and prestige of the individual and the industry is raised.

It may be argued that, in this mechanized age, creative skill and the necessity for creative work will become less and less. Nevertheless it is only those with a complete knowledge of their craft who can hope to retain effective control of the machine and to subordinate it to the service of man and so help to make a future in which he may be free to live a full and complete life. The power of knowledge is still greater than the power of the machine.

This book is intended as a guide for those who wish to study the technology of Breadmaking and Flour Confectionery, in particular the apprentice, and those studying on a part-time basis. It is hoped also that it will assist the part-time bakery teacher whose work is so valuable in bakery education.

INTRODUCTION

The subject matter of the book is based on the syllabuses compiled and approved by the Association of Bakery Teachers, to cover a course of study leading to the Basic Bakery and Advanced Craft Certificates of the City and Guilds of London Institute. Much will be of value also to those studying for the Technicians Certificate.

The volume is divided into two sections under the headings, Breadmaking and Fermented Goods and Flour Confectionery. Each section is further sub-divided into chapters the sub-headings of which correspond to the lectures arranged in the syllabuses. In this way continuity is effected, the subject-matter so arranged that study can proceed progressively, step by step until the end is reached. Inevitably this may lead to some repetition, but this will be in accord with established teaching practice when the important links in a course of study can only be forged by the hammer blows of repetitive emphasis.

Information on Bakery Law is readily obtainable in the form of booklets from H.M. Stationery Office and can easily be kept up-to-date by additional publications as and when they become available. Bakery machinery and equipment—ovens excepted—are not dealt with fully because design and construction is inevitably in constant change. Students and teachers are advised to study the excellent illustrated brochures provided by the leading manufacturers, who are at all times pleased to give advice and assistance to those engaged in education.

Mechanical dough testing was an item on the old Breadmaking Final syllabus which has been discontinued. The subject, however, is of special benefit to the student anxious to study for the Technician's Certificate.

The writer has drawn on the sum total of technical and practical knowledge at the time of writing and freely acknowledges the debt owing to his teachers at the National Bakery School, London, during his student days; to the authors of the many fine textbooks both old and new; to the work of the British Baking Industries Research Association; the service bakeries and the technologists and demonstrators who give so freely of their specialist knowledge, and to the bakery journals for the publication of up-to-date knowledge.

It is important, however, for the student to be ready for constant revision of his notes, and to seek at all times to add to his store of knowledge as a result of the introduction of new materials, techniques and scientific discoveries and as a result also of his own thinking and experiment.

PART ONE

Breadmaking and Fermented Goods

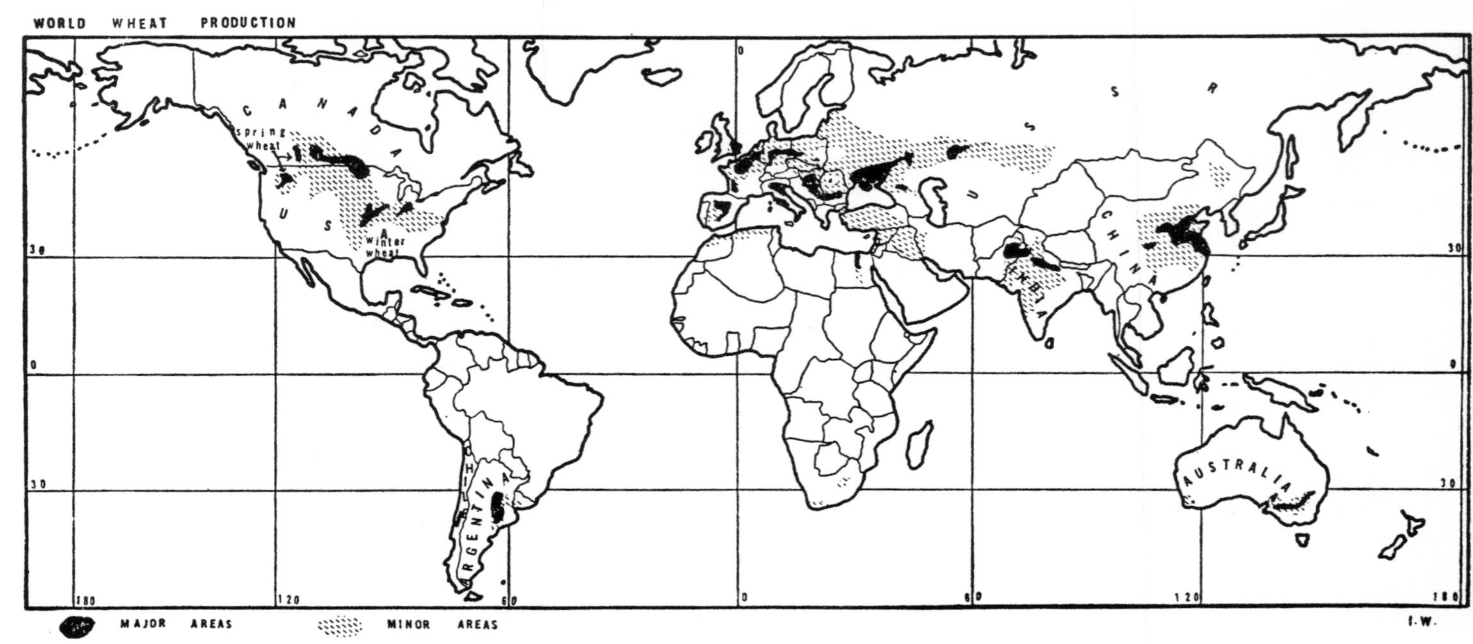

Map of the World's Wheatlands.

1

Food Hygiene; The First Mixing; Calculation of Water Temperature; Calculation of Yeast Quantities; Salt: Usage in Bread and Fermented Goods; Some Experiments; Water: Usage and the Effects of Temperature

FOOD HYGIENE

THERE is one subject common to all manufacturing activity in the baking industry and that is hygiene.

From the educational viewpoint, it is considered quite wrong to give greater emphasis to one subject at the possible expense of all others. The author makes no apology for emphasizing this subject by placing it first. There can be no craftsmanship in the baking industry without cleanliness and a sense of responsibility to other people.

Food poisoning is due to contamination by certain bacteria, or it may occur from the use of unsuitable metal containers where acids may form harmful salts. It can be caused by foods containing toxins (which are poisonous products produced by the action of bacteria) or foods already infected by, or inoculated with, pathogenic bacteria.

The natural hosts of many of these bacteria are man and certain animals. In man the common reservoirs are the nose and skin, for toxin-producing bacteria, and the bowel from which bacteria causing such diseases as typhoid, para-typhoid and gastro-enteritis and dysentery may be transmitted by human carriers. The animal sources could be meat, milk and eggs, which may already be infected, and food such as milk and eggs that may have been soiled by excreta, or foods contaminated by rodents and insects.

Food poisoning occurs only if the bacteria present can multiply. This requires four factors: suitable food, time, temperature and moisture. If any one of these factors is absent bacterial growth will not occur, The effects of time and temperature are shown in Figs. 1 and 2.

In general, foods which will not be heated immediately before use

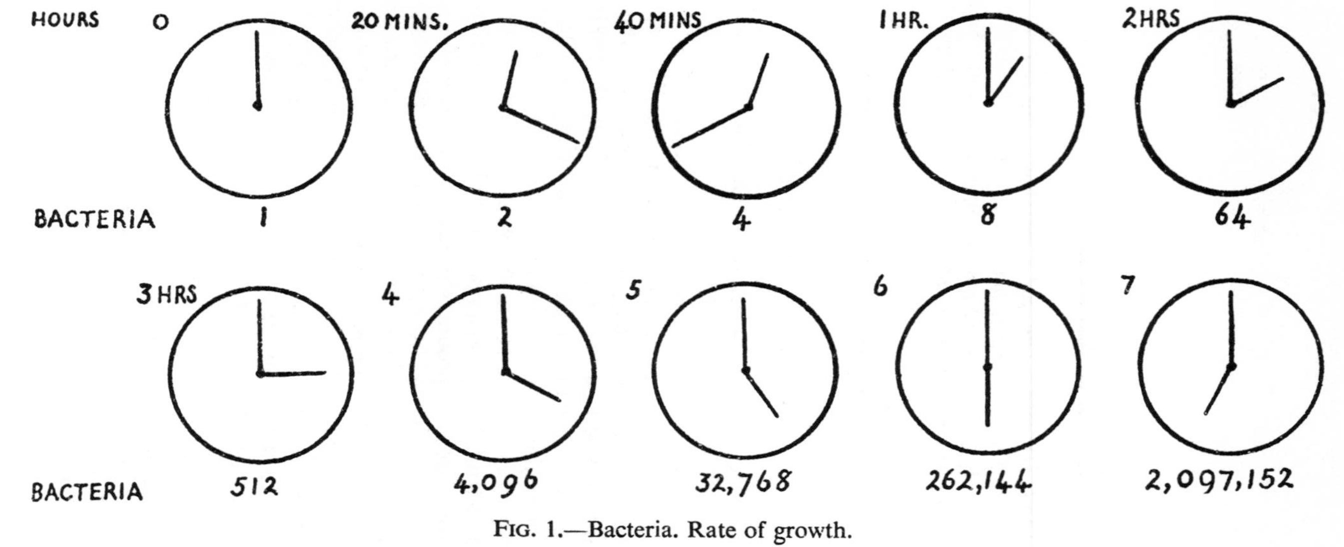

FIG. 1.—Bacteria. Rate of growth.

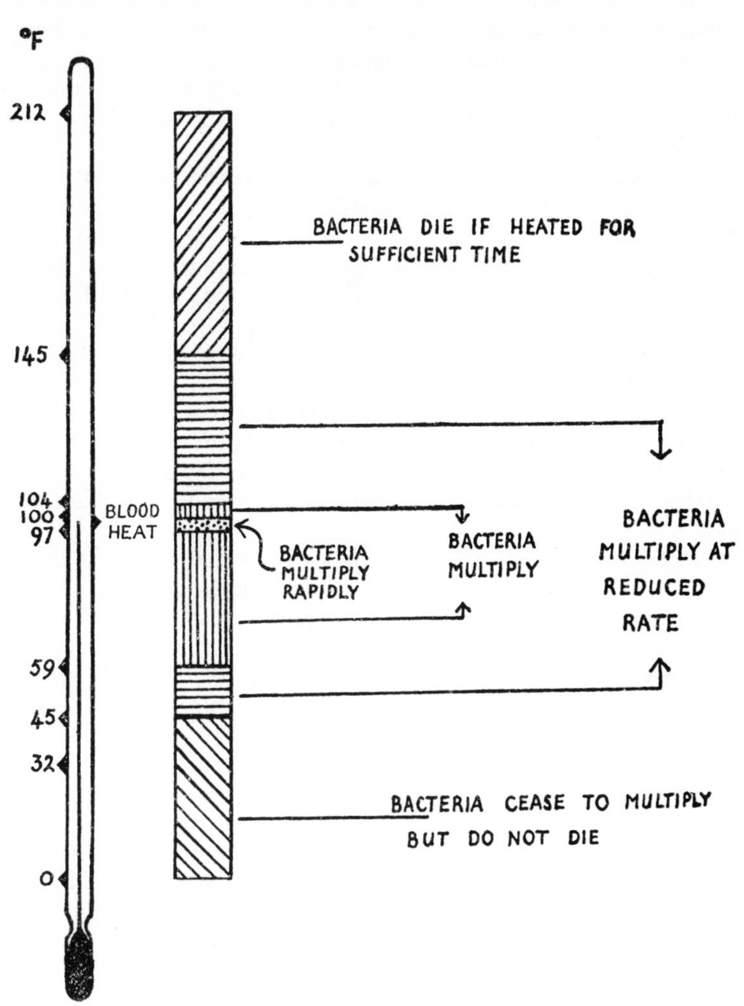

FIG. 2.—Bacteria. Effects of temperature.

are more likely to become dangerously contaminated; these could include fresh and made-up meats, milk and milk products, ice-creams and eggs (whether fresh, defrosted or reconstituted). Bacteria cannot grow in dehydrated foods that contain less than 10% moisture.

Dried eggs may contain salmonella bacteria, which can multiply in time after reconstitution. This type of egg, therefore, can be doubly liable to cause trouble and should only be reconstituted and used as required.

The student must remember that food hygiene regulations are strictly enforced by the Ministry of Health and local authorities and that standards are maintained and even exceeded by responsible firms engaged in the manufacture, processing and packing of food-stuffs. It is at the delivery point that the responsibility of those engaged in the baking industry begins.

It is of the utmost importance for all those who enter the baking industry to remember that:

(1) They are entering an industry primarily engaged in manufacture of bread, which is one of the basic foods of mankind; for the production of other goods of high food value, such as cakes, pies and pastries, and for the decoration of some of these goods so that they may be more attractive.

(2) Bearing in mind that food is being processed, it is absolutely essential for everybody concerned to be conscious of his or her responsibility to this necessary and important calling, and to the community, by attending to personal hygiene. Dirt is a criminal and those who encourage it are assessories after the fact. Therefore wear clean protective clothing, including headgear; see that hands and nails are always clean (remember the danger from bowel-borne bacteria); report at once any illness, any cut or skin infection; never put the point of a piping tube in the mouth and do not smoke in the bakery.

Remember that there is enough necessary work in this world without creating that which is unnecessary. A little thought and system will make work easier for yourself and others and will add dignity to your labour and command respect from those around you.

Tools—other than personal property—are for the use of all concerned and not for yourself alone. Look after them; clean them when you have finished and put them back in the proper place. You may be the one who will need them next.

Tables and all other equipment (refrigerators, cupboards, packing boxes, baking-sheets, bread-tins, etc.) must be kept clean. Any neglect, apart from advertising bad workmanship, will make the task harder when eventually it has to be done. Floors, walls, sinks and drains must be kept scrupulously clean. Savoy bags and all cloths should be sterilized after use.

Remember that, in the City and Guilds practical examinations, 20% of the marks are awarded for such qualities as cleanliness and neatness during work and that questions may be set on hygiene in the written examinations.

THE FIRST MIXING

A study of any dough-making formula will show that a finished dough temperature is always mentioned; generally it is between 76–80° F., and it is therefore necessary to make and maintain the dough at the temperature given. There are good reasons for this, for it is known that dough temperature, amongst other equally important factors, controls the speed of fermentation. As the temperature of water can be readily adjusted, it becomes the medium by which the calculated dough temperature can be achieved. Here are two methods of calculation in common use:

(1) First ascertain the desired dough temperature figure and double it. Subtract from it the temperature figure of the flour and the result will give the approximate water temperature necessary to achieve the given temperature. Here are two examples.

Desired dough temperature:	78° F.	Desired dough temperature:	80° F.
78 × 2	156	80 × 2	160
Flour temperature	64	Flour temperature	62
Water temperature	= 92	Water temperature	= 98

It may be necessary to add from 2 to 4 degrees to the calculated water temperature according to conditions and the size of the dough. There is a greater proportional heat loss in small doughs because of the relatively greater surface area from which heat may be lost.

(2) *Major Factor Method.* With this method the temperature of the bakery is taken into consideration.

On a day when the bread produced in a particular bakery is considered satisfactory, the temperatures of the flour, water and bakery are added together.

This figure, subject to adjustment over a period, is adopted in that particular bakery, and remains constant, and is known as the Major Factor Figure.

To find the water temperature, add flour and bakery temperatures together and subtract from the major factor figure:

Example:

	°F.
Bakery temperature	64
Flour temperature	60
Water temperature	100
Major factor figure	224
Flour temperature	56
Bakery temperature	62
	118

Subtract 118 from major factor figure 224 = Water temperature 106° F.

Yeast is a living organism and is in danger at 120° F. If the calculated water temperature is at, or over, this figure, a little of the water will have to be slightly cooled before the yeast is dispersed in it or the yeast will be damaged.

Here are twelve important points that should become habitual routine when making small doughs.

(1) Make careful note of formula and method.

(2) See that scales are accurate and that scale-pan and weights are clean.

(3) Carefully weigh the flour, sieve it, and place the thermometer into it.

(4) Weigh accurately the rest of the ingredients, except water.

(5) See that all necessary tools and equipment are ready.

(6) Read flour temperature, calculate water temperature, and record these figures.

(7) Weigh water at correct temperature.

(8) Disperse yeast in a little water. Dissolve salt in the rest; put both into a bay made in the flour.

(9) Mix thoroughly.

(10) Take dough temperature and record it.

(11) Weigh the dough and record the weight.

(12) Cover the dough to prevent skinning and let it prove in a place approximating to the temperature of the dough.

It is important that dough-mixing is done correctly, or the resulting dough will be insufficiently mixed and in the case of hand mixing, a great deal of hard work will be necessary to effect a proper clearing of the dough.

When the water, yeast and salt are ready in the bay, draw in some of the flour with the fingers and so make a batter within the bay. Still using the fingers, draw in the rest of the flour and using no pressure, shake the mass until the materials are thoroughly dispersed and no free flour is visible; then, and only then, pressure and stretching can be applied to make a well-mixed plastic dough.

Later it will be learned that, when wheat protein is hydrated, it forms an elastic substance known as gluten which is toughened by manipulation. It then follows, that, if part of the dough is over-manipulated, it becomes increasingly difficult to mix in the remainder, except by much time and energy. The alternative is a dough full of scraps. It is much easier to do the job properly!

CALCULATION OF YEAST QUANTITIES

Fermentation by the use of yeast is referred to as 'panary' fermentation from the Latin *panis* meaning bread.

Yeast is a living organism of the fungi family of plants and is capable of changing sugar into carbon dioxide, alcohol and other by-products. The gas (CO_2) is caught up in the gluten network and, in consequence, the dough rises. At the same time there are other physical and chemical changes taking place within the dough. These changes will be explained later in greater detail.

It is known that time, temperature, water content, quantity, quality and choice of raw materials all have an effect on the speed of fermentation. It will be seen, therefore, that it is far from easy to calculate the necessary quantity of yeast for a given dough under different conditions. It has been said that it is virtually impossible to reduce fermentation to mathematics.

There is, however, some guidance, because it has been shown that there is a relationship between yeast content and fermentation time; this can be proved, for if the normal amount of yeast in a sack dough at 80° F. be multiplied by the fermentation time of the dough, it will be seen that the figure 9 will be the result. For example:

A one-sack (280 lb. of flour) dough in bulk for 3 hr. normally has 3 lb. of yeast—$3 \times 3 = 9$. A one-sack dough in bulk for 6 hr. will need $1\frac{1}{2}$ lb. of yeast—$6 \times 1\frac{1}{2} = 9$. It follows, then, that one method of calculating the yeast necessary for a one-sack dough is to divide the bulk fermentation time into the factor 9. For example, a sack dough to ferment in bulk for 4 hr. $9 \div 4 = 2\frac{1}{4}$ lb. of yeast. By the same calculation a 5-hr. dough would need approximately $1\frac{3}{4}$ lb. of yeast.

This is known as the factorial method of yeast calculation. The factor number can vary under differing conditions of temperature, salt and water contents, type of bread and the amount of mechanical manipulation the dough receives. Factor 9, however, can be assumed to be a fairly good guide under average conditions, always remembering that it is based on one sack (280 lb.) of flour made into a dough 76–80° F. in temperature and containing approximately 5 lb. of salt per sack. For no-dough-time and 1 hour doughs, see page 15.

A different factor number is used when calculating the yeast required for smaller doughs. This is because there is a greater heat loss, due to the relatively larger surface area of the dough, thus slowing down fermentation speed. The figure 11 is suggested for doughs under 1 sack (280 lb.) and over 1 bag (140 lb.) and the equation is as follows:

$$\frac{\text{Factor No.} \times \text{Proportion of sack}}{\text{Bulk fermentation time}} = \text{Yeast}$$

Example 1. $\frac{3}{4}$ sack to ferment in bulk 4 hr.

$$11 \times \frac{3}{4} \div 4 = \frac{11 \times 3}{4 \times 4} = 2 \text{ lb. } 1 \text{ oz. of yeast}$$

For doughs of one bag or under the factor 12 is applicable.

Example 2. 14 lb. of flour ($\frac{1}{20}$ sack) to ferment in bulk for 2 hr.

$$12 \times \frac{1}{20} \div 2 = \frac{12 \times 1}{20 \times 2} = \frac{3}{10} \text{ lb.} = 5 \text{ oz. of yeast (approx.).}$$

Mr. W. E. Spencer, M.B.E., F.Inst.B.B., suggests the following calculation for two-sack doughs:

Take the sack figure for yeast, based on factor 9, double it and subtract 8 oz. Here is an example of yeast calculation for a two-sack dough to ferment in bulk for 4 hr. Yeast for one sack = 2¼ lb. 2¼ lb. × 2 = 4½ lb.

4½ lb. less 8 oz. = 4 lb.

We know that there is a relationship between yeast content and dough temperature; the cooler the dough is made the more yeast is used. It follows, of course, that the warmer the dough, the less the yeast used, the adjustments being progressive in each case. Dough temperatures can be classified under three group headings; cold, cool and hot.

Doughs with a temperature below 74° F. can be referred to as 'cold' doughs. For these it will be necessary to use approximately double the amount of yeast. For example:

A one-sack dough at 78–80° F. fermented for 4 hr. needs 2¼ lb. of yeast. For a cold dough use 4½lb. (approx.).

Doughs with a temperature between 74–84° F. can be referred to as 'cool' doughs.

A 'hot' dough is one made at a temperature exceeding 84° F. It is useful in emergencies when there is a serious shortage of yeast; otherwise it is not to be recommended. Here is a formula for tin bread using a hot dough:

lb.	*oz.*		*lb.*	*oz.*	
280	0	Flour		12	Yeast
4	0	Salt	155	0	(15½ gallons) water (approx.)

Dough temperature 88° F. Bulk fermentation 3 hr.

It is of the utmost importance for the student to remember that the data given is of value as a guide in practical work and as a basis for answering questions on a written paper.

It is essential also to remember that in breadmaking there are so many variables. Flours, for instance, have differing maltose figures and gluten strengths; there can be additions to doughs such as enriching agents, yeast foods and bread improvers. Bulk storage temperatures may vary and, above all, the human element must be considered.

There is much more to be learned concerning the science of fermentation before arbitrary tables can be used. This will give emphasis to what has often been stressed by competent craftsmen; and that is that successful breadmaking is a complex and highly skilled craft, calling for knowledge, skill and experience. The student must study closely and apply his knowledge day by day, observing results and so building up the measure of practical experience that is essential to good technological craftsmanship.

SALT

Salt confers many qualities on the dough and on the resultant bread.

(1) It confers flavour.

(2) It confers stability on gluten.

(3) It has a controlling influence on fermentation.

(4) It assists in the retention of moisture.

(5) Because of its control of fermentation it has a marked effect on crumb and crust colour.

Salt (sodium chloride) is essential to the making of good bread, provided that it is used within the limits imposed by the reasons given above. Amounts used vary according to the process being followed, the strength of the flour, the water content of the dough and the taste of local consumers. Amounts have varied between 3½ lb. and 5 lb. per sack; in Scotland it is in the region of 7 lb. per sack, because of the longer fermentation processes employed.

Common salt is now readily available to the baker in powder form; because of this there is a greater ease in handling and storage as against the use of block salt in the past. Salt from reputable firms is generally guaranteed 99% sodium chloride, the rest being moisture and very small amounts of other chlorides and sulphates. Salt is very hygroscopic; that is it readily takes up moisture. This can be prevented by correct storage in a dry atmosphere. If the salt is excessively moist, then it must be understood that water as well as salt is being weighed and the salt balance of the dough will be affected. Its ability to hold moisture probably explains why salt is considered a factor in delaying staling and in keeping bread moist.

One of the chief reasons for using salt in breadmaking is to confer flavour and palatability; without it bread would be insipid and uninteresting. In cakes, salt in correct quantity offsets blandness and insipidity and has the effect of bringing out other flavours present.

Not only does salt confer flavour on bread but it also has a marked effect on the stability of the gluten. The student can see this quite clearly if he will take several glass jars; the first with plain water, the rest with differing salt solutions ranging from 1¼% (¼ oz. of salt to 1 pt. of water) to 20% (4 oz. to 1 pt.), all water to be at the same temperature. In each jar suspend a piece of gluten on a wire hook, each piece of gluten being the same weight. After leaving the jars together in an even temperature, it will be seen that, as the strength of the solution increases so the gluten is rendered more tough and stable, until in the higher amounts it becomes almost intractable.

The average amount of salt used today is 4½–5 lb. per sack, which at 150 lb. of water per sack is approximately a 3% solution. When considering solutions, it is interesting to know that in most modern plants the sack basis for salt calculation is superseded by the method of assessing salt quantities on the weight of the water content. This is clearly of value when water contents per sack vary considerably; for instance, if 5 lb. of salt is added to 280 lb. of flour and 160 lb. of water, there would be 5 lb. of salt in 445 lb. of dough; if 5 lb. of salt is added to the same amount of flour which takes only 140 lb. of water, then there is 5 lb. of salt in 425 lb. of dough. Clearly it makes for greater uniformity. If, say, 5 oz. of salt per gallon of water is used (3% solution) then the first dough would need 5 lb. of salt and the second 4 lb. 6 oz.

Salt has a controlling effect on fermentation. Again the student can study this for himself if he will make up a number of small

I The effect of varying amounts of salt in bread

II The effects of varying amounts of milk in bread

III Symmetry of shape

IV Irregular structure of Vienna bread

doughs, all being exactly the same except for the salt content; the first having no salt, each of the rest having an increased amount, until the last has the equivalent of 30 lb. per sack. It will be noticed that there is a marked difference in the speed of fermentation, the 'no-salt' dough being extremely rapid and the others progressively slower, until at the last there is no evidence at all of gas production. The dough with the normal salt content is used for the control.

The same timing is given each dough, both for fermentation and for knocking back, and in due course the doughs are scaled, moulded and put into tins. When the control loaf is ready for baking, it will be found that the 'no-salt' loaf is large in volume and in danger of collapse; the rest being smaller and smaller until, at the end, the heavy putty-like piece of dough will be found to be lifeless and devoid of gas. All the loaves are then put into the oven at the same time. An examination of the cut bread afterwards will emphasize the differences in volume, crumb stability and colour and, of course, the flavour.

The effect of too little salt will be clearly seen. With the control lifted, fermentation is rapid; there is a greater breakdown of sugar into gas and, because the gluten is weakened, it offers less resistance to the gas expansion; volume in consequence is too large, the crumb structure is loose and lacks brightness, and the flavour is inspid.

With too much salt, yeast activity is seriously retarded; with excessive amounts fermentation is stopped. With this progressive slowing down of yeast activity there is a corresponding tightening of the gluten; both resulting in a smaller loaf volume, until in the last of the loaves the result is a dark, heavy, rubber-like mass. The taste of salt is excessive. The effect of salt on the volume of the loaf can be clearly seen in Plate 1.

Another simple experiment from which a useful lesson can be learned is to mix some dry yeast and salt together in a saucer. In a short time the mixture will be seen to liquefy; the liquid is the protoplasm from the yeast cell, which has been seriously damaged. Therefore never put yeast with dry salt or in concentrated salt solutions; the yeast will be damaged or inactivated according to the degree of concentration.

In dough-making the salt can be dissolved in some of the dough liquor, while the yeast is dispersed separately. As an alternative the salt can be sieved on to the flour.

It is interesting to place some small lumps of salt into a piece of dough which, when baked, will show slimy patches in the crumb. This will emphasize the importance of either sieving or carefully dissolving the salt before use.

If salt is accidentally omitted from a dough, it can be sieved over it and well mixed in. If by chance the salt is doubled, then the same weight of dough without salt should be made and the two doughs thoroughly mixed together.

In the introduction to this volume, the student is advised to keep himself up-to-date by constant revision of notes. Study of new text-books, trade journals, attendance at demonstrations and lectures will show that new facts and theories are being revealed, some confirming existing knowledge, some advising caution and some giving cause for doubt on the accuracy of hitherto accepted explanations. It has been taught that salt is largely responsible for crust colour in bread made from normal flours, because of its controlling influence on fermentation. If the speed of fermentation is retarded by the use of an increased amount of salt, there will be less sugar used by the yeast to produce gas. In consequence there will be more sugar caramelized on the crust, producing a high crust colour. If there is too little salt used, the opposite happens and there is little crust colour.

A report on *The Maillard or Browning Reaction in Breadmaking*, which has been published, suggests that the accepted theory is not wholly correct and that browning is the result of reaction between sugars and amino-acids. Obviously there is still much to be learned on this subject. It seems, however, that the student would be correct in stating that salt, because of its controlling effect on fermentation, plays a large part in crust coloration, because the degree of fermentation of normal flours determines the amount of sugar and other substances available for the crust colour reaction.

Here must follow a warning for those who would aspire to City and Guilds and National Diploma qualifications. Never throw aside hitherto accepted theories in favour of the new—except under competent advice. Until the old is completely rejected, it is safer to give the whole picture—old and new.

WATER AND TEMPERATURES

Water, of course, is essential in breadmaking.

(1) It hydrates the insoluble wheat protein, forming gluten.

(2) It takes up the soluble substances, salt, sugar, soluble proteins, etc.

(3) It is the means of dispersing the yeast and all ingredients to form a plastic dough.

It is known that the water content has a marked effect on the speed of fermentation. A ferment (which is a thin batter), for instance, will have a greater speed than a sponge (which contains more flour), which in turn is faster than a dough (which is quite plastic). There is also a pronounced difference in the speeds of a slack dough and one that is tight. Water contents in doughs will vary according to the water-absorbing quality of the flour.

Referring again to temperature, it is seen that it has a bearing on the speed of fermentation, which is at its best between 78–82° F. This is known as the 'optimum temperature range'. At temperatures over 90° F., fermentation is rapid but gets progressively weaker; under 75° F., it slows up until at 45° F. it is arrested.

It becomes obvious, then, that there is a relationship between the balance of raw materials, time and temperature. This balance can be controlled and this is best illustrated by the following chart which in practice, however, should be used as a guide only, for it may have to be adjusted to suit differing conditions.

Bulk Fermentation in Hours	*Quantity of Yeast*	*Dough Temperature ° F.*	*Salt Content (lb.)*	*Water Content (gal.)*
0	* 7 lb.	82	4½	15½–16
1	† 6 lb.	82	4½	15½–16
2	4½–5 lb.	80	5	15 –15½
3	3 –3½ lb.	78	5	15 –15½
4	2¼–2½ lb.	78	5	15 –15½
5	1¾–2 lb.	76	5	15 –15½
6	1½ lb.	76	5	14½–15½
7	1¼ lb.	76	5	14½–15½
8	18 oz.	76	5	14½–15
9	16 oz.	75	5	14 –15
10	15 oz.	74	5	14 –14½
11	14 oz.	74	5	14 –14½
12	12 oz.	74	5¼	14 –14½

* 2½% of flour weight † 2% of flour weight

It will be seen that, as the bulk fermentation time is increased progressively, so there is a decrease in the yeast and water contents with, at the same time, an increase of salt; all these adjustments slow down fermentation speed, which is necessary because, as will be seen later, time itself plays an important part in the ripening of dough.

Yeast is the fermenting agent; it must be reduced, together with the temperature, as the fermentation time lengthens. More salt and less water increase the potential strength of flour, and this extra stability is necessary as the fermentation time is lengthened.

The object of controlling fermentation is to pre-determine the period of dough ripening, so that the bread goes to the oven with the gluten extensible enough to 'give' to the expanding gases whilst strong enough to retain them.

Here is a formula for a practice batch of three tin loaves to be weighed in at 1 lb. each.

lb.	*oz.*				
1	14	Flour	Finished dough temperature 80° F.		
	1	Yeast	Knock back after	50	min.
	½	Salt	Scale at	75	,,
1	1	Water (approx.)	Hand up. Let stand	10	,,
			Mould and put into tins		
3	0½	Dough weight	Final proof about	25	,,

Bulk fermentation time
(Dough-making to scaling)—75 min.

Total fermentation time
(Dough-making to baking)—120 min. (approx.)

Yield 3 loaves weighed at 1 lb.

2

Reasons for knocking back; Brown Breads: Reasons for Different Processes; Bun Doughs: Reasons for a Ferment; Should a Ferment Drop? Fermented Small Goods

REASONS FOR KNOCKING BACK

BEFORE machine mixers were introduced into the bakery, all doughs were made by hand. Even by the best workers, despite the tremendous amount of hard work put into the mixing, the dough was never mixed as thoroughly as it is by the machine today. 'Cutting back', as it was known in the past, was therefore a necessity, because it gave the opportunity of further mixing.

When a dough is first made it is extremely tough, due to the development of the gluten. After a period of fermentation, generally about three-quarters of bulk fermentation time, the dough becomes full of gas and the gluten relaxes; it is then easier to spread and manipulate, and when the dough is in this condition the operation is carried out.

In the past, it was done in the trough by cutting off pieces from the end of the dough, expelling the gas and so stretching the gluten by folding and spreading; the pieces after being dealt with were put, one on top of the other, at one end of the trough. The same process was gone through until the dough was returned to its original place. It was then kept in place by the pinboard. Now, of course, it is done by simply wheeling the machine bowl to the mixer at the appropriate time, and giving a further few minutes' mixing, or what is now called 'knocking back'.

Not only was cutting back essential in the past to ensure thorough mixing, but it was found that the resultant bread was much better from this extra manipulation. Now we know that manipulation helps to condition the gluten in the dough, resulting in better shape and volume and a more stable crumb structure in the finished loaf. Manipulation is partly responsible for the high standard of modern exhibition bread; pioneers in this field found that rolling and folding gave the bread an enormous volume. This standard has now been modified but the principle remains, that thorough mixing and judicious manipulation will raise the standard of breadmaking, always assuming that first-class materials are used and fermentation is controlled. Knocking back is part of that manipulation.

When the dough is fully extended in bulk, the process of knocking back breaks down the dough fabric and, in consequence, most of the CO_2 is expelled. The gas expulsion, in turn, causes the breakdown of large gas holes; the degassing reduces the dough volume and renders the gluten temporarily less extensible.

During knocking back there is also an equalization of dough temperature, particularly in cases where doughs are stored under uncontrolled thermal conditions.

Finally knocking back is a means whereby the salt is incorporated in the 'delayed salt' method of breadmaking, which will be referred to in a later chapter.

To summarize, knocking back has the following benefits:

(1) Assists in dough conditioning.
(2) Stretches gluten.
(3) Equalizes dough temperature.
(4) Is the means of adding salt in the 'delayed salt' method.

REASONS FOR DIFFERENT PROCESSES FOR BROWN BREAD

There are many types of meal on the market at the present time for making brown breads, and the student should understand as far as possible their composition, the effects of fermentation on the constituent parts and the reasons for the different processes employed, if brown breads of the highest standards are to be produced. The meals can be grouped under three headings: wholemeal and wheatmeal; germ meals; special meals.

Wholemeal and wheatmeal will contain all or some of the bran and all or none of the germ. Here are the official standards:

Wholemeal—100% extraction from clean wheat without dilution.

Wheatmeal—Any extraction in excess of 85%.

Any new product licensed must comply with the above, but for the present, to avoid disturbance, any old-established brands of wholemeal can be 95% extraction and over.

There are brands of wholemeal that are guaranteed by the makers to be 100% extraction, that is, the whole of the grain is ground to a meal. Some firms also advertise that their meals are stone ground and similar to the meals from which bread was made before the introduction of roller milling.

Wheatmeals vary considerably in composition; some contain almost all of the grain, less the germ; others have the coarse bran removed and are, in consequence, much finer. There are other meals which are a mixture of white flour and fine branny particles; these will stand more fermentation than ordinary wheat meals, which in turn have a greater stability than 100% wholemeal.

Special meals are invariably sold under a trade name; these contain various admixtures of which malt flour is the most common.

Brown loaves are smaller in volume compared with white loaves of the same weight. For this there are two main reasons. First, according to the extraction rate and the composition of meals, there is present more or less bran and sometimes the germ, neither of which contains gluten. Gluten is an elastic substance which entangles the gas generated by yeast and then becomes the girder or framework of the loaf when it is baked, the amount and quality of it having a bearing on the volume of the loaf. Secondly, the bran particles, according to size, also tend to alter the coherency of the dough structure, having a cutting effect on the gluten strands which, in turn, has an effect on the volume of the loaf.

The bran coatings and the germ contain active substances known as enzymes. These have a powerful effect on dough ripening, which is, in consequence, much faster than in a dough made from white flour. Enzymes, and there are some in yeast as well, are substances that can speed up great changes; more will be learned about them later.

Wholemeals and wheatmeals have high water-absorbing power, so that the water content of the dough should be high; the doughs should be cool and have a short fermentation period; as low as 30 min. in the case of 100% extraction wholemeals and about 1½ hr. for wheatmeals, according to the extraction rate and degree of fineness in milling. Longer periods of fermentation are necessary for the 'made up' meals according to the strength of the white flour content.

Germ breads are recommended by the makers to be made on a 'no-dough-time' or, on a very short time process. Germ meals consist of 75% white flour and 25% added cooked, salt-preserved wheat germ. Again the percentage of gluten is low and the active enzymes in the germ help to ripen the dough almost as soon as it is mixed.

No salt is added by the baker when making these breads, because it is added by the miller to retard rancidity of the wheat germ oil. The makers recommend hot doughs to bring out the flavour of the cooked germ.

Here is a diagrammatic summary of three constants and two differences which should be borne in mind when making wholemeal/wheatmeal and germ breads.

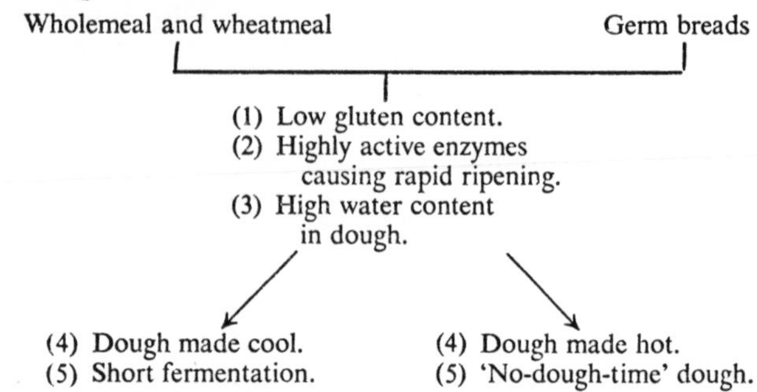

Here are six recipes illustrating the differences in formulae and method when making wholemeal, wheatmeal, germ and special brown breads, the yield in each case being three loaves weighed in at 1 lb. each.

Allinsons
(100% stone ground wholemeal)

lb.	*oz.*	
1	12	Wholemeal
	1	Yeast
	½	Salt
1	4	Water

Dough 80° F.
Knock back at 30 min.
Scale at 40 ,,

Wheatmeal

lb.	*oz.*	
1	12	Wheatmeal
	1	Yeast
	½	Salt
	½	Fat
1	3	Water

Dough 80° F.
Knock back at 1 hr.
Scale at 1½ ,,

Hovis
(Germ bread)

lb.	*oz.*	
1	12	Hovis
	1	Yeast
1	4	Water (120° F.)

Cool a little of the water and disperse the yeast, and add after partial mixing. Mould and place at once after thorough mixing into warmed Hovis tins.

Vitbe
(Germ bread)

lb.	*oz.*	
1	14	Vitbe
	1	Yeast
1	3	Water (110° F.) (approx.)

Dough 82° F.
Knock back at 15 min.
Scale at 20 ,,

Bermaline
(Special meal)

lb.	*oz.*	
2	0	Bermaline
	1	Yeast
	½	Salt
	½	Fat
1	1	Water (approx.)

Dough 80° F.
Knock back at 1½ hr.
Scale at 2 ,,

Turog
(Special meal)

lb.	*oz.*	
1	12	Turog
	1	Yeast
	½	Salt
1	3	Water (approx.)

Dough 78/80° F.
Knock back at 1½ hr.
Scale at 2 ,,

It is important that the tins provided by the millers be used.

REASONS FOR A FERMENT IN A BUN DOUGH

We know that yeast works best under certain conditions; where there is food in solution, and at a suitable temperature; where there is no concentration of sugar or salt and where fat is not excessive. Such a medium is a ferment, which is a thin mixture of the water, yeast, a little sugar and a small proportion of the flour at a temperature within the optimum range of 78–80° F.

Because it has a high water content, all the food in solution is readily assimilated and gassing is vigorous and it is almost certain that there is reproduction of the yeast cells. There is a minimum resistance to expansion, so that the ferment rises quickly and soon the watery mixture is a frothy mass of yeast activity, in a healthy and robust condition to carry out the much more difficult task of fermenting the bun dough into which it is to be made.

Yeast works best in a 10% sugar solution; a bun dough has in solution a sugar concentration of about 30%; at this figure fermentation is retarded. Food is assimilated by yeast through the porous membrane of the cell wall and fat in excess acts as a barrier to that assimilation. When it is considered that the fat content of an average bun dough is about 30 lb. to the sack of flour, it can be seen that such amounts of sugar and fat are not conducive to vigorous fermentation.

Modern yeasts are less effected by concentrations of fat and sugar. The use of ferments, therefore, is receding into history; the preference is for short-time doughs with plenty of yeast.

SHOULD A FERMENT DROP?

If left long enough a ferment will drop. This is due to the gluten, which is the girder-work of the ferment, being so distended and ripened by the generation of gas, the softening action of water and also by enzymic activity, that it can no longer retain the gas and the ferment collapses.

Craftsmen of the past maintained that the ferment must drop before it was made into dough. Many were the surreptitious kicks on the ferment tub by impatient operatives who wished to get on with their work. If the collapse was imminent, the kick soon brought it down, but with the strong gluten flours of the past and the sparing use of yeast, much more than a kick was necessary to cause an under-ripe ferment to drop.

A dough will ripen more quickly using a ferment that has dropped because the gluten in the balance of the flour used to make the dough has to be ripened only. Because fermentation has been carried to its maximum in the ferment, it has increased in acidity; this also assists in subsequent gluten ripening.

The old-time craftsman knew from experience that he would get rapid ripening in a dough made with a dropped ferment. With our greater technical knowledge we know that there are many factors that will vary the speed of fermentation and the subsequent maturing of the dough; such factors as the maltose figure of flour and the strength and quality of the gluten, the amount and quality of the yeast and the temperature of the ferment.

Any ferment, given time, will collapse, but nowadays time is more valuable, economically, than it was in the past and we can more readily control fermentation because of our greater knowledge.

If a ferment has not dropped, it will still produce good bread or buns provided that extra time is given in the dough stage.

To sum up, a ferment that has dropped will ripen a dough more quickly than one that has not. Both will produce good buns if the maker understands the fermentation process and his raw materials, and makes the necessary adjustments under the varying conditions.

The initial ferment can of course be omitted and the straight dough method used, but either the yeast or fermentation time will need to be increased.

FERMENTED SMALL GOODS

From the introduction to ferments, the reasons for their use and the timing of them, to the application of them to practical work is a logical step.

The term 'fermented small goods' covers a wide range of products from bun goods, plain and fancy rolls, baps, muffins, crumpets and tea-cakes to the more sophisticated babas and savarins. Because all these goods are fermented by yeast, they are included in the breadmaking syllabuses and the teaching of them is arranged to cover the work of four sessions. Most bun goods are made from a standard ferment and basic dough as follows:

Ferment			*Dough*		
lb.	*oz.*		*lb.*	*oz.*	
1	4	(1 pt.) Water (110° F.)	2	4	Flour
	2	Yeast		5	Fat
	½	Sugar		4	Sugar
	1	Milk powder		4	Egg
	4	Flour			Salt
					Flavour as desired

The ferment is allowed to stand for 20 min.

Knock back at 30 min.
Scale at 45 ,,

If compound fat is used in bun goods, salt should be used at the rate of 1 oz. to 8 lb. of flour. The salt content of margarine is about 2%: it is therefore suggested that, if margarine is used $\frac{3}{4}$ oz. of salt to 8 lb. of flour is added. If required to be fruited 8 oz. of currants and 1 oz. of chopped peel may be added to each pint of bun dough.

A bun dough should never be tight; a softer dough is necessary, not only for quicker fermentation, but to confer a soft, mellow crumb on the buns. More water may therefore have to be added at dough-making to adjust the consistency.

A breadmaking flour of good quality is ideal for bun-making, giving stability and fairly rapid gluten maturation. The yeast should be of the fast type for the shorter ferment and dough method, because it assists in gluten ripening in the dough stage and gives ample gas production in the final proving stage.

A better quality bun is produced by the addition of eggs, for not only is the food value increased but an extra stability is given the dough; eggs also confer on gluten a greater extensibility and the volume of the bun is thereby increased. An experiment will show that, with decreased weight, the volume of the egg-enriched bun is equal to a heavier bun made from a dough containing no eggs.

Most buns, when taken from the oven, are immediately washed to produce the familiar glaze. It must be clearly understood that glazing is a form of cake decoration designed to give finish and to attract the eye; therefore it should be done properly and with thought. Nothing looks worse than a bun half washed with a sickly-looking, sticky sugar solution.

Eggs, gelatine or sugar will glaze and water will disperse or dissolve them. Here are three recipes for bun glaze:

(1) Two parts fresh eggs and one part water, well whisked together.

(2) Two parts egg, one part sugar, and one part water, well whisked together.

(3) Take to the boil. 1$\frac{1}{4}$ lb. sugar and 1$\frac{1}{4}$ lb. (1 pint) water, skimming off any scum arising during the boiling. Add, after removing from the heat, $\frac{1}{2}$ oz. of powdered gelatine dispersed in a little of the water.

The judicious addition of lemon essence to the wash, imparts a delightful additional flavour to the goods glazed.

BREAD ROLLS

People who have travelled in Continental countries are often amazed at the wonderful variety and high quality of the rolls displayed in restaurants and bakery establishments. These rolls are generally enriched with butter and fresh milk and a good deal of work is put into the making of them, so that the finished rolls are appealing and a credit to the art and skill of the craftsman baker.

A well-made roll is a delight and it is sad indeed that rolls are so neglected in this country and not readily available to delight the consumer and enhance the prestige of the baking industry. Scotland is an exception, for there, tea-breads and morning rolls are made in great variety. Too often, rolls are made from ordinary dough, partly boiled in a prover and finished in the oven, so that they bear more resemblance to synthetic rubber than an article of food.

It is important to remember that rolls can be eaten at every meal, but the roll, crisp and crackly, suitable for eating with soup, may not be ideal on a buffet table, and the soft silky bridge roll is completely unsuitable with eggs and bacon at breakfast. Therefore the roll must suit the occasion.

Mr. W. E. Spencer, as an authority on breadmaking, has given definitions for dinner, breakfast and tea (bridge) rolls. A dinner roll should be of the Vienna type, enriched but not unduly sweet, with the easily-broken, characteristic, crisp shell crust and with a soft, open internal structure. The breakfast roll should also be enriched, but with a crust a little less crisp than the dinner roll. The tea roll should contain not only milk, but eggs and an increased amount of fat, so that the roll is soft and silky to the touch—in fact a bridge roll. Here are formulae for all three. The differences in fat content should be noted.

	Dinner		*Breakfast*		*Tea*	
	lb.	*oz.*	*lb.*	*oz.*	*lb.*	*oz.*
Flour	1	2	1	0	1	1
Milk powder		½		½		½
Fat		½		1		1½
Salt		¼		¼		¼
Sugar		¼		¼		¼
Egg						1
Water (approx.)		10½		9		10
Yeast		2		1		1
Dough temperature	75° F.		80° F.		80° F.	
Bulk fermentation	60 min.		60 min.		30 min.	
Scaling weight	2 oz.		1½ oz.		1 oz.	
Yield	16		18		30	

The sugar content of bridge rolls should be kept low, for they are prepared for the table, mainly with savoury fillings.

Plate VII shows examples of fermented small goods.

3

Wheat and the Wheat Grain: Wheat Growing Countries; Stone Milling; Roller Milling; The Fragmentation Process

WHEAT AND THE WHEAT GRAIN

As flour is one of the principal raw materials used by the baker, and as it is obtained from the milling of wheat, the student should seek to understand the wheat plant, its growth and development under differing conditions and in different countries. He should study the wheat grain and its constituent parts so that he will more readily understand the milling process, extraction rates, flour grades and qualities.

Wheat is one of the most widely cultivated cereal crops in the world and one of the most important, dating back to prehistoric times. Wheat is a member of the family of grasses and has the botanical name of triticum. Authorities estimate that there are between 12,000–30,000 varieties of wheat in existence. The wheats of commerce are divided into three groups, and the botanical term—*triticum vulgare*—is given to varieties milled to produce flour for the baker. The second of the group is Durum wheat (*triticum durum*) which is grown in the U.S.A., Canada and the U.S.S.R. It has a high sugar content and a starch that is very susceptible to diastase and for these reasons it is used to adjust the maltose level of flour in milling. Flour milled from Durum wheat is used extensively for the manufacture of macaroni. The third of the commercial wheats is Club wheat (*triticum compactum*). Flours milled from it are too soft for breadmaking.

It must be remembered that the wheat grain is a seed used by nature for the continuity of the species and is packed with all the food necessary for the first stages of growth. Fig. 3 shows the wheat grain in longitudinal section. Structurally it can be divided into three main parts; the bran coatings, the germ, or embryo, and the endosperm.

The bran coatings constitute approximately 13% of the wheat

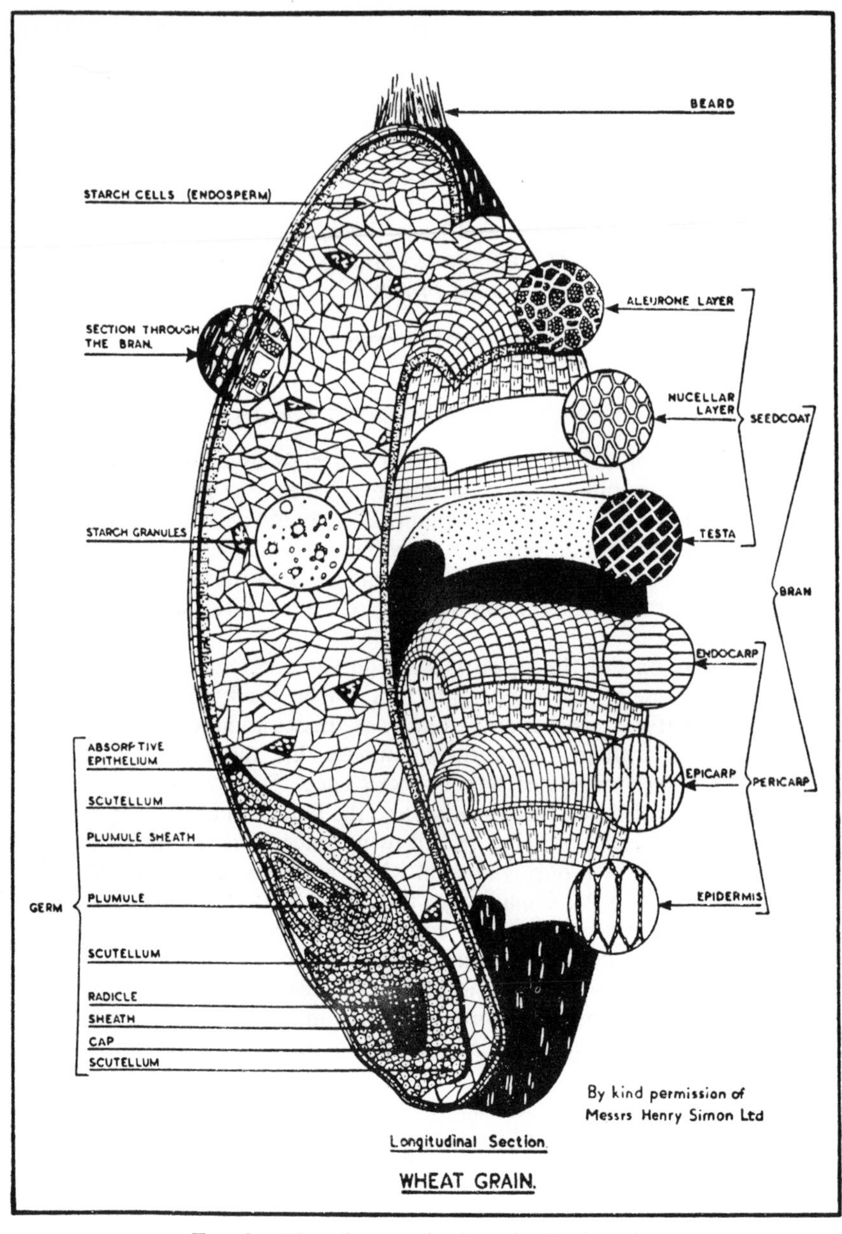

FIG. 3.—The wheat grain. Longitudinal section.

grain and consists of six principal layers. The outer three layers together form the pericarp; this consists of the epidermis 0·5%, epicarp 1·0%, and the endocarp 1·5%. Thus the pericarp constitutes about 3% of the grain, and is the protective covering. The inner layers form the seed coat of which the testa, 2% of the grain, contains the colouring matter by which the wheat can be classified as either red, white or yellow. Next to the testa comes the nucellar layer 1%, and finally the aleurone cells which constitutes 7% of the grain. The aleurone cells contain soluble protein and, with some of the other layers, an enzyme of the proteolytic group, which, if fermentation is excessive, breaks down the extensibility of the gluten.

The germ is approximately 2% of the grain and is the wheat plant in embryo. It has three main parts; the plumule which becomes the green shoot; the radicle or radix, which becomes the rootlet; and the scutellum which contains by far the greater percentage of the vitamin content of the wheat grain. The germ also contains a large proportion of diastatic enzymes which convert starch into sugar. The whole of the wheat germ is rich in food value, including valuable vitamins. The germ is cooked and salted and used in the composition of the various germ meals that have previously been mentioned.

The endosperm which is approximately 85% of the grain, consists largely of tightly packed starch cells, amongst which are dispersed soluble and insoluble proteins, oil, moisture, sugar and mineral matter. The outer starch cells are large and coarse; the inner cells small and fine. It is from the endosperm that white flour is milled.

Climate and soil conditions have a profound affect on the quality and the strength of the gluten of wheat. The strongest wheats of the world are grown in Canada, U.S.A. and the U.S.S.R. These are suitable for milling into breadmaking flours. Very rich soil, hard winters and hot summers are the main factors, although rainfall is of major importance. Nitrogen is the most important soil element for gluten strength and quality; if the rainfall during the growing period is unduly heavy, the nitrogen will be diluted. If the rainfall is light, there will be less soluble nitrogen available for the growing plant.

Starches and sugars are known scientifically as carbohydrates, and they are formed in the growing plant by a process known as photosynthesis. The leaves of the plant take in carbon dioxide which, under the influences of sunlight and chlorophyll (the green colouring matter in plants), splits; the oxygen is given off and the carbon is united with the water drawn up from the soil and synthesized into cellulose, starch and sugars.

WHEAT-GROWING COUNTRIES

Wheat can be grown in many parts of the world, but the bulk of it is grown in the temperate zone belts of the northern and southern hemispheres. The quality of the grain varies from country to country and at times from one farm to the next. This variation is a reflection of slight differences in soil, climate, breed of wheat sown and the degree of skill in the farmer.

Wheat can be classified in a number of ways. One of the simplest is a division into winter wheat and spring wheat. Winter wheat is sown in autumn or winter and harvested the following summer. Spring wheat is sown in spring and manages to complete its cycle of growth in a shorter period than winter wheat. It is usually planted in areas that have a severe winter; areas where the action of frost would bring the seeds back in the surface had they been 'winter' sown. Exposure would then kill them.

Wheat is also described according to the colour of the testa which may be red, yellow or white. The grain may further be considered as being 'strong', 'medium', or 'soft', these gradings being based on the gluten strength.

All these groupings are important to the miller and the baker because of the variations in quality of the flour produced. Winter wheats usually yield a soft wheat, although this is not true of the drier regions of south-west U.S.A. Texas, for example, produces a fine hard winter wheat.

In the colour groupings it is considered that the white wheats yield flours of excellent colour; the yellow wheats are associated with dryness; the red wheats are characteristic of strength, producing flour with a bright bloom and with a tough tenacious gluten.

Strength in wheat and flour is measured by gluten quality; elasticity and extensibility is the measure of that quality. The soft wheats have a gluten that is short and friable, suitable for such products as do not require the structural strength of a strong and stable gluten.

The map of the wheatlands of the world (page 2) brings out the fact, previously mentioned, that the greater part of the wheat comes from the two temperate belts. The table (page 29) shows the main countries concerned arranged in hemispheres, the figures record percentages of total world production.

The two totals account for about 84% of the world production; the remaining 16% is grown in small quantities in a large number of countries all over the world. Most of the wheat grown is consumed within the producing country, but about 20% does enter into world trade; the United Kingdom exporting about 13,000 metric tons per annum from a total production of about 2,500,000 metric tons per annum. The main wheat exporting countries are the U.S.A., Canada, Australia and the Argentine. These four sell 90% of the total amount of wheat that is put on the world's market. Canada, Australia and the Argentine export about one half of their total production.

	%		%
Northern Hemisphere			
U.S.S.R.	26	India	3
U.S.A.	16	Pakistan	2
China	11	Germany	2
Canada	6	Spain	2
France	4	United Kingdom	1·8
Italy	4		
Southern Hemisphere			
Australia	3	Argentine	3

On the other side of the picture, the United Kingdom emerges as the largest importer (nearly 5,000,000 metric tons per annum) with Germany second.

Some of the strongest wheat in the world is grown in the prairie provinces of Manitoba, Alberta and Saskatchewan; elsewhere in Canada softer winter wheats are also grown. In the U.S.A., strong Spring wheats are grown in the States of North and South Dakota and Minnesota. They are graded into three classes: (*a*) Dark North spring, (*b*) Northern spring and (*c*) Red spring. Of the hard winter wheats, the largest crop is grown in and around the State of Kansas. Red winter wheat, which yields a weaker flour, is produced in the Pacific North-West of the U.S.A.

The U.S.S.R. is now one of the leading wheat producing countries of the world, the Ukraine in particular producing wheats of good quality and strength. The U.S.S.R. and China are leading the world as the largest wheat-producers, and because of the differing climates within these vast countries, wheats of varying strengths are produced.

India grows great quantities of wheat that is hard and brittle, which requires extra cleaning and conditioning before it is milled into flour; it has no outstanding quality.

The best Hungarian wheats are of the highest quality, yielding a flour of good colour and with exceptional stability, a fact that at one time made Hungarian flour world famed for the production of Vienna bread. English, French and German wheats are all weak, generally of good flavour. The flours produced are used for blending with strong flours and used also in biscuit-making.

South of the equator the great areas watered by the River Plate produce large quantities of medium strong wheats. The three chief varieties of Plate wheat are Rosafe, Barusso and Baril; although varying little in quality, Rosafe is considered the best. Chile produces a very high quality wheat, very little of which is exported. Australian wheat yields flour of outstanding good colour and bloom, the strength varying from soft to medium-strong providing excellent flour for blending with the strong Manitobas.

Scientific work is going on all over the world on the selection and breeding of wheat suitable for growing in different countries or regions under differing climatic conditions. The skill of the miller in choosing grists for milling the flour into different grades, and the skill of the baker, in using these flours for the many bakery products, are still of paramount importance in providing the people with their daily bread and the other important products of the bakery that help to give variety in the daily dietary of the nation.

Here is a general summary of the characteristics of the world's principal wheats grown in different countries.

(1) *English.* Soft and weak but with good flavour. Yeoman, Holdfast and Warden wheats are stronger and more stable. Excellent biscuit flours are milled from English wheats. Average gluten content 7–9%.

(2) *European.* Similar to English, except Hungarian which varies; the best being medium-strong and of fine quality.

(3) *U.S.S.R.* Varies according to the area of growth; the greater proportion is of good strength, the best being equal to Manitoban. The famous breeds of hard spring and winter wheats of North America, originated in Russia. The average gluten strength is 10–14%

(4) *N. American* (*Canada*). Manitoban, grown in the prairie provinces of Manitoba, Alberta and Saskatchewan approximate to 95% of the total Canadian wheat crop. Canadian wheat possesses a high percentage of excellent quality gluten. The average is between 11–15%. Manitoban is the basis for breadmaking flours milled in this country. The remaining 5% of Canadian wheat is weaker with gluten contents of between 8–10%.

(*U.S.A.*) Northern spring, similar to Manitoban, is of excellent quality. Red winter, less strong, but flour milled from it produces excellent bread. Pacifics are a soft, white wheat with the gluten averaging 8–10%. Ideal for blending purposes.

(5) *Indian.* Generally flinty, hard, dry and brittle. Dough made from Indian flour is stable but lacks extensibility. The gluten content varies between 10–13%.

(6) *S. American.* Plate wheats from the Argentine and Uruguay

are of medium strength. Rosafe and Barusso are extensively used for blending with stronger wheats. Baril is weaker, and in blending must be used with discretion. The average gluten content is between 10–11%.

(7) *Australian.* Varies from soft to medium in strength, with an average gluten content between 8–11%. Flour milled from Australian wheat is noted for its excellent colour.

MILLING

Milling is the conversion of grain into flour and by-products. There are two distinct methods of milling wheat: stone milling and roller milling.

Stone milling is the method of antiquity and has been practised for many centuries. It is known that prehistoric man consumed the seeds from cereal grasses. It is not known whether at first he consumed this grain unbroken or whether it had a preliminary grinding. It is certain, however, that it was not long before the grains were reduced to a coarse meal by pounding between two stones.

Throughout the ages the same principle has survived, although the size and shape of the stone has altered, until the familiar round, flat, grooved stone is almost universal. As economic conditions altered, motive power changed and larger stones were used; slaves and animals were harnessed to provide power for the grinding. It was the Romans who introduced water power. About A.D. 600 the wind was also harnessed and the familiar windmill began to appear on the landscape. Stone milling in its various forms is still in practice today.

In stone milling the upper stone revolves on the lower stone, which remains stationary. The cleaned wheat is fed into a hole in the centre of the upper stone, sheared open and crushed to a coarse meal. The heat caused by friction lowers the viscosity of the wheat germ oil, which is readily absorbed by the meal. Bread made from stone ground wholemeal is thus given a distinct flavour, which is delicious. As the oil will become rancid, 100% wholemeal will not keep so long in storage as white flour, therefore it should be used more quickly.

Roller milling was introduced into this country from Hungary about 1878, and today most of the world's flour is produced by this method. The process may be roughly divided into three stages—cleaning and conditioning, breaking and reduction.

Cleaning

When the grain comes to the mill it is dirty and has mixed with it, amongst other things, chaff, straw, soil, pieces of metal and foreign seeds. It is obvious that these must be removed on the grounds of cleanliness, possible damage to machinery and the ultimate quality of the flour.

The first operation in the cleaning process is *Screening*, when, after weighing, the grain is passed through a series of sieves to remove objects that are much larger and smaller than the wheat grain. During this process, metal objects are removed magnetically and air currents remove the lighter impurities such as chaff and pieces of straw; this use of air currents is known as aspiration.

The next operation is *Sorting*, by which foreign seeds such as barley, oats and rye are removed. This is done by passing the grain through separators, which are horizontal drums that are indented. These indentations are too small to hold the wheat grain, but hold the smaller seeds, which are removed. The grain is passed to a similar separator, but in this case the indentations are of a size that will hold the wheat grains, and the larger seeds are removed. This type of separator is being replaced by what is known as the disc separator, which employs the same principle but in a different form.

The next cleaning stage is *Scrubbing*. In this the wheat is passed through scourers which remove the beard or tuft. Adhering dirt is also removed together with the cellulose grain covering known as 'beeswing'. The scourers are lined with emery, which effectively removes these extraneous products which are taken away by aspirating air currents.

The rest of the dirt is taken off at the next stage, which is *Washing*, when the grain is propelled through water by an endless screw. During this operation any stones that may have escaped the separators, sink, and are removed. The surface moisture is then taken off in machines known as 'whizzers'.

Scrubbing and washing are two very important operations in the cleaning process, because micro-organisms on the fine hairs of the beard and in the dust and dirt on the grain, especially in the crease of the grain, will, if not removed, adversely affect the quality of the flour.

Conditioning

We know that wheat will differ according to the type, country of origin and soil and climatic conditions; in consequence, the constituent parts of the wheat will not be uniform. This would be extremely difficult for the miller as far as moisture content is concerned because, if it is too high, the wheat would flatten and clog the rollers; if too dry, it would burst on pressure and it would be difficult, if not impossible, to remove the tiny bran snips from the finished flour.

Conditioning also has a physical affect on the bran coatings, rendering them tough enough to be removed in fairly large pieces during the operation of 'breaking', while the endosperm remains brittle and in a condition for satisfactory milling.

The operation of conditioning is of the utmost importance in the milling process, since its purpose is to adjust the moisture content to uniformity, and at the same time to toughen the bran coatings. To effect the adjustment the wheat can be allowed to absorb moisture during the washing stage, or moisture can be reduced by radiators or warm air currents afterwards.

Breaking

The wheat, cleaned and conditioned, is next passed to the break rolls, a series of machines containing grooved rollers, geared so that the top roller rotates in an opposite direction and two and a half times faster than the bottom roller. They are enclosed in dustproof, wooden cabinets, with inspection windows. In the No. 1 break, the evenly distributed wheat is held in the grooves of the bottom roller, and sheared open by the faster upper roller. The product of this breaking is sent to scalpers, which are of many types, comprising reels, centrifugals, plan-sifters and oscillating sieves, where it is divided into three streams as follows: (1) The large pieces, sent to the second series of break rolls, where they are further opened out by rollers set closer together and with finer grooves. (2) Semolina (coarse flour) which is graded into various particle sizes, including dunst, which is very fine, and break middlings, intermediate between dunst and flour. All these are passed to the reduction rollers. (3) Some flour which is sent direct to the bag.

At the second series of break rolls the break stock, as it is known, is given a further separation, which is followed by a similar grading. The same operations are repeated at the third and fourth breaks where the separation of the endosperm from the bran is completed.

Reduction

Before the semolinas, dunst and break middlings reach the reduction rollers, they pass through purifiers where by aspiration any branny particles are removed. The object of reduction is to reduce the stock to fine flour. The reduction rollers are smooth and the difference in rotating speed is not so great as that of the break rollers and they are set according to the size of the fractions that are to be reduced.

After each reduction the stock is sieved, and the flour sent to plan-sifters or centrifugals similar to scalpers, but covered with fine silk instead of wire mesh. The coarse particles that are sieved out are passed to finer reduction rollers for further reduction; this procedure is repeated until the stock is reduced to flour and by-products. The germ, which is tough and oily, flattens during the early rolling and is easily removed.

After treatment with improvers and the statutory addition of calcium and, in the case of 72% extraction white flour, certain nutrients, the flour is bagged and weighed ready for dispatch.

FRAGMENTATION MILLING

The student should be aware of a new milling technique by which it is possible to control the protein quality and quantity of flour. This new technique is known as fragmentation or fractionization and is effected by a combination of normal milling and centrifugal air separation.

In the normal milling process, the grist is calculated by the miller according to the type of flour to be produced, bearing in mind that there are critical differences between the protein qualities of such distinctive wheats as Manitoban, Plate, Australian and European. With the new system the grist is no longer an all-important factor.

The student will remember that the endosperm is approximately 85% of the wheat grain. This part of the grain is made up of very thin cellulose bags containing many starch granules embedded in a dry matrix composed of protein, mineral matter, sugar, enzymes, etc. During milling the break rollers splinter the endosperm into particles of differing sizes. These particles can be measured scientifically and the measurement is the micron which is expressed by the symbol μ; the micron is one millionth of a metre.

After the breaking process the particles of endosperm can be sorted into three sizes: some, over 40 microns, are simply smaller pieces of the parent endosperm and similar in composition; those between 15 and 40 microns are largely starch granules and therefore low in protein and the particles smaller than 15 microns are starch granules together with a high percentage of protein. The student will see quite clearly that if the fractions can be separated by particle size, then flours of high or low protein content can be produced simply by addition or subtraction.

The separation is carried out by a machine known as a centrifugal air classifier. This machine has been so far perfected that air speed within it is constant and not subject to frictional speed losses on the inner walls of the chamber. This is done by spinning the walls of the chamber at the same speed as the air flow. In this way a much finer particle separation is effected.

With the development of fragmentation milling, it is possible to produce from comparatively poor quality flour, fractions which may be suitable for special baking purposes, such as the production of biscuits or high-ratio cakes. High protein fractions can be removed and added to flours considered too weak for breadmaking purposes or to breadmaking flour for the production of high protein bread. By the use of this new technique the miller, with a greater control over flour grading and quality, will be able to sell flour by specification. The baker in turn, with the variability of flours reduced to a minimum, will be able to exert a greater technical control over fermentation and cake-making processes.

4

Flour Grades: Extraction Rates; Constituents of Flour; Nutritional Value; Simple Flour Tests; The Function of Gluten; Self-Raising Flour

FLOUR GRADES

THE essential difference between stone and roller milling is that in roller milling, flour and meal of any extraction rate can be produced. In stone milling the whole of the wheat is ground to a meal and is thus of 100% extraction. The only adjustment possible with stone ground meal is by sieving through silks so that the coarser particles are removed.

The extraction rate is the amount of meal or flour that the miller produces from a given amount of clean wheat. It is possible, for example, to produce the following from 100 lb. of wheat:

		By-products	*Extraction per cent*
100 lb.	Wholemeal	—	100
90–95 lb.	Wheatmeal	5–10 lb.	90–95
70–72 lb.	Straight-run	28–30 lb.	70–72
20–40 lb.	Patents	60–80 lb.	20–40

From a suitable grist, the miller can produce from 100 lb. of wheat: 40 lb. of Patents, 30 lb. of flour of a lower grade and 30 lb. of by-products. The two grades together represent Straight-run of 70% extraction. During the last war and until 1955, flour mills were controlled by the Ministry of Food and, due to the exigencies of war and its aftermath, the Ministry fixed the extraction rate of 'National Straight-Run' flour; this figure fluctuated from 80 to 90%.

The student will know from his study of the wheat grain that the endosperm is approximately 85% of the whole and consists mainly of starch with a quantity of protein, oil, sugar, moisture and mineral matter and that it is the insoluble protein which produces gluten when it is mixed with water.

Protein is not evenly distributed throughout the endosperm; even the quality varies according to where it is found in the grain. There is a greater percentage nearer the bran coatings but the quality is better nearer the centre. A further point is that the nearer the miller gets to the bran coats, the greater the possibility of including bran snips which will darken the flour.

From one wheat, the miller can produce: (1) flour of a better colour, containing less of a higher quality gluten; (2) flour from the outer section of the endosperm, of poorer colour but with a higher percentage of lower quality gluten; (3) a straight-run flour which is a blend of both.

In the mill, the break and the reduction rollers are always numbered, so that the flow of the various grades of flour can be controlled. Break 'chop' from 1 and 2 break rollers is eventually directed to 1 and 2 reduction rollers and it is from these that some of the best flour is produced: from the next rollers flour of a lower grade is produced, and from the last rollers, the lowest grade of all.

Reference has been made to soft and strong flours but within this rough division are many grades depending on the grist used by the miller or on the country of origin. Very strong flour can be milled from grists containing practically all Manitoban wheat, the extraction rate being approximately 60%. Soft flours can be milled from practically all English and Red Winter wheats or from wheats similar in strength. Some of the finest biscuit flours are milled from a grist containing all English wheat with an extraction rate of up to 70%.

In addition, the baker can buy imported flours, such as strong Canadian or softer Australian flour which is of excellent colour. These flours can be used for blending with home-milled flours or used for special types of bakery products.

The baker has today, the choice of three grades of home-milled flour for breadmaking and for products requiring similar flour; they are, Patents, Baker's Grade and Straight-Run. In addition, quite apart from special meals, there are 100% wholemeal and wheatmeals of extraction rates between 85% and 98%.

The grades of flour suitable for cakemaking are dealt with in Chapter 23.

CONSTITUENTS OF FLOUR (1)

Flour is not just a dusty substance from which many articles of food can be made; it is a wonderful mixture of chemical compounds, all of which can be separated with very little difficulty.

The amount of these constituent parts will vary according to the type of wheat, the source and the growing conditions. It has been stated previously that flour can be graded under three headings—strong, medium and weak. Generally speaking, this rough grading is a reference to the character of the flour.

Strong flours are such that they will produce a bold, well-risen loaf over a fairly long fermentation period. Very strong flours are capable of prolonged fermentation with a resultant bread of good quality.

The medium-strong flours will make good bread on shorter fermentation processes. Soft, weak flours are unsuitable for breadmaking except with a blend of stronger flour.

Flours vary in both the content and quality of gluten; flour strength is measured by gluten quality and not by quantity. Flour with an average gluten content of high quality is much more suitable for breadmaking than a flour with a high quantity of gluten of poor quality. Gluten quality is measured by elasticity and extensibility together with a certain tenacity. Here is a typical analysis of a breadmaking flour:

	%
Starch	70
Moisture	13
Gluten	13
Fat	1
Sugars	2·5
Mineral matter	0·5

The figure given for mineral matter does not include calcium (*creta preparata*) which is added by the miller at the rate of 14 oz. per sack (280 lb.).

(*a*) *Starch.* The student can separate some starch from flour by making a small flour-and-water dough and soaking it for about 30 minutes in water. After soaking, place the dough in a piece of muslin and squeeze it in a bowl of clean, cold water until what is left in the muslin is a greyish, rubbery substance which is gluten. Let the 'milky' water stand for some hours, when a white precipitate will form. This is starch, which can be recovered by filtering and then air drying.

(*b*) *Gluten.* Gluten is very important to the baker; without it in dough, the gas generated by yeast or baking powder would escape, and there would be no aeration. Without it there would be no structure in bread, or in any cake made without eggs, because gluten coagulates or sets at about 140° F., and the loaf or cake becomes rigid and does not collapse.

If the gluten is soaked in cold water for thirty minutes and then stretched between the fingers, it will be found that different glutens vary according to the type of flour from which they are extracted. If, for instance, it offers considerable resistance to stretching and then breaks, the flour from which it was extracted can be considered very strong. If it is fairly extensible and has elasticity, then the flour is suitable for breadmaking, buns and anything requiring a medium-strong flour. If it breaks easily and is short and friable, then the flour is suitable only for such products as short pastry and biscuits.

Gluten contains about twice its weight of water, so that if the weight of gluten from a given weight of flour is divided by three, a rough idea of the dry gluten figure in flour is obtained.

(*c*) *Moisture.* Flour contains moisture, the percentage of which depends on the wheat grist and the moisture adjustment in the milling process. For the baker it is economically important that the flour should not have a high moisture content; first because it lowers the water-carrying capacity of flour in breadmaking and secondly because the flour is more liable to mustiness, or the collection of 'off' flavours during storage.

It is interesting to note that flour, which seems such a dry powder, contains an average of about three gallons of water per sack (280 lb.).

CONSTITUENTS OF FLOUR (2)

(*d*) *Oil.* All flours contain a small amount of oil. Of the constituent parts of wheat, bran contains about 3·5% and the germ anything from 6 to 11%. The average for the whole of the wheat grain is 2%. Thus it can be easily understood that, as the extraction rate is lowered, so the oil content becomes progressively less as the bran coatings and the germ are discarded. The approximate figures are:

Extraction rate	*Oil per cent*
100% Wholemeal	up to 2·5
95% Wheatmeal	1·6–2·2
85% Flour	1·5–2·0
72% Flour	1·0–1·5

Wheat oils, like all other oils, are liable to oxidative changes and become rancid. This may be hastened by bad storage and temperature conditions. As far as white flour is concerned, the miller goes to a great deal of trouble to eliminate the oil as far as possible.

One hundred per cent wholemeal has not such a long storage life as white flour and until used, should be stored under ideal conditions; a cool storage temperature is essential. Germ meals, all of which have a high oil content, do not have a long storage life, despite the fact that the germ is cooked and salted to retard rancidity.

Wheat oil is a pale yellow in colour, although oil extracted from flour that has been bleached is almost colourless. Wheat germ oil is rich in vitamin E, which is considered to be the vitamin responsible for fertility.

(*e*) *Sugar.* Flour contains small but important amounts of various sugars, such as sucrose, maltose and dextrose, without which, in the presence of yeast, there could be no fermentation. Dextrose is directly fermentable by yeast to CO_2 and by-products; sucrose and maltose only after they have been converted to dextrose by enzymes in yeast and in flour.

The sugar content of flour actual and potential (known as the maltose figure) is of the utmost importance to the baker because, during bulk fermentation, intermediate and final proof, the gas production in dough is influenced by the amount of sugar available at each stage.

The sugar content of flour increases as the extraction rate is lengthened. Here are some examples:

Extraction rate %	*Sugar %*
72	1·5–2·0
85	2·0–2·5
100	2·0–3·0

(*f*) *Minerals.* The mineral content of flour is calculated by burning a given quantity; the ash which is left is the indestructible mineral matter which chiefly consists of the phosphates of potassium, magnesium, calcium, with traces of iron.

Earlier it was learned that the higher grade flours are milled from the centre of the wheat grain, and the lower grades from nearer the bran coatings, so that fine bran specks will be present causing the flour to be darker. Bleaching will improve the colour but the bran snips will remain. Bran has a higher ash content than endosperm, so that ash determination is a guide to flour quality, provided that due allowance is made for possible mineral additions to flour and for the calcium addition (*creta preparata*). The constituent parts of flour and the methods of separation are shown in the diagram opposite.

WHITE BREAD VERSUS BROWN BREAD

At this stage the student must expect homework or examination questions on the relative merits of brown and white bread or breads made from flours of different extraction rates. Questions such as

CONSTITUENTS OF FLOUR

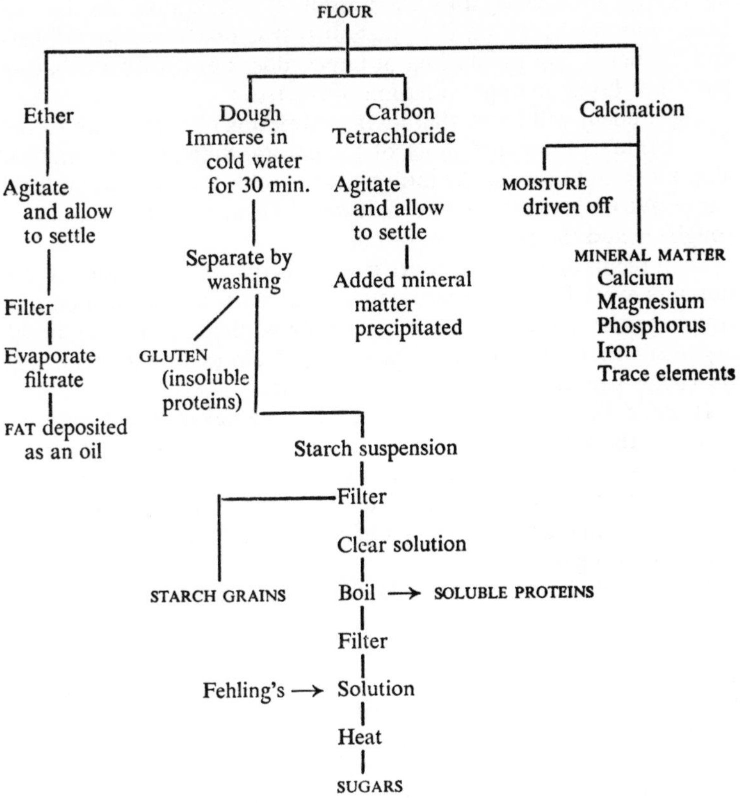

In all but wholemeal flours the mineral matter will include *creta preparata.* Approximate composition of low extraction flour:

	%
Moisture	13 –15·5
Mineral matter	0·3– 1·3
Protein	8 –13
Fat	0·8– 1·5
Starch	65 –70
Sugar	1·5– 2·5

these have occupied quite a lot of space in the press and are generally controversial. The student, however, will answer them factually, using the knowledge he has on the subject. The alternative is the controversial approach and this is not wise, for in the whole field of controversy it is a common practice, as a last resort, to bestow names on a doughty opponent, especially if he has a good case. Controversy on food in general, and bread in particular, is no exception and the parties are divided into 'food faddists' and 'cranks' on the one hand, and 'die-hards' on the other. It is true that there *are* faddists and die-hards, but the hurling of names does not clarify a debating point nor bring an approximation of the truth.

The student will know that as the extraction rate increases so the flour contains more and more of the natural nutrients. It contains, also, more and more of the indigestible roughage which has no food value. As the extraction rate is lowered so also is the amount of roughage and the percentage of nutrients.

So it seems on this quantitative analysis that the protagonists are honours even. But as the nutrients are far more important than the roughage the 'faddists' have a case. Against them, of course, is the argument that 'men do not live by bread alone' and any nutrient deficiency can be made up with other foods.

It could be expected that, in the past, the baker would raise his voice on the side of the retention of the natural nutrients as a sales factor of some importance, but it was never heard. The exigencies of war, however, made it necessary for the people to be well fed, and in national bread the people had a loaf of high nutritional value without too much roughage.

Because of the shortage of dairy products during and after the war, bread was made the vehicle for increasing the calcium intake of the consumer. Accordingly 7 oz. of *creta preparata* was added to each sack of flour. As the extraction rate increased, so also did phytic acid, a natural factor in wheat. Phytic acid was thought to retard the assimilation of calcium in the human digestive system and so *creta preparata* was increased to 14 oz. per sack (280 lb.).

It seems now that the 'faddists' have proved their case, for the Flour Order (1953) requires the following addition to be made by the millers:

(1) All flour (other than flour containing the whole product of the milling of wheat and no addition whatsoever): 14 oz. *creta preparata* per sack:

(2) Flour of an extraction of less than 80% in sufficient quantity to ensure a minimum content of:

Iron	1·65 mg./100 gm.
Vitamin B_1	0·24 mg./100 gm.
Nicotinic acid	1·60 mg./100 gm.

The nutritional value of white 72% extraction straight-run flour and 80% extraction straight-run is thus, at the present time, approximately the same, the white being a little lighter in colour.

It seems that there is now little to argue about, except whether there is any good reason for taking out the natural nutrients and replacing them synthetically, and whether the addition of *creta preparata* is now necessary,

SIMPLE FLOUR TESTS

(1) *Colour.* Flours, as distinct from meals, vary in colour from dead white to creamy yellow, and from yellow to grey, according to the wheats or grist from which they are milled, the milling process, the grade or extraction rate and possible bleaching.

A high-grade low extraction flour, if examined in a good light, will be seen as a creamy yellow in colour and have a surface sparkle—a bright reflection of light-known as 'bloom'.

A simple method of examining flour colour is the Pekar test. This is a comparison test of colour only, and it is advisable to have a flour of known good colour as a control against which the colour of other flours can be compared. The method is as follows:

On a narrow strip of glass or plywood, arrange small heaps of the flours to be tested; placing them side by side, and flattening them with a smooth scraper, and then trimming the edges off wedge shape. Any marked differences in colour will be clearly seen.

To accentuate any differences, immerse the board in clean cold water, introducing the thin edge of the wedge first, and keeping it submerged until the bubbles have subsided. Then withdraw the board, again with the thin edge first. Any slight differences in colour will be more clearly seen.

(2) *Gluten.*—Weigh accurately 20 grams of the flour to be tested, and place in a clean porcelain or enamelled dish; add 11 c.c. of tap water and mix to a clear dough with a glass rod or a metal spatula, taking care that none of the flour or water is spilled during this process. Place the piece of dough in cold water for about 30 min., and then wash it out under the tap, working it all the while with the fingers until the water running from it is clear and no longer a 'milky' white.

It is advisable to place a sieve under the stream of water to catch any small pieces of gluten, so that they may be easily recovered. Squeeze between the fingers to expel as much of the water as possible, and then lay it aside on a smooth surface for about 10 min. when more water will settle out.

On average, wet gluten is two parts water, so that to estimate the percentage of dry gluten, multiply the weight by 5 and divide the result by 3. Here is an example:

From 20 grams of flour, 9 grams of wet gluten is extracted.

Therefore $9 \times 5 \div 3 = 15\%$ dry gluten.

If gluten estimating is to be done regularly, the whole operation must be standardized. The mixing time must be always the same; the period of soaking must be constant; the temperature and rate of flow of the washing water and the period of washing time, must be always the same. It is only in this way that reliable estimations can be made.

If the student is less concerned with accuracy and more with the practical test, then with 3½ oz. of flour make up a dough with 2 oz. of tap water. When thoroughly mixed, allow to soak for 30 min. and then wash out as described above. This larger piece of gluten can then be soaked in cold water for about 30 min., then the stretching test for quality can be applied as described earlier in this chapter.

The gluten colour of high-grade flours is yellow. Strong flours and low-grade flours yield glutens greyish in colour, as do bleached flours, but in the latter case the gluten darkens on exposure to the air. Weak glutens are usually pale yellow in colour.

As an experiment the student should make a series of gluten extractions at timed intervals, all from a single fermenting dough, starting from dough-making. It will be noticed that as fermentation proceeds, the gluten colour brightens until, when the dough is ripe, it reaches its maximum colour brightness.

(3) *Water Absorbing Power.*—Water-absorbing capacity or power is generally referred to, for short, as W.A.P.

All flours differ in their capacities for absorbing water, so that in all breadmaking, whether on a commercial or a student scale, care must be exercised when adding water to a flour of unknown W.A.P. It is because of this varying capacity in flours for taking up water that, in all formulae for bread and fermented goods, the water content is always given as approximate, and this the student must always bear in mind.

It is well for the student also to know how to carry out a test for estimating the W.A.P., not only for its usefulness in practical work, but to enable him to answer a possible question on the subject in a written examination.

Take 28 grams of the flour to be tested and place it into a porcelain dish; from a graduated burette, run in 12 c.c. of water and mix carefully with a metal spatula, without spilling any of the flour or water. If the dough is too tight, run in water, 1 c.c. or even ½ c.c. at a time, until the right consistency is reached. A good deal of experience is necessary in assessing the correct consistency in so small a dough. To compute the W.A.P., calculate each c.c. of water used as 1 gallon per sack.

(4) *Baking Test.*—In competent hands this is an excellent test for flour quality, especially as a follow-on to confirm the conclusions

V A fine photograph illustrating the qualities of sheen and texture

VI Wheatmeal loaf showing crumb vesiculation

VII Examples of fermented goods

reached from the preceding tests. Not only does it give the opportunity of detailed examination of the internal and external qualities of the finished bread, but also of studying the fermentation during all stages of manufacture. The study can be extended, if necessary, to the staling of the loaf and the formation of moulds.

A useful formula for a test batch of bread is given; it is extended to show how it can easily be used to calculate the proportion of raw materials on a sack basis.

lb.	*oz.*		*oz.*	
1	12	Flour	28	× 10 = 280
	½	Salt	0·5	× 10 = 5
	15	Water (approx.)	15	× 10 = 150
	¾	Yeast	0·75	× 10 = 7½

Dough temperature 80° F.
Knock back at 1 hr.
Scale at 1½ „

It will be seen that, taking the 280 as pounds, there is the equivalent of 5 lb. of salt, 150 lb. (15 gallons) of water and 7½ lb. of yeast per sack in the small test batch. The student is reminded, however, that 7½ lb. of yeast would not be needed in a sack batch at this fermentation speed. He will remember the calculation of yeast quantity using the factor 9. Using this figure with a dough fermenting for 1½ hr., approximately 6 lb. of yeast would be needed for a sack dough.

If baking tests are to be carried out regularly, then everything, as far as possible, must be rigidly standardized, so that any differences in the finished product can fairly be ascribed to variations in flour quality.

In baking tests the following points should be systematically recorded:

(1) The 'feel' and consistency of the dough at making. This will give the opportunity of checking the W.A.P. of the flour.
(2) Alterations in consistency during fermentation; i.e. note any marked tightening or softening.
(3) Feel of the dough at the time of knocking back.
(4) Retention of shape after handing up.
(5) The speeds of intermediate and final proof.

When the loaf is baked and sufficiently cooled it can be examined for the following:

Exterior	*Interior*
Bloom	Colour
Crust colour	Flavour and aroma
Oven spring	Moistness
Volume	Structure
Shape	Crumb softness and stability

THE FUNCTION OF GLUTEN IN BREADMAKING

Gluten is that part of wheat protein which, when hydrated, is not soluble in a water/salt solution. It can be washed out from a mixture of flour and water or from a piece of fermented dough. The procedure for washing out has been described.

It is considered that there are five constituent parts in wheat protein; (1) Albumin, (2) Globulin, (3) Proteose, (4) Gliadin, (5) Glutenin.

These can be further divided into four groups: (1) those soluble in water; (2) those soluble in a salt solution; (3) those soluble in 70% alcohol; (4) the remainder, insoluble in all three.

The first three of the constituent parts, amounting to about 1–2% of the flour, are known as the soluble proteins and provide the basis for the necessary nitrogenous yeast food during fermentation in the dough.

It is gliadin and glutenin that together form gluten. The former, it is considered, confers elasticity on the dough. Glutenin confers stability and tenacity. It is considered also that the sticky gliadin acts as a binding agent to the tough glutenin. The ratio of these two to each other is about 50/50.

Without gluten in dough there could be no bread, as we know it, for gluten provides the means whereby the gas generated by yeast is trapped and held in the dough structure. When it coagulates under the influence of heat during baking, it becomes the framework or girderwork of the loaf, so that it becomes comparatively rigid and does not collapse.

Flours differ in gluten quality and quantity, but it is always important to remember that it is quality rather than quantity that is essential in good breadmaking. According to the qualities of stability and elasticity it possesses, gluten has the important power of retaining the gas generated by yeast, thus giving volume to the loaf.

It can be said that the whole art of dough fermentation is to have the gluten at the oven stage so ripened that it will give easily to the expanding gases, at the same time retaining them without breaking down. The result of this can be seen in the examination of a slice of well fermented bread. If the slice is held to a strong light, the whole vesiculated structure can be clearly seen.

Gluten is conditioned as the result of a combination of many factors; such as the amount of yeast and its activity, the amount of salt and water in the dough, fermentation time, dough temperature, the acidity of the dough, manipulation and the effect of additions.

We have seen that the amount of yeast, among other things, will regulate the speed of fermentation and consequent ripening; so also will the amounts of salt and water. In addition, the amount of salt influences the potential strength of flour, because salt increases the stability of gluten.

Fermentation time has an appreciable effect on gluten, because this will give water the opportunity of exerting a softening action. Time also will increase the acidity of the dough, which beyond certain limits begins to undermine the stability of gluten.

Dough manipulation has an extremely important effect on gluten development, especially in the dough-making stage. It is no exaggeration to say that, given good materials and in the correct balance according to the process being used, nothing contributes to good breadmaking more than a properly made dough. Apart from the thorough dispersal of ingredients, proper mixing gives the gluten the opportunity of taking up the maximum amount of water and becoming thoroughly hydrated, all of which helps in the final conditioning.

Additions play their part in gluten conditioning. Some chemical flour improvers confer an artificial strength on gluten. The casein of milk has a tightening effect, while fat is considered to lubricate the gluten strands, giving an increased volume to the loaf.

SELF-RAISING FLOUR

It is necessary for the student to know what is meant by self-raising flour, both for the purpose of making it in commercial practice, and answering a possible question on the subject in a written examination. It is also necessary to know the statutory regulations concerning the composition and sale.

Self-raising flour is an intimate mixture of flour and a sufficient amount of baking powder. It was once a regular job in the bakery, done during a slack period in the week, generally by the bread bakers. The flour and baking powder were thoroughly sieved, after which it was packed into yellow coloured paper bags, generally into 1½ lb. units.

The bulk of self-raising flour is now pre-packed in the mill and sold to bakers and grocers, who retail it to the public.

Self-raising flour is subject to a Ministry of Food regulation which states that the flour shall yield not less than 0·40% of available carbon dioxide at the time of sale to the consumer. For this reason the packer will see that this figure is much higher so that (1) it allows for the loss of CO_2 consequent on prolonged storage before sale, and (2) the aerating material will give maximum activity during baking.

Acid calcium phosphate is the baking acid generally used, because it exerts a stabilizing effect on gluten, conferring an artificial strength. It reacts with bi-carbonate of soda more rapidly than does acid sodium pyrophosphate, but this, it is considered, finds favour with the housewife, because she prefers evidence of aerating activity, and in any case her products are generally placed into the oven without delay.

If A.C.P. of an effective acidity of 80% is used, 1¼ lb. will be necessary to ensure a complete reaction with 1 lb. of bicarbonate of soda. The percentage figure represents the number of parts of bicarbonate which can be neutralized by 100 parts of A.C.P. Here is a formula for self-raising flour using A.C.P. (80%),

280 lb. Flour
4½ lb. A.C.P.
3½ lb. Bicarbonate of soda

After sieving the chemicals separately, the A.C.P. is sieved with about 70 lb. of flour, and the soda with a similar amount. Both are mixed with the balance of the flour and the whole thoroughly sieved, until the chemical ingredients are intimately mixed.

Here is another formula using standard strength cream powder:

280 lb. Flour
6½ lb. Cream powder
3¼ lb. Bicarbonate of soda
1 lb. Salt

As the housewife uses self-raising flour for all types of cooking, the flour should not be too strong. A top patent Australian flour is suggested, because of its medium strength and good colour.

The test for determining the total available figure of CO_2 requires proper laboratory facilities. For a general test of acid/alkaline balance and comparative volume, it is considered that the steamed pudding test is the best. The self-raising flour is simply mixed with cold water, the dough weighed into pieces, placed into small containers and steamed. This is done under controlled conditions; all weights being predetermined and strictly adhered to; steaming time, size of containers and all else being standardized.

The crumb surface can then be spotted with phenol red or B.D.H. Universal Indicator, so that any errors in acid/soda proportions can be detected. The same test is useful for obtaining data on comparative volumes, using different types of flour and baking-powder.

5

Panary Fermentation: Historical Survey; Yeast: Structure and Life; Function of Yeast; Condition and Storage; Manufacture

PANARY FERMENTATION (HISTORICAL)

THE French say '*bon comme le pain*', which means as good as bread. The Arabs speak of bread as God's gift. All over the world bread means food and life. Well may we pray, 'Give us this day our daily bread.' Where there is no bread there is famine.

It is not known who was the first baker, for he or she practised in the dim ages of antiquity. If the student will go to the British Museum in London, some of the oldest bread in the world can be seen. It was found in Switzerland and is probably 5,000 years old. Samples of bread made 2,000 years ago, excavated from the ruins of Pompeii, can be seen in the museum of Naples, with the maker's name still visible on the loaf.

The Bible refers to leavened and unleavened bread. One thing is certain; the discovery of leaven or fermentation was accidental. When it occurred is unknown, but it is probable that it was in primitive times.

It is known that bread in the form of unleavened cakes was made, and it is easy to imagine a piece of unbaked dough from an old batch being mixed with a new dough, and to the delight of the primitive baker it was found to be leavened; in fact it was softer and lighter in texture because of fermentation.

For hundreds of years, bread was leavened by the addition of sour dough, and in the oldest book on breadmaking, written in 240 B.C., it is mentioned that old dough was made up into yeast cakes and used to ferment a new dough. In the Roman Empire, bakers were held in high repute and were the only tradesmen who were not slaves.

The large consumption of bread led to the development of a well-organized baking industry. The first baker's guild was founded in the reign of the Emperor Augustine, the guild sign being a baker's trough and three ears of corn. All tools and equipment were obtained collectively, the organization being perfect. Bakery craftsmen were eagerly sought after, master craftsmen earning up to 100,000 sesterces per annum, which is the equivalent today of about £800–£900.

The medieval baker used barm as a leaven. This was a carefully made mixture of malt and hops with water, and some of the coarse meal then milled. It was inoculated by air-borne yeast micro-organisms (although this was not known at the time), and it began to ferment, after which it was made into a dough. A little of this dough was saved to serve as a starter for the next barm, and so the process went on. In many parts of the world the sour dough method of fermentation is still used, especially in the making of rye bread.

In the seventeenth and eighteenth centuries, those who had need of the processes of fermentation began to apply the practical knowledge gained by innoculating successive barms or ferments, and it is recorded that in the Hebrides a hazel twig was dipped into a ferment and then carefully dried. All that was necessary to start a new ferment was to stir it with the twig. During these times the yeast rising to the top of home-made wine was collected, washed and dried; this however was not completely successful for breadmaking. It was during these times also that a considerable amount of brewers' yeast was used by bakers and by women who did home baking. Many methods of preserving and refining this yeast were tried, the most successful being the slow drying after spreading on a cloth. It was then stored for use as required.

Brewers' yeast imparted a sweet nutty flavour to the loaf, and in competent hands made excellent bread. At first, being in unlimited supply, it was easy to obtain and fairly cheap to use, but as its use became general, and in consequence the supply more limited, it not only increased in price, but also became an object for adulteration, and this, together with the introduction of other yeasts, practically put an end to business between brewer and baker.

The new 'patent' yeasts were an excellent substitute as far as fermentation was concerned, but did not impart the distinctive flavour of brewers' yeast.

Up to the year 1859 it was thought that fermentation was something that just happened, but then the great French scientist, Louis Pasteur, showed that it was the result of micro-organisms converting sugar into carbon dioxide gas (CO_2), which is the gas that aerates the dough. With this discovery, science began slowly to enter the bakery and the baker who made his own 'patent' yeast became aware of the importance of scrupulous cleanliness, at least as far as the making of yeast was concerned.

With the 'patent' yeast came the ferment, which was the means of multiplying and strengthening the yeast still further. Thus a small amount of yeast used initially was induced to do a great amount of work in time.

There were several types of ferments or barms, each of them having adherents according to local conditions, the raw materials available, and personal preferences. In principle, however, they were the same, all being media containing the necessary food for the life and reproduction of the yeast organism.

One was the 'Spon' or virgin barm, 'Spon' being an abbreviation of 'spontaneous' which, as already mentioned, was the explanation of the fermentation process, before Pasteur made his discoveries. This barm was prepared in the usual way and allowed to be inoculated by air-borne yeast spores.

Compound barms were also popular. These contained malt and hops, and were started by the addition of small amounts of the yeasts available, such as brewers', patent, or compressed. Some draught beer or a bottle of stout, both of which contained yeast, were also used as starters. Craftsmen of the day added other ingredients to the barm, such as boiled mashed potatoes, brown sugar, and even ginger and carraway seeds, which they termed 'strengtheners' or 'correctors'.

In the early days of the century the compressed yeast as we know it today was made available to the baker. Made under scientifically controlled conditions, it arrives at the bakery beautifully fresh and pure, a wonderful and essential raw material which plays a major part in the production of daily bread that is the pride of the British baker.

YEAST STRUCTURE AND LIFE

First of all, the diagram overleaf shows clearly the classification of yeast in the pattern of living organisms.

Yeast is a living micro-organism belonging to the fungi family of plants. It is devoid of the green colouring matter in plants, known as chlorophyll. Because of this it cannot obtain carbon from carbon dioxide as do other plants. Instead this element is obtained from carbohydrates.

Sugar is the carbohydrate necessary for yeast fermentation. It is because of this that yeasts are called saccharomyces, which means a sugar fungus. There are many types of yeast that come under the

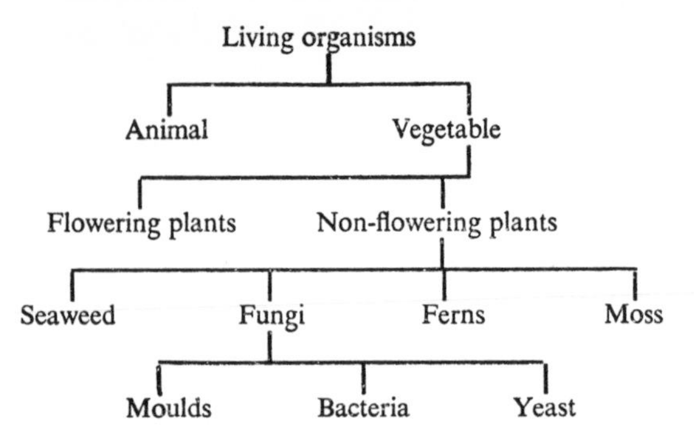

general heading of saccharomyces, each having different characteristics, in much the same way as in other forms of animal and vegetable life. For example, there are many types of dog in the animal world and roses in the world of vegetation, all of them coming under their respective generic headings. The type or strain of yeast used by the baker is known as *saccharomyces cerevisiae*.

Mico-organisms are so named because they are invisible to the naked eye and can only be examined under the microscope. Yeast cells are so small that over 4,000 could be placed side by side and equal the diameter of a penny, while 10,000,000 could be accommodated on the whole surface. Under the microscope the yeast cell

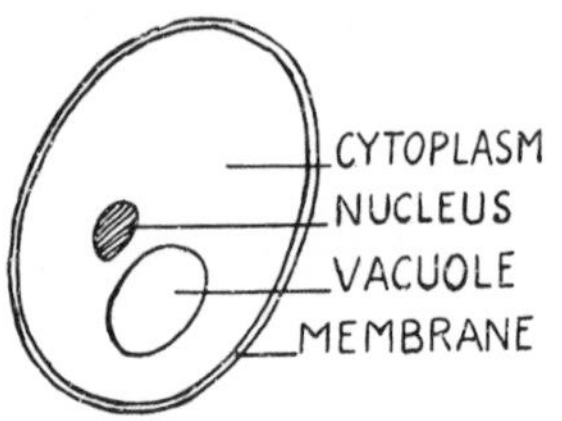

FIG. 4.—The yeast cell.

is seen to be round or slightly oval in shape (Fig. 4) with a semi-permeable double membrane wall, which controls the movement in and out, of dissolved substances.

Careful observation will show that within the cell itself there is one or more well defined areas known as vacuoles, a name derived from the word 'vacuum', since it was thought that this area was devoid of any substance. It is now known to contain the cell sap which is considered to be the reserve for the nucleus.

The nucleus itself is seen as a small dark spot near the vacuole; it is the 'life' of the yeast and carries the characteristics of the particular strain. Surrounding the vacuole and within the yeast cell is an aqueous solution known as cytoplasm. It is a reserve for the yeast, and consists of an intimate mixture of fatty particles, glycogen, which is a carbohydrate, mineral matter and water. In addition it contains certain enzymes. The average percentage composition of yeast is as follows:

Water	68 –73	Carbohydrate (cellulose and starchy matter)	9 –11
Proteins	12 –14		
Fat	0·6 – 0·8	Mineral matter	1·7– 2

Yeast has two life cycles:

(1) *Reproduction by Budding* (Fig. 5).—When in a suitable medium for growth, the yeast cell will reproduce itself. This can be seen if a very small amount of yeast is dispersed in water, with a little added sugar, and a spot put on to a microscope slide, covered with a cover slip, then placed under the microscope. The yeast cell will be seen to develop buds which grow and become as large as the original or parent cell, becoming in fact new cells.

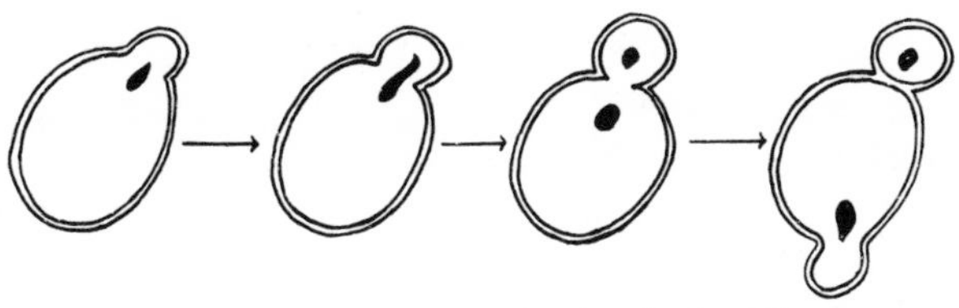

FIG. 5.—Yeast. Reproduction by budding.

The new, or 'daughter', cell is then capable of reproduction in turn, and at the same time the parent cell is still reproducing, resulting in an accumulation of yeast cells.

There are great changes taking place in the cells immediately before reproduction takes place. The composition of the cytoplasm changes as a consequence of the absorption of food. The vacuole and the nucleus become extended towards the bud that begins to form on the outer wall. As the bud grows, the nucleus divides and, complete with a new vacuole, enters the new cell; the connection between the cells closes and the daughter cell becomes a complete and separate unit. The cells remain in contact in doughs, or in still ferments and sponges, but separate in thin ferments, especially if they are vigorously stirred.

(2) *Reproduction by Sporulation* (Fig. 6).—In the absence of food and moisture the cytoplasm becomes fairly stable, but the nucleus is activated, using up all the food that is in the cytoplasm, and

dividing and sub-dividing inside the cell, until there are generally four spores, although there are sometimes as many as eight.

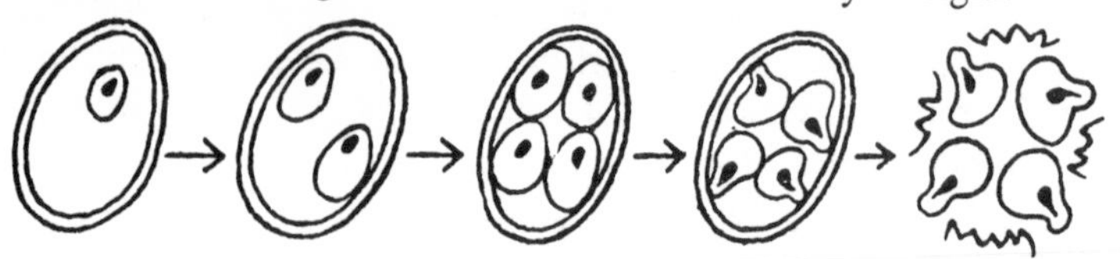

FIG. 6.—Yeast. Sporulation.

At the same time the cell wall thickens to form a protection or shield for the spores. These are known as ascospores from the Latin word ascus, meaning a shield.

It is known that these spores, which become air-borne, preserve their vitality for long periods, even up to six months under certain conditions. When they alight on a suitable medium for growth, the shield disintegrates and the spores behave as ordinary yeast cells and reproduce by budding.

FUNCTION OF YEAST

As well as the knowledge of the structure of the yeast plant and its life cycles, the student should have an elementary knowledge of the function of yeast in panary fermentation, and its importance to the baker. This knowledge will induce him to use yeast with greater thought and care.

The primary function of yeast is to change sugar into carbon dioxide gas, better known by its chemical formula CO_2 so that the dough in which it is generated is aerated. The second function is to assist in ripening or mellowing the gluten of the dough so that, when the loaf is in the oven, the gluten is in such a condition that it gives evenly to the expanding gases and at the same time retains them.

When yeast is dispersed in water at a suitable temperature, and mixed to a thin paste with sufficient flour, all the foods necessary for fermentation are present. There is sugar to act as food and soluble proteins to form the structure and building material for the new cells.

Activity starts within the yeast cell, as yeast exudes a substance known as an enzyme which changes a solution of sugar (sucrose) and water into a simple sugar (dextrose); this is absorbed within the yeast cell and changed to CO_2 and alcohol, together with other by-products. Other enzymes in flour and yeast change some of the soluble starch to sugar, which in turn is assimilated by yeast and changed, so that aeration goes on from this continued production of gas.

Soluble proteins contain valuable building material, and enzymes change these proteins to simpler compounds, so enabling them to pass through the semi-porous yeast membrane.

It would be well at this stage if the student were properly introduced to these wonderful substances that are known as enzymes. They are the products of living organisms or cells, and are able to effect great changes without themselves being changed at the end of the reaction. They are highly selective; one enzyme being responsible for one type of reaction, but unable to take part in any other. For example, an enzyme known as invertase can change sucrose and water to dextrose and levulose, but cannot change maltose and water to dextrose, which is effected by another enzyme known as maltase.

Because of the power they have to speed up reactions they are known also as catalysts; later the student will learn more about them.

The activity in dough known as fermentation, however, is only successful under certain conditions. These will be dealt with under the headings that follow.

YEAST: CONDITION AND STORAGE

Yeast must be in good condition if it is to do its work efficiently. This can be ascertained by examination. It should be cool to the touch and possess a creamy colour, breaking with a clean fracture; the aroma is best described as similar to that of ripe apples. If it is light in colour, dry, warm and crumbly to the touch and with a pungent odour, then it is in a poor condition. If dark brown in colour, with a soft, sticky consistency and an unpleasant odour, then the yeast is bad and completely unsuitable for the fermenting of bakery products.

Yeast can be kept in good condition at about 40° F. and should be used in strict rotation according to delivery. Small quantities can be kept in good condition if pressed into a stone jar and stored in a cool place. Yeast rapidly deteriorates if kept in a warm atmosphere; it quickly gets hot and crumbly. This is the beginning of self-fermentation, known as autolysis, and is brought about by the enzymes of yeast which break down the cell walls allowing the contents to escape; the semi-liquid mass has an unpleasant odour, is dark in colour and as yeast is useless.

There is a temperature range within which yeast works very well. It is 78–82° F. Above this figure fermentation is rapid, but gets progressively weaker as the temperature increases until, at 120° F., yeast is in danger. At 140° F., and over, it is killed. Between 74 and 78° F. yeast works slowly and regularly. Below 74° F. it is very slow indeed, unless extra yeast is used, until at 40° F. it is completely retarded, although at this temperature it must be emphasized that the yeast is in no way damaged.

Yeast should never be mixed with dry salt, or sugar, or dispersed in strong salt or sugar solutions. When dough-making, separate receptacles for yeast and salt should be used. Yeast is never dissolved; it is a living organism and cannot be dissolved in water; the mass is 'broken down' or dispersed, and to effect the separation of millions of yeast cells it is better to use a whisk.

YEAST MANUFACTURE

The commercial cultivation of yeast, generally referred to as yeast manufacture, can now be considered a science. A great deal of knowledge has been collected on this living unicellular plant, what is best for its growth, and why it is the best.

All life is subject to natural law. If meticulous control is exercised and an organism behaves in exactly the same way under identical conditions, then the result can be considered as definite as, for example, a chemical reaction.

The production of yeast is subject to this precision control at all stages of the process, and the result is the fine fresh yeast, strong, pure and of consistent high quality, ever at the service of the baker.

Stage I: Seed Yeast.—It is obvious that, if life is to be reproduced, then it is essential that the first generation shall be healthy and have the essential characteristics necessary for the environment in which it is to live and be active.

It is with this in mind that the bio-chemist uses his specialized knowledge and selects one healthy yeast cell, which is used to inoculate a prepared plate containing nutrient agar or gelatine. After incubation the cells are transferred to small flasks containing yeast food in solution; the incubation continuing until almost all the yeast food is assimilated, then the yeast is transferred to still larger vessels. This operation is continued progressively, until at last there is sufficient seed yeast to commence cultivation in bulk.

During this incubation period, rigid biological control is exercised, the yeast being examined at each stage to ensure that the yeast cell is the desired shape and size, and that there are no foreign bacteria present.

From the laboratory, the yeast is introduced to the smallest of a series of sterile containers, all containing food in solution. The yeast passes progressively, by gravity, to larger vessels until at last there is from two to three hundredweights of seed yeast, all from a single cell. The student will be interested to learn that, in the course of three weeks, one single cell can be grown into hundreds of tons. This represents an astronomic number of cells when it is considered that there are 215 thousand million to the ounce.

Stage II: Preparation of Wort.—Following the cultivation of seed yeast, preparation is made for reproduction on a large scale. It is necessary first of all to prepare the yeast food, which is known as wort. The food is mainly sugar in some form in solution, to which is added nitrogenous matter and mineral salts.

The form of sugar used can be produced from the saccharification of starch by the addition of malt, or by using molasses. Either of these methods give the name 'grain' or 'molasses' yeast to the finished product, although much yeast is made by a combination of these methods.

When barley is malted, the starch is changed to maltose sugar and at the same time the diastatic group of enzymes becomes highly activated; so that if the malted barley, after crushing, is added to gelatinized starch, it is changed, under controlled conditions, from starch to sugar. The protein of the barley, modified during the malting process, is present as a yeast food. With a sufficient amount of water the whole is filtered and rendered 'star bright'.

Molasses is the uncrystallizable residue of either cane or beet sugar juice. It is sterilized, filtered and has the addition of nitrogenous matter in the form of ammonium salts. This solution of yeast food in water, either grain or molasses, or a mixture of both, and known as wort, and with the acidity adjusted, is passed to fermentation tanks, some of which have a capacity of 20,000 to 50,000 gallons.

Stage III: Fermentation.—These huge tanks are fitted with coils, by which the temperature can be controlled. An aeration system is also fitted so that sterile air under pressure can be evenly distributed throughout the fermenting liquid.

It is then that the wort is inoculated with some hundredweights of the seed yeast, and fermentation begins; the aeration system is put into operation, causing the yeasty liquid to bubble furiously, giving the impression that the whole mass is boiling, although the temperature is only about 78° F. The impression of boiling is the explanation of the word 'ferment' which is from the Latin fermo—to boil. The yeast now multiplies rapidly, increasing by five times its original weight over the fermentation period. During fermentation, alcohol is produced and the density of the ferment is lowered. Molasses and yeast foods are added during the process. Finally the yeast comes to the top and fermentation is stopped.

Stage IV: Separating, Compressing and Packing.—From the

fermentation tanks the yeast is passed to centrifugal separators, which extract the exhausted yeast liquor. The yeast is then mixed with water and cooled to 38° F., the water washes the cells and the lowering of the temperature inhibits yeast activity.

From the cooler, the yeast is passed to filter presses, where under pressure most of the water is removed which renders the yeast a plastic mass. It is then removed to cold storage, from which it is taken, as and when required, to be shaped into 1 lb. blocks and wrapped in waxed paper.

A new type of yeast known as Higher Activity Granular Yeast has been developed for use with mechanical developed dough processes. This yeast can be used for conventional processes also.

Granular yeast is manufactured in the manner described for ordinary compressed yeast except that a different treatment is given at the stage of final filtration, resulting in the end product being granular in form. The moisture content is lower than that of compressed yeast, so that activity is approximately 10% higher, which must be allowed for when calculating yeast quantities.

The yeast is free running and must be kept cool, under refrigeration (about 40° F.) for preference.

Some yeast is dehydrated and packed in sealed tins for export to places where fresh yeast is not available. Drying is done in different ways. One method is to force fresh yeast through small holes in a metal plate, so that it forms into small rods. These are dried by passing through warm air currents; 1 lb. of fresh yeast yielding 4 oz. of dried yeast. Dried yeast is used as recommended by the packers and is usually guaranteed for six months.

Here is a simple test that the student might like to try for himself. First of all, make up a 10% sugar solution (2 oz. sugar, 1 pt. water) and pour into as many small glass jars as there are yeasts to test. Into each jar drop a ¼ oz. pellet of the different yeasts (they must be weighed accurately).

It will be seen that the pellets drop to the bottom of the jars. Soon tiny bubbles of gas form on the outer surfaces of the yeasts; when a sufficient number are formed the pellet suddenly rises to the surface. It is obvious, therefore, that provided care is taken in the test, the yeast coming to the surface first is the one with the quickest initial gassing power. This is not necessarily the best yeast.

Yeasts are produced for various fermentation speeds, according to the strain of the seed yeast used. A fast yeast is suitable for short fermentation systems, and would not be advisable for longer fermentation periods for which a slower yeast is the best.

6

Salt: Commercial Production; Water: Its use in Breadmaking; Water: Essential Work in Bakery Production

SALT: COMMERCIAL PRODUCTION

THE chemical name for salt is sodium chloride. It is composed of two elements, sodium and chlorine, in the ratio of 40% sodium and 60% chlorine. Both of these elements are deadly when on their own, but combined in these proportions they are, as common salt, indispensable to life. It is readily available in all parts of the world; in the sea, in lakes and springs, in the earth itself, in mountains and in swamps.

Its origin is uncertain. One school of thought asserts that it was formed millions of years ago by the evaporation of sea water; others say that volcanic upheavals were responsible for the deposits.

England is very rich in salt deposits. Salt has been raised in Cheshire from very early times, and the deposits are considered inexhaustible. The salt beds seem to be in a basin from Lymm in the north to Nantwich in the south, with Winsford, Middlewich, Northwich and Sandbach in between.

Salt is found also in the Carpathians, in Spain, Germany, Austria; in America, India and Australia. Some of the rock-salt beds are over 3,000 ft. in thickness; some being thousands of feet from the surface, others only about 200 ft., as in some parts of England. Salt is also found in the sea, but is not as pure as that made from natural brine. It is economic to recover salt from sea water only where the climate is very hot, such as in Aden and in parts of Australia.

The approximate salt content of sea water is about 2·7 to 2·9%. The water in the Dead Sea contains up to 7·5%, but the brine pumped up in Cheshire contains approximately 26%.

The world's estimated annual production of salt is 10 million tons, and on this enormous production other large industries depend. The production of vast quantities of hydrochloric acid, chlorine, caustic soda and hydrogen, etc., depends on salt and, in turn, these products are necessary for the manufacture of soap, bleaches, glass and explosives.

It is interesting to recall that the Romans who raised salt in Cheshire were paid in salt; it is from the word salt that the Latin salarium is derived, from which came the word salary. It is supposed that the word soldier, originated from *sal dare*, meaning to give salt.

Rock salt is mined by first breaking the rock with explosives. The lumps are sold either in large pieces for 'cattle licks' or crushed for agricultural purposes. Some are purified for table use.

Natural brine is produced naturally by water percolating through the earth strata until it reaches the deposit of rock salt which it dissolves. In Cheshire it is pumped up fully saturated; in other parts of the country fresh water is pumped to a salt layer to form a near saturated solution, before being raised again and passed to reservoirs.

If the student is in Nantwich, he will see in the museum there the leaden pans used by the Romans for evaporating the water from the brine; they were about 3 ft. long and 6 in. deep. Now the evaporating pans are 80 ft. long, 26 ft. wide and 20 in. deep.

The whole secret of salt crystallization is in the control of the heat; the slower the evaporation, the larger the crystal; the greater the heat applied, and the quicker the evaporation, the finer the crystal. Salt for the fishing industry has large crystals up to an inch in width, the crystals being produced after evaporation that takes between 7 and 14 days to complete. Quick boiling is employed in the production of the fine crystal table salt.

The crystals form on the surface of the brine, and then fall to the bottom where they are drawn off with rakes, lifted with perforated skimmers and thrown on to wooden stages to drain, after which they are dried.

Lump salt is produced by packing drained salt into wooden frames or moulds, and when the salt has settled it is wheeled to a hot room where the blocks are dried. These large blocks of salt are almost a thing of the past in bakeries; manufacturers now cut them up into small blocks and wrap them for sale in the shops.

Sea-water salt is present in enormous quantities in the seas and oceans of the world, washed from the land into the sea for millions of years. In the Mediterranean countries and the U.S.A. the sea is yielding its dissolved salt commercially, especially in France, in the mouth of the Rhone. Its chief advantage is cheapness in production.

Flat land below high-water level is surrounded by a wall, and these 'saltings' are sub-divided by internal walls. The sea runs in at high tide and evaporation proceeds in the hot sun to almost saturation point; the residue is then run into crystallizing ponds, where evaporation proceeds still further. After this, fairly pure sodium chloride is raked out and air dried. The process takes about 40 days.

Sea water salt is not ideal for fermented goods, because of the high proportion of other salts that may be present, such as magnesium chloride, magnesium sulphate, calcium sulphate, calcium carbonate, etc., all of which have an adverse effect on yeast fermentation. Before the Roman occupation of this country, the inhabitants poured brine over charcoal and scraped away the resultant salt crystals. They also produced the first salt ever manufactured in England by boiling brine in open pans.

Vacuum Process

Many attempts have been made to improve on the old methods of producing salt, but only one during the last two thousand years has been successful and that is evaporation by the vacuum process. Brine boils at ordinary atmospheric pressure at a temperature of about 226° F.

In a vacuum pan, where the pressure on the surface is reduced, the boiling point is only 100° F. Thus it will be seen that boiling under vacuum is much more economical. Before the brine goes to the pans it is artificially purified to prevent the deposit of calcium sulphate and calcium carbonate.

There are usually three conical-shaped vessels in a vacuum plant, each vessel containing hundreds of tubes. The steam is introduced to the first vessel and passes through the tubes, the heat boiling the brine. The heat given off in the form of steam from the first vessel is passed to the second, where it raises the temperature of the brine there, and so on to the third.

The steam from the last vessel is condensed and returned to the boiler plant for steam raising. As the salt is precipitated it falls to the bottom of each pan, and then down a pipe to a bucket elevator, where it is carried away to a vacuum filter and excess water is driven off, leaving a damp salt cake with about 3% moisture. This is marketed as unstoved vacuum salt.

If a drier quality is required, it is passed automatically to a drier heated with hot air, where the remaining moisture is removed. This is known as stoved salt and is the best quality produced.

WATER: ITS USE IN BREADMAKING

Without water all life would perish. Water is a component of every living thing; the earth, our food, the heavens, growing crops and decaying organic matter. As Banfield most truly states in *Manna*, 'water is the most general solvent and also the cheapest. It is the cheapest beverage, cleansing agent, means of transport and power; as ice it is the cheapest preservative.'

Most substances are more soluble in hot water than in cold. Water exists in three states: as a solid below 32° F. (0° C.); as a liquid between 32° F. and 212° F. (0–100° C.); as steam over 212° F. (100° C.).

Pure water is a chemical compound consisting of two parts hydrogen and one part oxygen. Distilled water is chemically pure. All natural waters contain dissolved solids, liquids and gases, some of which are impurities, while others are necessary ingredients of drinking water.

The largest source of water is rainfall. When one considers the fact that rainwater is polluted by the smokes and gases from factory and domestic chimneys, in the big industrial regions, it is clear that rainwater is far from pure; it is in fact considered to be quite unfit for human consumption. Apart from geographical reasons, water storage reservoirs are generally away from industrial areas, in places where there is less chance of contamination.

Drinking water, and all water used for the manufacture and processing of food, must be free of all harmful impurities. Among the many impurities that are found naturally occurring in water are organic matter and bacteria. The first is removed by oxidation and filtration, the water being sprayed over filter-beds consisting of layers of stones, the stones in each layer getting progressively smaller until the last layer is of sand. The air and light to which the water is exposed also destroys some of the bacteria.

Bacteria that are responsible for disease in man (known as pathogenic) must be removed; typhoid is an example of one of these and to render water free of this type of contamination chlorine is used.

The difficulty with which water produces lather is the measure of its hardness. There are two kinds of hardness—temporary and permanent.

Temporary hardness can be destroyed by boiling, although temporary hardness is rare without some measure of permanent hardness. Boiling deposits calcium and magnesium carbonates, as a scale which can be removed by acid treatment which dissolves the carbonates.

Permanent hardness is not removed by boiling, although it can be eliminated by distillation. This, however, is not an economic proposition on a large scale. Evaporation in a boiler causes calcium and magnesium sulphates to form a hard crystalline scale, which gives rise to over-heating of the boiler metal, and a lessened boiler efficiency. Both temporary and permanent hardness can be removed by water softeners.

The difficulty with which water lathers is measured in 'degrees of hardness', and each degree corresponds to one grain of calcium carbonate, or its equivalent, per gallon of water. It also corresponds to the using of 2 oz. of soap per 100 gallons of water. A water containing, say, seven grains of calcium carbonate and five grains of magnesium sulphate would be estimated as 12 degrees of hardness.

Waters containing over 30 degrees of hardness are referred to as very hard. Waters containing from 5 to 20 degrees are termed moderately hard, while waters with up to 5 degrees are referred to as soft. Swansea, Manchester and Glasgow have soft waters with 2–4 degrees of hardness. London water varies between 16 and 21 degrees depending on source, while water at Burton-on-Trent contains up to 48 degrees.

Hard water has a greater alkalinity than soft water. As yeast works better in a slightly acid medium, it can be seen that in this change towards alkalinity there can be a slowing up of fermentation in the initial stages until, in the process of fermentation, which in itself produces a certain acidity, the balance is restored.

It is found also that doughs made with hard water are tighter, probably as a result of the action of the mineral salts on the nature of the gluten. This tightness, in turn, makes it less easy for the yeast to develop because the food is less readily available. Very hard water contains in addition magnesium sulphate, which exerts a definite retarding action on yeast activity. Dough made with the same amounts of soft water are less tight and ferment more quickly, because the water is more extractive, and in consequence, fermentation is speeded up.

Good bread can be made from dough containing either hard or soft water, provided that due allowance is made for the physical effects and the necessary adjustments made. In the case of hard water, the dough could be made a little slacker, the fermentation time could be lengthened, the yeast content slightly raised or the amount of salt used slightly increased. Where soft water is used, exactly the opposite adjustments should be made, or a mineral bread improver could be used.

In practice, however, the effect of differing degrees in the hardness of water in breadmaking is slight; the student being more likely to find the problem put hypothetically on an examination paper, in which case the question must be answered logically and fully.

WATER: ESSENTIAL WORK IN BAKERY PRODUCTION

Water in bread and cakes is a solvent for the dispersion of salt, sugar and other water soluble ingredients, and for the hydration of insoluble protein into gluten. Without this gluten development there could be no aeration, either by yeast, baking powder, lamination or beating, because the gas and air incorporated by these methods would escape and be lost.

Water is also necessary in panary fermentation for the dispersion of yeast, and in chemical aeration, for the complete reaction of the constituent parts of baking powder in the oven.

Water is always present at the mixing stage of all bakery products, be it direct from the tap, or as a constituent of eggs, milk or emulsions. The water content of bakery mixes varies according to the water absorbing power of the flour, and the type of product being manufactured.

Banfield in *Manna* gives the following table of consistencies.

Consistency	*Type*
Batter	Hot-plate crumpets.
Exceptionally soft dough	Hot-plate muffins
Very soft dough	Oven muffins, barm cakes, tea cakes, buns.
Soft dough with a tendency to flow in final proof	All doughs baked in tins or pans, except malt bread.
Moderately stiff	Crusty bread and one-piece moulded loaves, crusty cottage bread, bricks, etc., requiring built-up moulding, malt and rye bread.
Very stiff	Fancy show-pieces—wheatsheaves, etc.
Cheesy stiffness	Biscuit doughs.

One of the first functions of water in breadmaking—and this has already been mentioned—is to dissolve the salt, so that being finely divided it is evenly distributed throughout the dough. At the same time, water disperses the millions of yeast cells so that they also can be evenly distributed throughout the liquor and, later, the dough.

When water is mixed with flour a putty-like mass is formed, which is known to everybody as dough. The structure or framework of the dough is gluten, which is the insoluble protein hydrated with approximately twice its weight in water. The greater amount of the water in dough is held by the starch which is the largest constituent of flour. It is held by surface tension (adsorption) in the early stages of mixing.

As the mixing continues, the dough gets less and less sticky until it does not adhere to the hands or the sides of the machine. In this condition it is considered that the dough is sufficiently mixed. By this time the protein is fully hydrated, and it is probable that the starch cells have absorbed the maximum quantity of water, which is about half its weight.

The student should make a habit of recording the weight of the dough immediately after making. This should be done for two reasons; first, to check the weighing of the raw materials used, and second, so that he may at different stages of fermentation be able to calculate fermentation losses, because dough loses weight as fermentation proceeds. Most of this is lost by way of the escaping gas as the dough is knocked back. Some of it is lost by surface evaporation, according to the amount of care taken in keeping the dough in a humid atmosphere.

In baking most of the weight is lost by water in the loaf changing to steam and its consequent escape as the loaf is baked. More is lost as the loaf stales, although the water content is not the dominant factor which controls the staling of bread. Because of these baking, cooling and staling losses, an extra 3–4 oz. of dough on each 1¾ lb. loaf is added, so that the weight of the loaf will be at, or over, that required by law at the time of sale.

A tight dough increases the potential strength of flour, and more water decreases it. The water content has a marked effect on the structure of the loaf; within limits, more water opens and softens the crumb. This can be clearly seen in properly made Vienna bread, which has a high water content. Stiff doughs generally produce bread with a close, bound crumb, a hard crust, and small volume.

Ice may be used in dough-making, under certain conditions, or for special breads. Its value is in its capacity to lower dough temperatures by using it as part of the water content, 10 lb. of ice being the equivalent of a gallon of water.

All washing in the bakery needs water, whether for personal use, laundering or the cleaning of the premises and equipment. It is nature's vehicle of thermal and chemical destruction in the fight against dirt and bacteria.

It is cheap to use, so use enough of it but, because it is of such value to the baker, do not waste it.

7

Malt and Malt Products: Malting; Types of Malt available to the Baker; The use of Malt; Malt Breads

MALT AND MALT PRODUCTS

MALT is a raw material of considerable importance to the baker. It is a yeast food and comes under the general heading of bread improvers, although diastatic malt could be termed a flour improver. From four basic materials—flour, water, yeast and salt—good bread can be made, provided that these materials are ideally suited to the purpose. Malt as an addition will only assist in making better bread if there are certain deficiencies in the constituent balance of these basic materials and/or adjustments to the system of manufacture. It is for this reason that a complete understanding of its nature, manufacture and use is so essential to the craftsman baker.

Malt was introduced to the baking industry about 1890, at a time when spring wheats from North America came into general use. Malt products are available to the baker in three forms: malt flour, malt extract (which is a thick, viscous, amber-coloured syrup), and dehydrated malt extract, which is in dry crystal form. All are products of the malting of grain, for which barley has been used extensively for centuries. Wheat also is used for malting, the products of which are ideally suitable for breadmaking. Most of the malt manufactured is used in the brewing and distilling industries.

The primary purpose of all seeds is the perpetuation of the species. When planted, seeds are in an ideal medium for growth, and they begin to germinate, the plant stem (plumule) and the rootlet (radicle) breaking through the seed coatings covering the germ. Food is obtained from the endosperm until the roots and stem are sufficiently developed to enable food to be obtained from the air and the soil.

Before the starch and proteins can be assimilated by the growing plant, they have to be changed into simple sugars and simplified nitrogenous compounds respectively; this is done by the activated enzymes, which also hasten the changes.

The whole process of malting is the artificial germination of grain under controlled conditions, so that the proportion of water soluble substances present is increased, and so to modify the grain that these essential substances can be easily extracted. In addition, another important object of the process is the formation and liberation of enzymes, especially of the diastatic group. Malting is a highly skilled commercial process.

Choice of Grain.—This is of great importance. The term 'malting quality' is applied commercially to grain with the maximum capacity for germination. The grain should: (1) be plump and uniform in size; (2) have no excessive moisture content; (3) be ripe; (4) be correctly matured; (5) be sweet and free from moulds and the micro-organisms of disease.

The best barley for malting is grown in Great Britain, in the Mediterranean countries, Manchuria, U.S.A., Chile, Australia and India, the maltster using home-grown and imported grains, each for a definite purpose.

The *Cleaning* of the grain at the maltings is similar to the cleaning of wheat at the flourmill. It is cleaned to free the grain from all extraneous matter such as chaff, stones, dust, and other seeds. The removal of dust is of particular importance because of the danger from dust-borne organisms which may find their way into the germination floors where conditions would be favourable for development.

Conditioning.—The keeping quality and the germination capacity of the grain is of the greatest importance, and careful conditioning becomes essential. Since the natural maturation of grain differs according to the country of origin and the weather conditions obtaining there and since, also, there is a relationship between maturity and the moisture content, it is important that steps should be taken to ensure some uniformity of the moisture content before malting begins.

Some maltsters use the 'sweating' process, as it is called, for new grain purchased before natural maturity is attained. Others kiln-dry all grain to a predetermined moisture level.

Steeping.—The grain, cleaned and conditioned, is taken from storage and soaked for about 60–100 hr., depending on the hardness of the water used and the type of grain. The water is changed every 12–18 hr., and air is bubbled through to free any unwanted particles. The grain will absorb water up to 50% of its weight, and after draining, the moisture content should not exceed 44%. Steeping is finished only after examination by an experienced maltster.

Couching.—After steeping, the grain is laid out on the floor to a depth of about 2 ft. 6 in. to 4 ft., depending on the season and the temperature. It is turned over periodically to equalize temperature and moisture content and to allow for the circulation of air. The rootlets now begin to appear.

It is during this initial germination that great changes take place in the grain, brought about by what is known as hydrolysis, a term applied when water takes part in a chemical change. The enzymic groups responsible for the breakdown of the food store of the grain are the diastatic group, which change the starch to sugars, and the proteolytic group which simplify the proteins for the purpose of supplying nitrogen for the growing plant.

As germination proceeds, so the sprout or acrospire lengthens and it is when it has reached to about three-quarters of the length of the grain that the maltster knows that growth has proceeded far enough.

Flooring is an operation whereby a steady controlled growth is maintained after the initial germination during couching. The grain is spread over the malting floor to a depth decided by atmospheric and temperature conditions; turning is frequent to control temperature, which is maintained at 56° F. and to expel CO_2 and incorporate oxygen.

On the fourth day, the temperature is allowed to rise to 58° F., and the grain is sprinkled with water; this is carried on to the sixth day with a temperature rise to 60° F. On the seventh and eighth days no water is used and the temperature is maintained at 60° F., during which time the grain is frequently turned.

During the next five days the acrospires are required to wither. This is accelerated by the retention of CO_2 and the controlled raising of the temperature, to 65° F. in the case of foreign barley, and to about 63° F. for home-grown. The moisture content should be approximately 43%.

Kilning (*Drying and Curing*).—The grain is loaded on to kilns, which are heated by anthracite, and the moisture content reduced to 10% after drying at 100° F. for 48–50 hr. The malt is now considered 'hand dry'.

To cure the grain, the draught system is closed and the heat lowered, so that the moisture content is further reduced and the diastatic value diminished. The latter, however, depends on the temperature during curing; if the temperature is low, then diastatic malt is assured; if the temperature is raised, then the diastatic and proteolytic enzymes are eventually destroyed and non-diastatic malt is produced.

The system of malting described is known as the flooring method and has been employed for generations. This method is now being superseded by the 'pneumatic drum' system common to Continental maltings.

MALT FLOUR AND EXTRACTS

After the removal of the rootlets, known as culms, the malt is allowed to age for a time. It is then ready for processing into malt flour and malt extracts.

The changes that have taken place during malting are shown in the following analysis given by Banfield in *Manna*. The analysis is of the same barley before and after malting. The change from insoluble to soluble nitrogenous matter can be clearly seen, as well as the great increase in the percentage of sugar present.

	Barley	*Malt*
Water	13·88	5·8
Soluble nitrogenous matter	1·7	6·71
Insoluble nitrogenous matter	12·4	6·38
Sugars	4·13	21·23
Starch	55.57	44·15
Cellulose	7·76	11·57
Fat	2·66	1·65
Salts	2·3	2·6

Malt flour is manufactured by passing the malted grain through fluted rollers, similar to the break rollers used in the milling of wheat. It is then sieved to remove the coarse particles. Malt being very dry and brittle, the outer coating breaks up into fine particles, so that the resultant flour is reddish-brown in colour. Malt flour is preferred by many bakers because it is easy to handle.

Because malt flour is very dry and is rich in malt sugar, it is very hygroscopic; that is it attracts moisture, so that it must be stored in an air-tight container.

Malt Extract is prepared by mixing the crushed malt with an equal amount of water and soaking it for about six hours. More water is added and the whole allowed to digest for one hour at a temperature not exceeding 130° F., so that the bulk of the starch present after malting can be converted to sugar, and at the same time there is a further modification of the nitrogenous compounds.

The liquor, after filtration, is transferred to vacuum pans where, at a temperature of not more than 130° F., excess water is removed and the extract reduced to a thick viscous syrup.

Dry Malt Extract.—After further vacuum drying the extract is ground to a fine crystalline powder which, because of its very hydroscopic nature, must be carefully stored. Dry malt extract finds much favour with the baker because it is much easier to handle.

Diastatic Paste.—This is a cold water malt extract manufactured in a similar manner to malt extract, but without the higher temperatures. In this way the enzymes are not impaired. Because of this, the diastatic value of these pastes is extremely high.

Diastatic Values.—Malts differ in diastatic value and it is essential that the student and the baker should understand this. Diastatic activity is lowered by the heat treatment of malt, and this activity is measured in degrees Lintner. The standard of computation is 100; 70 degrees Lintner is a malt of high diastatic value, while 20 is low.

Malt taken over a temperature of 170° F. is non-diastatic because the enzymes have been destroyed. This malt is generally dark in colour and, with inactivated enzymes, is useful in imparting a malty flavour to doughs not needing increased diastatic action. Because of its high sugar content it will also increase the gassing power of yeast.

USE OF MALT

If the four basic breadmaking materials, flour, yeast, salt and water, are not ideally suited to the purpose and there are certain deficiencies, then malt can be a valuable addition, both as a yeast food and as a bread improver, although it must be emphasized here that, in certain other conditions, bread will not be improved and may well be spoiled by the careless use of malt.

It follows then that both the student and the baker should have knowledge of the function of malt if they are to have complete control of the fermentation process.

The student will know that flour is not just an inert powder, but a complex mixture of substances, together with certain products of living organisms known as enzymes. In fact the whole fermentation process is the result of enzymic activity, directed to providing a readily available supply of sugar for the production of gas; for the breakdown of soluble protein, and for the mellowing and ripening of the hydrated insoluble protein, which we know as gluten. In this gluten ripening, manipulation, amongst other things, plays an important part.

Sugar is naturally present in flour in small quantities and, to supplement this amount so that gas production is maintained, starch is broken down to sugar by the diastatic enzymes also present in flour. This sugar content, available and potential, can be measured by means of the maltose test, the result giving a figure that is an important source of information both to the miller and the baker.

If the maltose figure is below 1·5 it is likely that there will be insufficient gassing in the final proving stage. If the figure is in excess of 2·3, then fermentation will be rapid, the bread will be difficult to bake, the structure weak, the crumb dark and sticky, and the loaf will have a high crust colour.

Flour with a very high maltose figure is milled from sprouted wheat; that is wheat that has germinated while still in the ear. This germination results in a partial change in the composition of the grain, precisely the same as that which takes place in the early stages of malting.

It follows then that, if this flour could be mixed with one of a low maltose figure, good bread could be made. This is not always possible, so that a method in which a good deal of the sugar present is fermented away is advisable. This method, perfected by Britain's leading research bakers, is known as the salt-delayed method of breadmaking, and gives a measure of success with this type of flour.

In the same way it is not always possible to correct a low maltose flour by mixing with one showing a high figure. In this case, however, the remedy is easy for diastatic malt has the same characteristics as high maltose flour, but in concentrated form. It increases the maltose sugar supply and adds to the diastatic activity in fermentation, so that the supply of maltose sugar is maintained. The enzymes responsible for the modification and ripening of gluten are augmented; this is of special advantage because strong stable glutens are invariably present in low maltose flours.

The problem can sometimes be complicated when a starch is highly resistant to alpha amylase, an enzyme in the amylolytic group, which is considered to break down the starch cell wall and release the soluble starch, which subsequently is changed to maltose and dextrin. In this case scalded flour can be used to provide soluble starch, because application of wet heat to the starch causes the cell wall to burst, so releasing the soluble starch within.

Bearing all these things in mind, and also the fact that there are several types of malt available to the baker and, in addition, that each type may have a different diatistic value, it becomes almost impossible to assess the amounts of malt to use per sack of flour with mathematical precision (malt breads excepted).

Assuming that malt is necessary with a particular flour, the correct amount to be used can only be assessed by trial and error, the margin of error being narrowed by experience and technical knowledge. Nevertheless the margin of error with malt of the lower diastatic values has to be great if it is to spoil the bread. If in any doubt, the technical advice of the malt manufacturers can always be sought; this will readily be given.

With the diastatic value of the malt in mind, malt flour is generally used in greater proportion per sack than malt extract, and malt extract in greater proportion than the dried product. Used correctly malt will confer the following qualities on bread:

(1) Increased volume, because of better gluten ripening.
(2) Improved crust colour. The increase in the sugar content resulting from diastatic activity, especially in the last stage of fermentation in the oven, before the enzymes are destroyed, has a marked effect on crust colour. The sugars, in conjunction with other substances in the crust, caramelize, giving a much better crust colour.
(3) Better bloom. This is a natural result of better dough fermentation.
(4) Brighter and softer crumb. Again the result of better gluten ripening.
(5) Better flavour, because of the characteristic flavour of malt as an addition to the natural flavour of well-fermentated bread.
(6) Better keeping qualities. Again the result of better fermentation.
(7) Increased food value. An increase in the calorific value of the bread.

MALT BREADS

Malt breads may be divided into three grades: lightly, medium and heavily malted breads, any of them being fruited or plain.

With the knowledge which the student now has about the nature of malt and the action it has on fermentation, he will more readily understand the characteristics of the various types of malted bread, how to balance and re-balance formulae for experimental purposes and how to produce malted breads to a predetermined standard.

Knowing that malt confers flavour, increases the sugar content of the dough and increases the diastatic activity during fermentation, according to the diastatic value of the malt and the amount used, the student can alter the balance of materials with understanding and with the knowledge that certain changes in balance will bring certain changes in the physical nature of the dough, and in the finished product.

In addition, he will know that by making changes, not only in the balance of materials but in the nature of them, he will have under his control many factors that will whet his appetite for experimentation and give not only satisfaction in practical tests, but valuable technical knowledge in his study of the fascinating science of panary fermentation.

Here are recipes showing the differences in three types of malt bread. A study of these recipes will provide a foundation on which the student may construct his own individual formulae:

	Light		*Medium*		*Heavy*	
	lb.	*oz.*	*lb.*	*oz.*	*lb.*	*oz.*
Wholemeal flour	1	4	1	4		8
White flour		8		8	1	4
Malt extract		1		1½		5½
Malt flour		—		—		1
Baking powder		—		—		¼
Fat		½		½		½
Treacle		½		1		2
Salt		½		½		½
Yeast		1		1		1¼
Water	1	4	1	4	1	1½
Dough temperature	80° F.		76° F.		76° F.	
Bulk fermentation	1 hr.		1½ hr.		1½ hr.	
Oven temperature	420° F.		400° F.		350° F.	
Baking time (approx.)	45 min.		60 min.		90 min.	

If required to be fruited, add 6 oz. of sultanas to the above recipes.

It will be noted that, as the bread becomes more heavily malted, the treacle content increases. In the last recipe the actual sugar present, and the potential from the diastatic action on starch, is heavy. Sugar in concentration has a retarding action on yeast fermentation and a solvent action on gluten. To compensate for this, the protein strength is increased by the addition of a greater proportion of white flour, and there is an increase in yeast and the addition of a small amount of baking powder to increase the gassing power in the first stages of baking.

Because of the progressively higher sugar contents, the baking temperatures are lowered and the baking times increased. If the oven is too hot, the crust forms too quickly and the heat does not penetrate to the centre of the loaf until the crust is burned and unpalatable.

It is normal for heavily malted bread to have a sticky crumb, due to the dextrin formed from the breakdown of starch to sugar; careful baking is therefore necessary, so that despite the natural stickiness, the loaf can be cut.

8

Chemical and Physical Changes during Fermentation Baking and Cooling

CHEMICAL AND PHYSICAL CHANGES DURING FERMENTATION BAKING AND COOLING

WITH his knowledge of the four basic materials used in bread-making, the student will have a greater understanding of the chemical and physical changes taking place in a dough during fermentation. The chemical and physical changes are interdependent.

Provided that the materials are of good quality, and are correctly balanced according to the type of bread being made and the method being used, then by far the most important operation in the manufacture of good bread is the thorough mixing of the ingredients in the first stage.

Stage 1: Dough-making.—In the vast majority of bakeries this is now done by machine; a great load has been lifted from the backs of men, with the further advantage that the machine will mix far more thoroughly and in a shorter time than any human dough-maker possibly could.

The first physical change is the equalization of dough temperature by means of the calculated temperature of the water. As mixing proceeds, the soluble constituents are taken up by the water and the insoluble proteins are hydrated to form gluten, the whole mixing constituting a colloidal structure of dough. A certain stability is conferred on the structure by the stabilizing action of salt on the gluten.

As mixing proceeds still further the mass becomes less sticky and tougher as a result of the thorough dispersion of all the ingredients and the complete hydration and development of the gluten. It must be understood that upon the quality of the gluten depends to a large extent the physical properties of the dough.

Chemical changes take place immediately, for the yeast cells dispersed throughout the dough commence activity by the breaking down of the naturally occurring sugar in the flour to CO_2 and alcohol.

During mixing a certain amount of air is incorporated and held within the dough fabric, although this is not evident when mixing is completed, for the dough is short and tough, appearing quite dormant for a while until, after a period, a degree of elasticity becomes manifest.

The mechanism of gas diffusion throughout the dough is in some doubt. It has generally been accepted that, as the yeast exudes gas, it is contained within a gluten bubble in the vicinity of the yeast cell. It is now suggested that in the initial stages of fermentation, the CO_2 remains in solution. As more CO_2 is produced, the solution becomes saturated and the excess, appearing as a gas, is diffused into the small air pockets incorporated by the mixing process, and so causes an expansion of the dough fabric.

Stage 2: Bulk Fermentation.—Fermentation is brought about by yeast which, in panary fermentation, has two functions:

(1) Production of CO_2 for aerating the dough.

(2) Assistance in the conditioning of dough before it is baked.

It is through enzymic activity that the above is brought about, which during fermentation follows two courses:

(*a*) The reduction of the natural sugars together with sugars from starch, for assimilation by yeast to produce ultimately CO_2 and alcohol.

(*b*) The reduction of proteins to simpler nitrogenous compounds for the growth and development of yeast.

The enzymes are active during the whole of the fermentation period, the changes in the sugars liberating energy which manifests itself as heat; in consequence the temperature of the dough rises.

The rate at which the dough temperature rises is dependent mainly on the speed of the dough as defined by the yeast content and, to a certain extent, on the temperature at which the dough is stored; obviously, if a dough is made at a certain temperature and allowed to ferment at one much lower, then any increase of temperature through activity within the dough is more than lost by heat radiated from the dough surface.

Dextrose is assimilated by yeast and, as the amount present in the initial stages of fermentation is small, then other sources of supply must be found if gas generation is to continue. For this purpose the enzyme, invertase, is excreted by yeast and is responsible for the breakdown of sucrose to dextrose and levulose. This chemical change is known as hydrolysis; the action of invertase is to speed the fusion of one molecule of sucrose and one molecule of water and to split the solution into a molecule each of two simple sugars, dextrose and levulose, which pass into the yeast cell. Within the cell they are broken down by the action of another group of enzymes, the zymatic group, to CO_2 and three other by-products, alcohol, succinic acid and glycerol. All these products are passed out through the yeast membrane, the gas to aerate the dough and the by-products to take a part in the final flavour and aroma of the loaf.

A further group of enzymes contained in flour, and in diastatic malt, provide another source of dextrose from the breakdown of starch; these are known as the amylolytic group; they act immediately on the starch cells fractured in the milling process. At the same time one of the enzymes in this group commences to liberate more soluble starch by its action on the cellulose membrane of the starch cell.

The first stage in the breakdown of starch is to maltose and dextrin. Maltose by hydrolysis is changed by the enzyme, maltase, excreted by yeast, to glucose. Thus gas production is assured, provided that all things are equal.

Some of the sugar within the fermenting dough is changed to lactic acid by lactic acid bacteria; very small amounts in short fermentation processes, increasing slightly as the process is extended, sufficient then being produced to exert a softening effect on gluten. Some of the CO_2 combines with water to form carbonic acid. Other products of fermentation are glycerine and fatty acids produced by the fat splitting lipase enzymes. In long process doughs there may be traces of butyric acid.

Some of the alcohol is changed to acetic acid by the action of acetic acid bacteria; this represents about 5% of the total acidity of the dough. The acids produced during fermentation alter the pH of the dough (pH is a measure of alkalinity and acidity), this increases the acidity of the dough which, within limits, has a beneficial effect on yeast activity and on the physical properties of gluten, particularly elasticity and extensibility. The effects, however, are slight. It is considered that various esters are produced from the combination of each organic acid with alcohol and that these make their contribution to the flavour of the finished bread.

The proteolytic enzymes are also active. The soluble proteins are modified into peptones and polypeptides so that they may be assimilated by the yeast for its growth and development, after being further broken down to peptides and amino acids. Proteolytic activity also assists in the mellowing of gluten. This can be seen in the changes in the colour of the dough, which gradually brightens as fermentation proceeds.

The salt which is present in the dough acts as a brake on enzymic activity, preventing this from becoming too fast, or going too far in the time calculated against total fermentation. The stabilizing action of salt causes the gluten to offer resistance to the CO_2 which is constantly being produced, and so the dough fabric rises.

The combined action to which gluten is subject is as follows:

(1) Being insoluble it is hydrated, taking up about twice its weight in water.
(2) Proteolytic enzymes gradually mellow it as fermentation proceeds.
(3) The salt strengthens it and so increases its stability.
(4) The gas produced within the dough stretches it.
(5) The colour gradually brightens.
(6) By manipulation and enzymic action it becomes finely divided into web-like strands.

Stage 3. Knocking Back.—Further chemical and physical changes take place during the operation of knocking back a dough, all of which, provided that the operation is carried out correctly, have a beneficial effect on the fermentation process and the resultant bread.

The first change is the expulsion of CO_2 which escapes as the dough fabric is collapsed. As the knocking back progresses, the many surfaces exposed to the air during the operation takes up oxygen which at one time was thought to assist gas production. This is now considered not to be the case. As the dough is degassed it collapses and the volume is decreased. The dough toughens and loses extensibility in consequence of the work hardening of the gluten. This explains the reason why, after manipulation, the dough must have time to relax and become inflated with gas again, ready for further manipulation or for baking.

The stretching action on gluten, given during knocking back, has a bearing on the finished loaf, helping to bring the dough to the correct condition for the final stages of fermentation. It is at this stage that the effects of over-machining can be clearly seen, for the dough fabric can be irreparably damaged and the resilience of the gluten lost. The term used for this damage to the dough is 'felling'. A further change is in temperature, which is equalized by this operation.

Stage 4: Scaling and Moulding.—The dough, having recovered from the knocking back, is now again in a fully inflated condition and now approaching its optimum ripening. It is then scaled to the required weight and 'handed up', these operations being done either by hand or machine.

Again the dough fabric is partially collapsed and a large amount of

CO_2 excluded. The gluten undergoes further manipulation and becomes much less resilient. Care is necessary at this stage when the work is done mechanically for, if the action of the divider is violent, the dough is mashed and the structure felled. There is no danger of this, of course, from hand scaling.

When at the required weight the dough pieces are moulded up into a round shape known to the industry as 'handing up', this is done either by hand or machine. After this operation the dough pieces are allowed to recover for about 15–20 min., so that they are again filled with gas and the gluten is resilient enough to allow for the final moulding without the use of excessive pressure.

In small bakeries, after handing up, the pieces are placed together on the table-top and covered to prevent skinning, or packed into boxes which are stacked to exclude air. In automatic plants the pieces are conveyed to an intermediate prover and dropped automatically into fabric pockets on a moving belt, where they travel for a predetermined time in an atmosphere of which the temperature and humidity are controlled, after which they are ejected, again fully expanded, to a moulding machine where they receive the final shaping.

This final moulding is of great importance, for not only is the shape of the baked loaf affected, but also the crumb structure. With hand moulding the craftsman has such a sensitivity of touch that any difference in gluten resilience is readily detected and moulding pressure is altered by instinct. The machine does not possess this instinct, so that it becomes necessary, if the dough structure is not to be improperly treated, for the machine operator to be skilled at his job. The pressure put on the dough must be such that it is neither loosely moulded nor so abused that the structure is torn and damaged.

Stage 5: Final Proof.—This very important stage in the manufacture of bread is the period between the final moulding and the placing of the bread in the oven.

As the dough piece leaves the craftsman's hands or the machine moulder, most of the gas is again expelled and the gluten tightened. If the dough is mature and the moulding done correctly, the dough piece is not only of the required shape but has the skin surface perfectly smooth, without tear or blemish. The object of final proof, therefore, is to allow the loaf to expand before baking. It follows than that, if the loaf is to have good shape and volume, the production of gas from the breakdown of sugars must, at this last stage, be vigorous and the gluten should be in such condition that it is strong enough to hold the gas and resilient enough to give to the expansion.

The stresses and strains imposed upon the structure during moulding are eased as expansion goes on, until the volume of the loaf is at its desired maximum and the loaf is ready for the oven.

Apart from the chemical and physical changes taking place within the loaf, the conditions under which the final proof is carried out are also important, for if there is a lack of humidity, the dough surface will dry, and there will be a loss of bloom on the crust of the baked loaf. Skinning, the result of draughts, will show as grey patches on a hard crust. There is also the possibility of uneven expansion while in the oven causing misshapen loaves. Excessive humidity and high proving temperatures will result in tough leathery crusts, a wrinkled surface and holes under the top crust of the loaf.

Stage 6: Baking and Humidity—The dough piece has by this time arrived at what is termed 'full proof' and is almost at its fully-expanded state. Once in the oven activity within the loaf is very rapid; the yeast continuing to produce gas until it is killed at about 127–140° F. As the heat penetrates, the gas in the dough fabric expands and the oven spring is produced. Steam and alcohol vapour pressures also assist in this expansion.

Enzymes are still active to about 170° F., producing sugars that remain internally to sweeten the crumb and externally to produce, with other substances, crust colour and bloom. At about 172° F. the proteins coagulate, the dough structure is 'set' and all activity within the loaf ceases.

As baking proceeds, weight is lost by the evaporation of moisture and alcohol from the crust, and from the interior of the loaf by way of the oven break. As the moisture is driven off, so the crust takes on a higher temperature, reaching eventually the temperature of the oven. The sugars, dextrin, and the breakdown products of the soluble proteins, blend to form the attractive colour of the crust. The sugars caramelize at about 270° F.

Inside the loaf, some starch is gelatinized as the heat penetrates, rendering it more sensitive to enzymic activity, and the temperature rises to a figure that is not much higher than 212° F. The loaf is not baked until the heat penetrates to the centre.

Assuming that the dough conditioning and the gassing power in the loaf are correct, baking conditions are of great importance, for care in all the stages of production is a waste of time if the bread is spoiled in the baking.

First of all the temperature of the oven is important. This thermal figure is adjusted according to the nature and shape of the bread and the number of loaves to be baked in relation to the size of the oven. If the oven is too hot, then a crust is formed too quickly;

there is uneven expansion and, as the pressure within the loaf is irresistible, it breaks through the crust formation, giving an exaggerated break and, in consequence, a bad shape and reduced volume. Because of the thickening crust, heat penetration is slower and, in consequence, the loaf is not properly baked; or, if left in the oven to complete baking, the loaf has a thick crust with a bitter and unappetizing flavour. Internally the crumb structure is close and 'cheesy'.

Humidity in the oven is also of importance for, if it is correct, the expansion of the loaf is gentle and even, thus ensuring a good shape. If the humidity is too great, the bread has a tough leathery crust and an excessive shine which is unattractive. Insufficient humidity causes rapid evaporation of moisture from the skin of the loaf, together with a rapid crust formation, and has almost the same effect as baking in an oven that is too hot, causing uneven expansion and a bad shape, although without the high crust colour.

Uneven oven loading will also detract from bread quality, for, in the case of overloading, the penetration of heat into the loaf is retarded, resulting in excessive volume and uneven crust colour. Under-loading, unless humidity is increased and the bread protected, will result in bad shapes, showing the effects of oven 'pull'.

The student will find it of absorbing interest to study these changes, especially the study of the oven break, for apart from the realization that the balance of gassing power and gluten conditioning is of the utmost importance in the production of good bread, he will also learn that many of the conditions in the actual baking can influence the resultant bread, most of which have been described.

Two other conditions are the position of the loaf in the oven, and the influence of variations of temperature during baking. It will be noticed that, in one batch of tin bread, for instance, according to the position in the oven, some loaves will have the break on one side, some on the other and some a uniform break round the crown of the loaf. A little observation will show that the bread from the centre of the oven, where the heat is equable, will have the uniform break; other loaves nearer the sides of the oven will have the break on the side nearer the centre of the oven.

It follows that the break must occur at the weakest part of the loaf and this must be where there is least resistance, which will be where crust formation has been delayed.

In the case of a loaf that has been cut before baking, here the break has in effect been pre-determined and, if properly done, it adds to the appearance, increases the crust area and, because there is more flavour in the crust, increases the total flavour of the loaf.

It is for this reason that a loaf that has been properly baked has a far better flavour than one underbaked.

Stage 7: Cooling.—When the bread has left the oven, it is essential that it should be cooled reasonably quickly so that it can be packed for distribution. The modern practice of slicing and wrapping makes this even more necessary, for bread that is insufficiently cooled before wrapping is subject to the formation of moulds and, unless the dough acidity has been increased as a preventative, the conditions inside the wrapper are ideal for the development of 'rope'.

The first effect of proper cooling is to allow for the evaporation from the loaf of steam which would otherwise condense on the crust surface. This condition is known as 'sweating' and the student can see this for himself by leaving a loaf for a short while in the tin in which it is baked. The condensation will show in moist patches on the crust. As cooling proceeds there is a loss of weight.

There are physical changes also taking place within the loaf, for the structure, composed of gelatinized starch and coagulated protein, gradually assumes a greater rigidity.

9

Characteristics of good Bread; Bread Faults; Causes and Prevention; Rope: Cause and Prevention; Acid Dough

CHARACTERISTICS OF GOOD BREAD (1)

A LOAF of bread is a product of creative work and is a link, by way of distribution, between the baker and the consumer. Obviously then, if the consumer is to be satisfied, it must be a good loaf, especially if one remembers that the art of salesmanship is the selling of something that does not come back to somebody who does.

To define a good loaf, one must have some knowledge of the desirable qualities of a particular type of bread and how these qualities are produced. This, in turn, means an understanding of raw materials, manipulation and the fermentation process.

There is no better plan than to make out a score sheet listing the desirable features of a good loaf under two headings, external and internal. The list can be short or long, according to the wishes of the assessor and to the degree of examination. Generally about six salient points under each heading are all that is necessary, with a seventh common to both.

External	*Internal*
(1) Volume	(1) Colour
(2) Symmetry of shape	(2) Structure
(3) Bloom	(3) Sheen, texture
(4) Crust colour	(4) Flavour and aroma
(5) Evenness of bake	(5) Crumb clarity and elasticity
(6) Oven break	(6) Moistness

(7) Cleanliness

It is a fundamental truth that the factors which make for a good loaf nearly always come together, because a good loaf is the result of:

(1) The use of first-class materials.
(2) The balance of those materials according to the process used.

(3) Correct manipulation.
(4) Overall control at all stages of manufacture.
(5) Good workmanship.

Volume

This is important from the selling point of view, because a small, heavy loaf has little or no appeal. A loaf of large volume would have more initial appeal, but would not please the housewife when cutting and buttering, in fact the loaf must be big enough to suggest value for money but not so big that it is difficult to cut, with a structure so open that it uses an excess of butter when spreading.

It is obvious then, that a volume that is 'right' is of importance and must be obtained. This will come from a dough in which the gluten has been properly conditioned and in which there is sufficient gassing power at the time of baking. It means, also, correct final proof and correct baking temperature and humidity.

Symmetry of Shape

There are many shapes in which bread can be made. If the shape is ugly or imperfect, then sales value is lost. The dictionary defines symmetry as a 'beauty resulting from right proportions, or a harmony between the parts'.

This describes symmetry in bread of any shape. It is brought about by correct dough fermentation, moulding and final proof. Any cutting before baking must be done at the right time and with care. Attention must be paid also to proving and baking conditions, oven loading and subsequent packing after baking. Plate III shows symmetry of shape in a coburg loaf.

A baking-tin too small for the weight of dough is a common cause of imperfect shape. Expansion within the loaf is not equal. The lower part of the loaf is controlled by the tin and takes on colour more quickly. In contrast, the upper part of the loaf, forced out of the tin, takes on crust more slowly, the expansion is greater and is uncontrolled, resulting in a bad shape.

Bloom

Bloom is not easy to define, for a loaf may have every other desirable attribute, including a nice crust colour, and yet without bloom it is short of perfection. If a loaf with a natural bloom and one without are placed side by side, the difference in the crust appearance is clearly seen. If the loaf with the natural bloom is put by the side of one with an artificial bloom, again the difference is clearly seen, for the artificial bloom appears as a glaze.

Natural bloom is the glow, or healthy flush, that denotes excellent fermentation, the use of first-class materials and fine workmanship. It is always a thrill to the true craftsman.

Crust Colour

This is not wholly the result of baking, for unless the dough is correctly fermented and made from good materials, the crust will lose the wonderful gradations of colour, ranging from the reddish-browns through the golds and yellows to the creamy white, discernible at the oven break.

The crust colour of bread made from under-ripe dough is less attractive, having a harsh red-brown colour with a greenish tint at the oven break. Bread made from over-ripe dough has a crust that is completely unattractive, as though all the natural crust colours have been rendered drab with grey. Bread made from hot doughs or from over-bleached flour also have an unattractive greyness in the crust colour.

Finally, a baking temperature under or over normal, or insufficient humidity in the final proving or baking, will spoil the attractive crust colour of otherwise well made bread.

Evenness of Bake

This is obtained by correct oven firing and maintenance. Overloading is a frequent cause of uneven crust colour. The packing too closely together in the oven of tin loaves, for example, prevents the even penetration of heat, with the result that one or more sides of the loaf fail to take on enough colour, spoiling the appearance of the loaf.

Oven Break

This is the result of expansion within the loaf during the initial baking period. If the dough is correctly ripened and the proving and baking conditions are correct, then the break is even and attractive. This is because the gluten is in such condition that it is resilient enough to 'give' to the expanding gases and yet stable enough to retain them.

Humidity in the proving and the baking prevents skinning and the rapid formation of crust, so that again expansion is even. Careful moulding and correct final proof are both contributing factors making for an even break.

Internal Colour

Colour must of course depend, to a certain extent, on the grade of flour used. Colour in bread can vary from the fine creamy white of high quality, low extraction flours to the characteristic brown colour of wholemeal bread. Correct fermentation and manipulation, however, will produce qualities of colour within each grade.

Flour from the same bag can, in different hands and under different conditions, produce a variety of crumb colours from creamy white to a drab grey. Similarly a wheatmeal or wholemeal loaf can be made with either a bright appetizing crumb colour, or one that is unattractive, depending on the skill and knowledge of the baker. Correct fermentation and manipulation will produce in the crumb a sparkling brightness that is absent from the under- or over-fermented loaf, or from a dough that has been incorrectly handled. This crumb brightness depends to a large extent on the size and shape of the gas cell.

If the student will cut several loaves from different batches or, better still, from different bakers, he will notice a general variation in the size of the cells in different loaves. Close study will always show that the shape of the cells may vary from loaf to loaf. He will understand that the loaf with the smaller cells will give the greatest aggregate light reflection. This again will depend on the shape of the cell for, if they are shallow, then there is the maximum light reflection from them.

The deeper cells will absorb light. The thinness of the cell wall is important because on it depends the maximum reflection of light deflected from cells immediately below the cut surface of the loaf.

Colour brightness, then, is determined by light reflection and refraction; light absorbed will lower the colour brightness. It follows that the first consideration is the use of first quality materials in correct balance; secondly, fermentation must be correct; thirdly, manipulation at all stages must be carried out properly; finally, proving and baking conditions must be ideal.

It is the quality of the materials used and the fermentation control that will largely determine the thinness of the cell wall, and manipulation that is mainly responsible for the size and shape.

Dark streaks in the crumb will, of course, spoil the picture of crumb brightness. Streaks are the result of carelessness and bad workmanship.

The student may like to try an interesting experiment with bread, showing the effect of manipulation on crumb structure and colour. First make up this small dough:

lb.	*oz.*		*lb.*	*oz.*	
1	14	Flour		$\frac{1}{4}$	Fat
	$\frac{3}{4}$	Yeast	1	1	Water (approx.)
	$\frac{1}{2}$	Salt			

Dough temperature 80° F.
Knock back at 1$\frac{1}{2}$ hr.
Scale at 2 ,,

Yield, 3 loaves weighed in at 1 lb.

After scaling and handing-up, let the dough pieces rest for about 15 min. to recover. Take one piece and divide it neatly into eight, moulding each piece up round. Pin them or flatten them slightly and stand each disc one on top of the other. No dusting flour should be used or the pieces will not adhere to each other.

Turn the heap over on to its side and carefully drop into a bread-tin, so that the top shows a corrugation with eight ridges. Halve the second piece of dough and mould into two baton shapes; place them side by side on the table and, before putting them into a second tin, twist together similarly to the strands in a rope. Mould up the last piece normally and place into a third tin. After sufficient proof, bake them all at about 480° F.

When cool and cut, there will be noticeable differences in crumb colour and structure, all the more remarkable in view of the fact that each loaf was made from the same dough. The first loaf, known as the 'supertex' if cut parallel with the ridges will be found to possess a fine regular structure with a very bright colour. The manipulation has the effect of fining the structure and producing small shallow gas holes that reflect light, giving the illusion that much whiter flour has been used.

The second loaf, known as a 'cross pan', will have a fine cutting surface and a bright crumb colour, although the structure will follow the course of the twist. The last loaf when cut, will show larger, deeper gas holes that absorb light and in contrast to the first loaf the crumb will appear less bright.

Structure

This refers to the build of the loaf and the size and shape of the cells. Structure must vary according to the type of bread. The vesiculation in the crumb structure of a tin loaf, for instance, should be round, fairly small, regular and evenly distributed. This would not do for a Vienna loaf, however, where the ideal is for large and irregularly distributed gas holes of differing sizes. Plate IV shows the irregular structure of Vienna bread.

The size of the gas holes in a wholemeal loaf must of necessity be small, firstly because of the low gluten content and, secondly, because the bran coatings present in the dough will break down the coherency of the gluten, thus making it less resilient to expansion. Plate VI illustrates a fine example of a wheatmeal loaf showing even crumb vesiculation.

Here again good quality materials, properly fermented, with correct handling and careful proving, are essential if the structure of the crumb is to be satisfactory. The water content of the dough is important, also, for too much water in doughs for ordinary bread will open the structure, producing large holes, with a consequent lowering of colour brightness.

Sheen and Texture

If the cut surface of a good loaf is held level with the eyes in a good light, it will be observed that the surface will reflect back what will look like myriads of tiny sparkling lights. This is called sheen, and again is the result of the same trio-quality materials, controlled fermentation and correct manipulation.

If the finger-tips are drawn lightly over the cut surface of the crumb, the sensation of touch will convey quite a lot of information to the skilled and experienced person. If the sensation is one of soft silkiness, yet with a certain stability, then the texture is good. If on the other hand, it is very soft, then it is termed 'woolly' and is the result of a dough that is too slack, or a loaf that has had too much final proof. A tight rough surface, one that is termed 'drummy', suggests a dough made from a tight dough, or one under fermented. Plate V is a beautiful photograph of a tin loaf of excellent sheen and texture.

Flavour and Aroma

However much care is put into the manufacture of bread, its final destiny is to be eaten; therefore flavour and aroma are important factors if it is to be enjoyed. The expert judge can assess both by the sense of smell, but a more accurate estimation can be obtained if the tip of the tongue is used on the crumb surface at the same time as the nose is used, thus giving a combination of taste and smell.

Flavour and aroma, given first-class materials, are the result of fermentation, plus salt and any other flavoursome addition such as malt. Both flavour and aroma will differ according to the process used; more pungency may be expected from the longer fermentation processes. Bread made from hot, over-fermented doughs will have a sour taste and smell, from the development of excessive acid fermentation. An aroma that could be described as that of bad pineapples, will denote the presence of 'rope', a bacterial disease in bread.

Crumb Clarity and Elasticity

If the crumb surface is pressed gently with the thumb any cores or seams are immediately felt. If a thin slice of the loaf is held to a bright light they can be seen. The crumb should be clear and free from such cores and seams.

Crumb clarity comes from the proper mixing of the dough in the dough-making stage, and care and attention during the subsequent stages, especially in preventing the incorporation of dough scraps.

If the crumb is pressed, it should return when pressure is raised. This elasticity is the measure of the tensile strength of the crumb and is important, because cutting and buttering depends so much on this quality. Again the degree of fermentation of good quality materials will determine the degree of elasticity of the crumb.

If the student will cut a thin slice from a loaf, then, after removing the crust, roll the piece like a Swiss roll, it should, if elasticity is at its maximum, slowly unroll and return to its original shape without crack or breakage.

Moistness

This is not determined by the water content alone, but by fermentation, the action of salt and by additions, such as fat and malt. Baking and storage conditions are also important.

A well-made loaf from a long process dough will generally be moister and retain that moisture for a longer period than a loaf made on a very short process. This is due to the greater changes possible in time, in the insoluble constituents of the dough.

Moistness in relation to keeping quality is important if the housewife is to be completely satisfied with the product.

BREAD FAULTS

Bread faults are not easy to diagnose, because they can arise from so many causes. For instance flours vary in grade, in gluten content and quality; colour varies as do the maltose figures. In addition flours can take on off-flavours from contact with other materials or from bad storage. Extraneous matter may be accidentally or carelessly mixed with the flour or, by chance, some foreign seed may inadvertently be milled in with the grist, although this is extremely rare.

The quantity and quality of other materials used in breadmaking can also cause faults. Temperatures; timing and methods of manipulation, carelessness in the addition of materials; insufficient mixing at the dough-making stage; errors in the setting and timing of machinery; all must be taken into account.

Faults in proving and baking conditions; the use of baking tins too small for the weight of dough; carelessness in cooling, packing and storing and, lastly, lack of hygienic principles; all can cause faults. To complicate diagnosis, two or more of the above causes can produce the same fault or, worse still, a loaf may have different faults, each from a variety of causes.

Faults and the reasons for them are finally diagnosed, by examination, reasoning, deduction, elimination and by experiment; all this pre-supposing that the baker has a sound knowledge of his raw materials, the fermentation process and of men and machinery. It can be seen, quite clearly, that a great deal of skill, knowledge and experience is necessary before the student can become a competent craftsman in breadmaking and one able to diagnose and define faults in bread.

Exterior faults will be dealt with first and these may be put under six headings.

(1) *Lack of Volume.*—There are at least nine possible causes for this fault, ranging from the balance of raw materials to the baking. A dough that is too tight, more especially with tin bread, will certainly be responsible for a loaf of small volume, unless longer final proof is given. A dough, the fermentation speed of which has been checked by chilling; one with too little yeast for the system employed; the use of too much salt; all, in effect, causing under ripeness, are conducive to small volume. Insufficient final proof, an excessive baking temperature—the two together will accentuate the fault—are also possible causes.

Flour with a low maltose figure, because there is insufficient gassing power at the critical final proving stage, will produce bread of less than the normal volume. In the same way, a badly over-fermented dough, wherein the sugar has been fermented away, producing practically no gas during final proof, will produce a similar result.

Lastly an over-bleached flour, or an over-use of chemical improver in the bakery, will produce the fault; in this case, however, it is because of the serious damage done to gluten strength and its stability.

(2) *Excessive Volume.*—Obviously, this fault can be due to the direct opposite of some of the causes given above.

An excessively slack dough, unless timing adjustments are made, is a cause of excessive volume, especially if the oven is too cool, which last, according to degree, will apply to normal doughs.

Doughs with a low salt content, which decreases the stability of gluten, and excessive final proof are two other causes of this fault. Loose moulding decreases gluten stability and because of it, final proof may be excessive, is another possible cause.

(3) *Lack of Crust Colour.*—There are five possible causes, apart from the obvious one of a cool oven. Badly over-ripe dough, due to an over-extended fermentation period, to lack of salt, or to an excessive water content, will detract from crust colour, as will the use of low maltose flour. A hot dough and/or skinning during final proof will most certainly be a cause of lack of bloom and healthy crust colour.

(4) *Shell Tops.*—This fault in tin bread is easily recognized because the top crust of the loaf can readily be taken off in the form of a large shell. This is due to the formation of crust on the top of the loaf before maximum expansion has taken place; the pressure from within the loaf exerts itself in such a way that the top of the loaf lifts in the form of a lid. The fault can be due to under-ripeness, insufficient final proof or the use of low maltose flour. The fault can be accentuated by baking in too hot an oven, especially if there is little or no oven humidity.

(5) *Cleanliness.*—If there is an absence of all other exterior faults, and the loaf is dirty or otherwise soiled, then those responsible for manufacture cannot be recognized as craftsmen. The ultimate purpose of breadmaking is for it to be eaten; if it fails in that purpose, then not only has time been wasted, but also raw materials.

Extraneous matter that may, by accident, have been baked into the crust, such as string, splinters of wood and calcined bread crumbs are bad enough, but there can be no excuse for dark smears from dirty tin grease, finger marks or dirt from unclean racks or boxes. A dirty loaf is the mark of a slovenly worker.

Internal faults can be conveniently put under six headings.

(1) *Holes.*—There are many causes of holes in the structure of the loaf and there are many types of holes. Generally speaking it is the size and shape of the holes that give a clue to the probable cause.

A dough made from flour with a weak gluten, especially if the yeast content is high, will cause holes, because the gluten has little power of gas retention and the weaker cells break down during baking. The expanding air and gases escape into other cells, which in turn break down until the coagulating protein at last traps the gases in large pockets.

The use of a very strong flour with a large quantity of yeast will cause holes. In this case the gluten is not resilient enough for even expansion; it ruptures and again the gases are collected into pockets that eventually form large holes.

A further cause is an excessively hot oven, especially the oven sole. The elasticity of the gluten is destroyed quickly near the surface of the loaf and, in consequence, expansion does not proceed evenly, breakages occur and large holes are formed.

A different type of hole is the slit or break, which is caused by the excessive use of cones or flour when moulding. It may also be caused by skinning while the dough piece is recovering from handing up. This may be accentuated if the dough is unduly tight.

Fat not properly dispersed during dough-making, or oil introduced during dividing, handing up or moulding, may again be a cause. All these things prevent the dough from knitting or cohering together during the manipulation so that, during baking, there is a greater expansion where the surfaces meet.

Small holes are generally caused by an undue incorporation of gas generated during bulk fermentation and its presence is a direct result of discarding the knock back and/or handing up, with faulty manipulation at the final moulding stage.

A dough with a high water content will have quite an open structure; if, however, the flour is strong or the dough under-ripe, water holes may occur. These are distinguished by a glossy surface unlike the gas holes, which are dull.

Yeast or salt not properly dispersed in the dough will cause holes. The salt hole is easily recognized. It is slimy, and has a pronounced saline taste.

(2) *Cores, Seams, Streaks and Condensation Marks.*—If the student will take a cut loaf in his hands and press the surface gently with his thumbs, the sensation of touch will indicate the presence of cores which are usually felt as small dense spots in the crumb. Before the advent of the machine mixer, cores in bread were prevalent, because in hand mixing there was not such a complete dispersal of ingredients and the dough, therefore, was not so thoroughly mixed.

It was the small unmixed patches that, remaining unfermented, provided the cores in the finished loaf. The most common cause nowadays is the incorporation of pellets of hard flour or dough particles during dusting. Another common cause is skinning during bulk fermentation. The skin is broken up during the knock back, dividing and moulding, showing up as cores in the crumb structure.

Seams can be seen in the form of dense layers. They can be caused by the careless handling of the fully expanded loaf during setting, or the violent movement of bread in the oven before the structure is set. Putting a warm dough piece into a cold tin, or a cool dough piece into a very hot one, will cause seams. In both cases fermentation at the point of contact with the tin is stopped, if not destroyed; this layer of virtually unfermented dough shows as a seam next to the crust. A sandwich loaf in too small a tin will show a seam near the crust; this is due to the pressure on the metal surface from the expansion within the loaf.

Streaks are evidence of uneven manipulation of the dough in the final stages, that is, loose moulding and/or insufficient final proof. Correct final proof is of great importance, for not only is volume desirable for itself but during this stage the dough fabric must fully relax from the tension given during the final moulding. Dark streaks can be caused by the use of high maltose flour or the excessive use of malt products.

Condensation marks are interesting. When the loaf leaves the oven it contains steam, some of which may condense in the crumb structure causing dark patches. Mr. W. E. Spencer, of the Cereals Research Station, St. Albans, has investigated this problem at great length. He emphasizes the importance of each loaf being properly cooled before it is packed. The student can learn quite a lot if he will take several tin loaves straight from the oven and place them in various positions on the table; one on its end, one upside down, one on its side, etc. After cutting, the condensation patches may be seen in different parts of the crumb structure.

(3) *Dryness and Rapid Staling.*—This may be due to making bread from an excessively tight dough, especially if baked in a cool oven. Low baking temperatures mean prolonging the baking time, with a consequent increase in the evaporation of moisture. A hot dough will produce bread that will dry rapidly, partly due to the excessive evaporation of moisture during fermentation and partly because the speed of fermentation limits the time in bulk, when the gluten is more effectively mellowed and softened.

Because salt is hygroscopic, i.e. it attracts moisture, a low salt content in the dough may hasten drying. An over-fermented dough (a low salt content may cause this) loses moisture and may also result in dry bread. Under-fermentation is a cause of rapid staling, in this case it is because there has been insufficient time for gluten softening and maturation. Mineral improvers used in excess will also cause dryness.

(4) *Damp, Clammy, or Close Crumb.*—By using a high maltose

flour, milled from sprouted wheat, or by the use of excessive amounts of malt, a clammy, sticky crumb may be expected, due to an excess of sugar and dextrin in the dough. The presence of a higher proportion of dextrin (which is a gum) and sugar, prevents a complete baking out. In this case, although sticky, the crumb is quite open.

A damp, clammy, discoloured crumb that smells sickly sweet, denotes the presence of 'rope', a disease in bread caused by soil-borne bacteria. This should never be allowed to develop.

Bread not properly baked, or proved and baked in atmospheres that are excessively humid, may have a clammy crumb. The over-use of enriching agents, such as milk and fat, will tend to cause closeness in the crumb structure. Milk has a closing effect on the crumb, due to the tightening effect of casein on gluten; this can be counteracted by using fat with the milk. Fat, on the other hand, has a shortening effect on gluten. Used excessively it destroys resilience, producing a close crumb with a greasy feel.

Dough felling will so break down the structure that the crumb will be close and clammy. Bread made with weak flours, with the use of too much salt and from very cold under-fermented doughs will show the same fault.

(5) *Crumbliness.*—One of the fallacies often met with among bakers, is that a slack dough will produce crumbly bread. Any type of dough can be made to produce crumbly bread by simply under or badly over-fermenting it. A properly made Vienna or proprietary germ loaf with a high water content will never be crumbly. A tight dough, if properly fermented and baked, should not necessarily produce crumbly bread either.

Crumbliness is due, almost always, to the degree of fermentation; if it is insufficient, then the gluten is not conditioned, and the crumb has neither the resilience nor tensile strength necessary to withstand the action of cutting the loaf. If fermentation is over prolonged, then the gluten is weakened and the cutting pressure breaks down the crumb structure.

If mineral improvers are used excessively, thus damaging the gluten strength, or if the salt content is low so that it does not confer sufficient stability on the gluten, then crumbliness in the finished loaf may occur. The use of excessive quantities of fat with their consequent shortening effect on gluten will also cause this fault.

(6) *Colour Spots.*—Colour spots on the crust or in the crumb are nearly always the result of carelessness. Brown spots on the crust are due to either salt or sugar that may have been picked up on the surface of the dough piece during or after final moulding. Larger patches could be caused by pellets of milk powder that have

escaped complete reconstitution or thorough mixing during dough-making.

Carelessness in the use of confectioners' colours is an obvious reason for colour streaks in bread. Cocoa powder or chocolate are also possible causes. Another possible source of colour spots is from the dye used in the printing of the brand name on flour sacks. The remedy for all this, of course, is care. Finally the student must be warned against the use of indelible pencils in the bakery, or violet streaks may appear in the bread as a result of carelessness. It is an unwritten law that this type of pencil must not be used in the flour mill. The same law must be strictly observed in the bakery.

J. R. Irons, the author of *Breadcraft* and a great craftsman who, during his lifetime, won over 7,500 awards for breadmaking, used to say that, if he were a teacher he would, after showing his students how to make good bread, teach them how to produce every possible fault. He would do this to such effect that, not only would they be able to exactly produce a particular fault, but would recognize it, and its cause, in commercial practice. The deliberate production of faults is an excellent means of gaining experience and knowledge of the use of raw materials, the complexities of fermentation and the effects of manipulation.

ROPE

The student will know that there are many ways of making bread, all successful provided that the baker has the necessary knowledge and experience. The craftsman of the past gained his knowledge in the school of experience only; the modern baker has the way shortened and made easier by the technical facilities now so freely available.

Fermentation in primitive times, as the student will also know, was carried out by the use of soured dough saved from a previous batch. This method was used for hundreds of years, until other forms of yeast became available. Nevertheless sour dough is still used in many parts of the world where breadmaking is still carried out in the primitive manner.

In the cosmopolitan quarters of the world's great cities, it is still used in the making of rye and similar types of bread, although a proportion of compressed yeast is used to speed up the process. This method has not only a historical significance but a gastronomic one as well, for bread made by this method has a characteristic flavour that is not imparted by the use of compressed yeast alone.

It is from the past that modern technical research obtains assistance in the solving of problems of the present. In this way the sour dough method was applied some years ago to rid the baker of the effects in bread of the disease known as rope, which was prevalent during the hot humid months between July and September. Rope is first seen as a discoloured spot in the centre of the crumb of the loaf, which will spread until the whole of the crumb is discoloured and emits an unpleasant odour, not unlike that of rotting pineapple.

Bread that has been infected, when broken open shows fine web-like strands, and it was from those strands that the expression 'rope' was derived. The condition is caused by spores of soil-borne bacteria of the *subtilis-mesentericus* group, which are introduced into the flour during milling, despite the most thorough cleaning that is given to the wheat in the modern mill.

It is virtually impossible for the miller to remove it from the crease of the wheat grain; in any case it can only be destroyed by the prolonged application of heat at a high thermal figure, or by the use of powerful germicides, both of course impracticable during the milling process. At the same time the student will understand why the bacillus is not destroyed during baking.

Rope is unpleasant and soon renders the bread uneatable, but it is not really dangerous to health. Brown breads are much more liable to the disease than white bread, for meals contain some or all of the bran coatings on which the bacillus is present.

Investigation into the problem of rope revealed the fact that, although difficult to destroy, its growth could be inhibited by the rapid cooling of the bread to a temperature below 70° F., which is extremely difficult during the hot summer and early autumn months. It is inhibited also by increasing the acidity of the dough. The alteration in the *p*H of the dough can be carried out either by the use of vinegar, acetic acid or acid calcium phosphate. These are used at the rate of two pints of vinegar per sack, 12% acetic acid at one pint per sack or 1–1½ lb. of acid calcium phosphate (80%) per sack.

Another method of increasing the acidity is by the use of sour dough and this method developed by British Arkady Ltd., was given the approval of the Ministry of Food during the last war.

Starter Dough

lb.	*oz.*	
14	0	Flour
	3	Salt
	½	Yeast
7	8	Water

Dough temperature: 70° F.
Let ferment 24 hr.

Sour Sough

lb.	*oz.*	
140	0	Flour
2	0	Salt
17	8	Starter dough
75	0	Water

Dough temperature: 72° F.
Ready in 24 hr.

The sour dough is made up daily and sufficient is left each day for use as the next day's starter. As an inhibitor against the development of rope it is used in the following way:

Bulk fermentation time in hours	0	1	2	3	4	6	8	12
Sour dough-pounds per sack	30	20	12	8	5	2	1	½

If in small quantities the sour dough is first broken down in part of the water with the yeast. If larger quantities are used it is best added in pieces at the beginning of dough-making.

The use of mould inhibitors give at the same time, a moderate protection against rope.

The practice of using sour dough as an aerating agent is sometimes termed the M.P.D. (Mature Parent Dough) method and here is a formula that the student may like to try:

Bread-using sour dough

lb.	*oz.*		
1	14	Flour	Dough temperature: 78° F.
	½	Salt	Knock back after hr.
	¾	Yeast	Scale at 1½ ,,
1	0	Sour dough (saltless)	
1	1	Water (approx.)	

Yield four loaves weighed in at 1 lb. each.

BREADMAKING

Historical Evolution

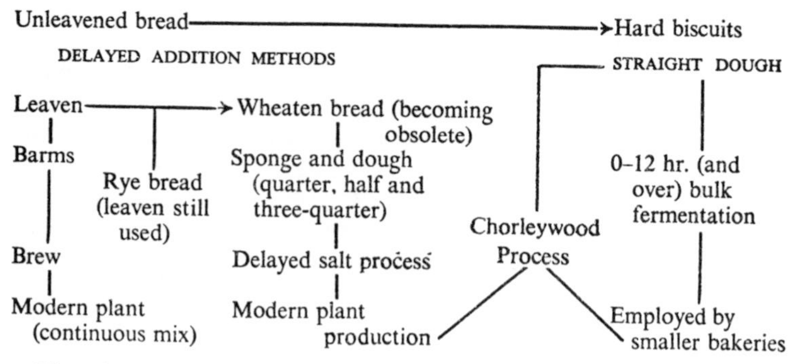

The above diagram shows the historical evolution of breadmaking from the earliest times, before fermentation or leavening was discovered, to the various present-day methods of yeast fermentation. The diagram on page 104 show the unit processes in the three principal methods of breadmaking.

10

Breadmaking Processes: Straight Dough; Ferment and Dough; Sponge and Dough; The Salt-Delayed Method; The Continuous Breadmaking Process

BREADMAKING PROCESSES

THERE are many satisfactory ways of making bread. Generally they come under three headings—straight dough, ferment or sponge and dough and the new continuous method. There are modifications of these, but the underlying principles are the same.

Straight Doughs

With this method all the ingredients are mixed together in one operation. It is the method most widely used in this country. It is simple and straightforward and this no doubt accounts for its popularity.

A straight dough can be timed to ferment in bulk from 30 min. to from 14 to16 hr., according to the amount of yeast, water and salt used, the type of flour, the temperature of the finished dough, and the room where it is stored.

The quickest of all straight doughs is the no-dough-time dough, when, after thorough mixing, the dough is scaled and moulded straight into the tins. Usually this type of dough has a minimum of 2½% yeast, based on the weight of flour. The method is useful in an emergency, although the quality of the finished loaf is not generally satisfactory, the bread staling rapidly and having little of the crumb resilience that one expects from the well fermented loaf.

This is due to the fact that ripeness is not attained in a process so short that there is little or no time for gluten softening. The characteristic aroma of well-fermented bread is absent, although there is a pronounced aroma of yeast.

The method, however, is one into which constant research is going on, in view of the restriction in night baking. Two important points being studied are, the type of flour most suitable for the process, and the possibility of using organic acids to improve flavour (for example, lactic acid from the use of milk).

The short processes are generally accepted to be from one to five hours, although some authorities include the six-hour-dough in this category. It may be well to emphasize at this point that these times are calculated from dough-making to scaling, which is what is meant by bulk fermentation. Probably the three- and four-hour processes are the most popular and the most widely used.

The late J. R. Irons, the well-known bread craftsman, considered that two hours bulk fermentation was the minimum period in which most of the essential characteristics of the loaf could be obtained. It can be said that a dough with a fermentation period of under two hours is gassed rather than fermented, the desirable characteristics of good fermentation not having time to develop. This does not of course include roll or bun doughs.

The student must always remember that every stage of breadmaking is controlled by the speed of fermentation, and a greater control is possible with the shorter process methods.

The long process group will include the doughs from five or six hours to anything up to sixteen hours bulk fermentation and, provided that the flour is sufficiently strong, satisfactory bread can be produced. During long fermentation periods the gluten softens to a greater extent than it does in the shorter processes. For this reason the water content is reduced, the yeast content is lowered, and also the temperature of the dough. The salt content is increased to confer a greater stability on the gluten.

The very long processes are not to be recommended, because of the virtual impossibility of controlling temperature and consequent speed during this long fermentation time. A long process sponge followed by a short time dough, is far more satisfactory than a long straight dough, for in this way the desirable flavour that is one of the characteristics of long fermentation, is preserved.

Ferment and Dough Process

Bread and buns can be made on a two-stage method known as either a ferment and dough, or a sponge and dough. By this method the total bulk fermentation is divided into two stages. The length of either stage is a matter of preference controlled by the yeast content.

An old textbook on breadmaking—one preferably published before the beginning of the present century—will give the student a fascinating picture of the bakery scene long before there was any technical or scientific understanding, by the ordinary baker of fermentation.

In those days the craftsman was trained in the hard school of trial and error and practical experience. Flour quality varied to a greater extent than it does today, and the craftsman baker brought the blending of flour to a fine art. Yeast had to be made by the baker himself, or if bought, had to be nursed and developed if it was to carry out the fermentation process successfully; now, yeast of high uniform quality, delivered fresh is taken for granted.

Temperature control by the use of the thermometer was practically unknown, the baker was guided by the weather, by the use of the hand and to a certain extent by instinct. Dough ripeness was determined solely by the sense of touch. The development of yeast was carried out by the use of ferments and sponges, and this method of breadmaking became the rule almost without exception.

The ferment is a mixture containing a proportion of the water, the yeast, any yeast food and sufficient flour to make a thin batter. The yeast immediately begins to ferment and multiply, and soon is active and vigorous, so that it is in a first-class condition to undertake the harder work of fermenting the rest of the flour. A ferment is generally allowed to stand until it shows signs of collapse, although this is not strictly necessary.

A 'flying ferment' is a mixture of the yeast, a haphazard guess at an amount of water and flour, which together with any yeast food, when mixed, will make a thin batter. It is allowed to stand only while the rest of the ingredients are being weighed and prepared for doughmaking. It has enough time for vigorous activity to commence and is in fact a fermentation 'boost'.

When the rest of the materials are ready the ferment is added, and the dough made up; the dough is then allowed a period for the second stage of fermentation. The ferment and dough method is still popular in the making of bun doughs, enriched rolls, and any type of dough where speed is necessary, or when the dough carries a large amount of fat and sugar, which will retard fermentation: the initial 'boost' then becomes necessary.

Sponge and Dough Process

A sponge can be described as a stiff ferment or a slack dough. It is made up by mixing a proportion of the flour, the yeast, some, or all of the salt (but sometimes none at all), and some or all of the water. Speed is controlled by the amount of yeast, the amount of salt used, the consistency, and the temperature of the sponge and the room where it is allowed to ferment.

When the sponge has dropped, the balance of the water in which the salt has been dissolved is added to the sponge and thoroughly mixed in; after which the rest of the flour is added and the dough made. The process of adding and mixing the salt solution to the sponge is known as 'breaking down', and in the days when doughs were made by hand, the experienced dough-maker did this properly because he knew that failure to do so meant far harder work in clearing the dough after the rest of the flour was added.

The size of the sponge in proportion to the finished dough gave it its name; thus, if a quarter of the total weight of flour was used in it, it was known as a 'quarter sponge'; if half or three-quarters was used, then it was a 'half-sponge' or a 'three-quarter' sponge.

Another type is known as a 'flying sponge'. This is one standing two hours or less, and containing the larger amounts of yeast necessary for the processes of less than five hours' fermentation.

Ferment, Sponge and Dough

The breadmaking process can be split into three stages, by first of all setting a preliminary ferment, which, when ready, is made into a sponge by the addition of more water and flour. After a sufficient fermentation time the final stage is completed by the incorporation of the rest of the materials.

It is considered that bread made from a sponge and dough method is superior in flavour, texture and keeping qualities to bread made from a short process straight dough. These results are attained with a control of fermentation that is virtually impossible with long straight doughs.

Salt Delayed Method

This method of breadmaking has become exceedingly popular during the last decade, being introduced during the last war as a result of the use of a large proportion of strong Canadian wheat in the milling grist. The gluten in this wheat was harsh and tough, and experiments were made as to the best method of breadmaking to adopt so that the gluten could be conditioned without the use of more yeast, higher dough temperatures, or by longer fermentation periods.

It was eventually found that by making a dough in the ordinary way, giving about two-thirds of the mixing time and leaving out the salt, the gluten mellowed in a reasonable time. The salt was added at the knocking back stage, when the balance of the normal mixing time was given to effect a thorough mixing.

As is usual with all breadmaking processes, there are modifications; some craftsmen insist that the salt shall be added in the dry state, others keep back some water and flour from the dough and add the salt as brine, using the flour to adjust the consistency of the dough during the final mixing. Some suggest that a proportion of the flour should be sieved with the salt before adding, others mix the salt with some fat before addition, lastly there are bakers who will add a proportion of the salt at the dough-making stage, adding the balance in one of the several ways mentioned.

Again many bakers have experimented with the timing of the salt addition, some adding about two-thirds of bulk fermentation time, while others make the addition as late as possible, allowing, of course, sufficient time for the dough to recover from the mixing. It seems that the correct timing is dependent on flour strength, bulk fermentation, and the amount of machining that the dough will get after bulk fermentation is complete.

It is considered that by this method the crumb of the loaf is much brighter and has a much greater stability, and that there is a better oven spring.

Continuous Breadmaking Process

This method has aroused great interest in the baking industry in recent years, although it was the subject of experiment in Germany as far back as 1883.

Experimentation has proceeded in many countries since; until in 1951, the method was put into commercial practice in the U.S.S.R.; now it is in an advanced stage of development and well over 200 bakeries in the Soviet Union are making bread by this system.

In Sweden and the U.S.A. there have also been great technical developments. Bread is now being made by this process in this country. The process is essentially the same in all the countries concerned, except that in the U.S.A., the product appears to have been influenced by the machine, while in European countries the machine has been designed to fit the bread standards of the countries using the system.

Briefly, the process is a speeding up of the old barm, ferment and dough process. Bulk fermentation has been eliminated, the fermentation taking place in the barm stage, the barm being renamed, 'brew' or 'broth'. The broth contains the yeast, water, salt, milk solids, malt and yeast foods, and is fermented for 6 hr. at 100° F., being constantly agitated. The fat is emulsified.

The dough ingredients are fed continuously in controlled amounts into a pre-mixer and given a partial mixing, then entering a developing mixer where, under pressure, and by rotating impellers, the dough is conditioned. It is then extruded and fed at the required weights into baking-tins. The total mixing time is about 90 sec.: 30 sec. in the pre-mixer and 60 sec. in the developer.

The resultant product has the attributes of good bread, particularly with regard to flavour.

Here are four recipes employing different processes, with which the student may like to experiment.

No-dough-time dough

lb.	*oz.*	
2	8	Flour
	¾	Salt
	3	Yeast
1	8	Water (approx.)

Dough temperature 80° F.
Mix the ingredients thoroughly; scale, mould and place into warmed tins immediately.

Yield two loaves weighed in at 2lb.

Ferment and no-dough-time dough

Ferment

lb.	*oz.*	
	8	Flour
	1½	Yeast
1	2	Water

Temperature 80° F.
Let stand 30 min.

Dough

lb.	*oz.*	
1	6	Flour
	½	Salt

Mix the ingredients thoroughly; scale, mould and place at once into warmed baking-tins.

Yield three loaves weighed at 1 lb.

Sponge and dough

Sponge

lb.	*oz.*	
1	0	Flour
	2½	Yeast
	1	Milk powder
1	0	Water

Temperature 80° F.
Let stand 45 min.

Dough

lb.	*oz.*	
2	10	Flour
	1	Salt
	½	Sugar
	1	Fat
1	1	Water (cold)

Rub the fat into the flour. Dissolve sugar and salt in the cold water and add to the sponge and mix well. Add the flour and mix all together thoroughly. Rest the dough for 15 min. then scale and mould. This dough will make excellent London bloomer loaves. It is an enriched bread. Yield three loaves weighed at 2 lb.

Three-quarter sponge and no-dough-time dough

Sponge

lb.	*oz.*	
1	14	Flour
	2	Yeast
1	8	Water

Temperature 80° F.
Let stand 60 min.

Dough

lb.	*oz.*	
	10	Flour
	¾	Salt

Mix thoroughly; scale and mould and place at once into warmed tins.

Yield two loaves weighed at 2 lb.

Calculation of Water Temperature for a Sponge

Here is a simple method of calculation. First take the flour temperature and deduct the figure from the desired sponge temperature. Multiply the result by the weight of flour in pounds. Divide the result by twice the weight of water in pounds. The result, added to the desired sponge temperature gives the approximate water temperature.

Here is an example:

A sponge containing 7 lb. of flour and 8 lb. of water is to be set at 80° F. The temperature of the flour is 62° F.

$$\frac{(80-62) \times 7}{8 \times 2} = \frac{63}{8} = 8 \text{ approx.}$$

Required water temperature is therefore $= 8 + 80 = 88°$ F. This calculation allows for no heat losses in weighing or mixing.

Chorleywood process

This process, which is based on the principle of mechanical dough ripening, has been developed by the British Baking Industries Research Association. The process has been perfected and applied to commercial production, both large and small.

The straight dough method is used, the dough materials are subjected to an intense mechanical mixing within a short period, in a special type of machine fitted with an automatic watt hour meter. The work input is thus carefully controlled. In practice the baker multiplies the dough weight by five. With the meter set, the machine automatically stops when the required watt hours are consumed.

This process eliminates the bulk fermentation period altogether. This is achieved by the intense mechanical mixing which, in the space of only a few minutes, develops the dough in a manner which take several hours in conventional processes.

The addition of ascorbic acid is necessary at the rate of 9.5 g. or $\frac{1}{3}$ oz. (5 oz. ascorbic acid to 15 pints of water using 1 pint per sack, simplifies the addition).

Fat also is necessary at the rate of 2 lb. per sack and approximately 1 gallon of water extra per sack is also necessary depending on the degree of enrichment. The yeast level is raised above normal by 50-100%. Weaker flours may be used to make bread of excellent quality. All varieties of bread can be produced by this process.

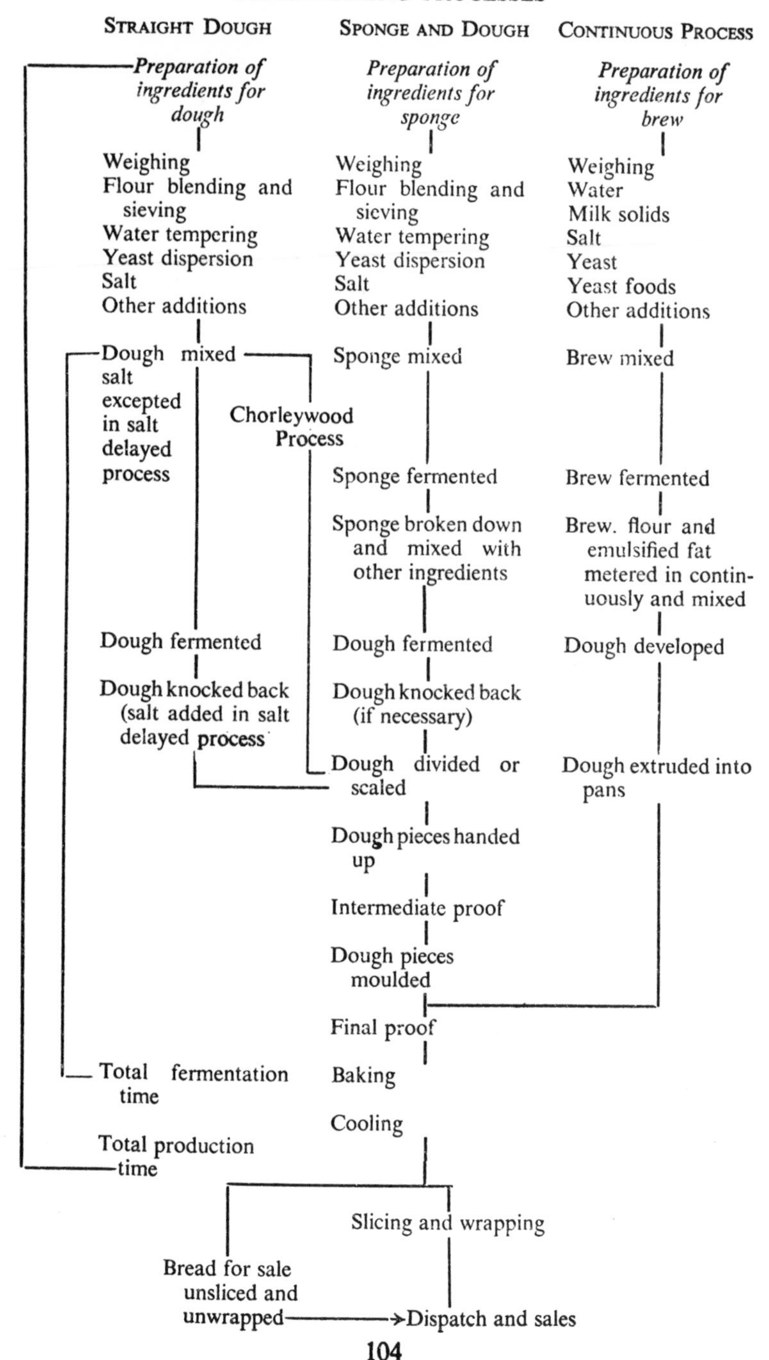
BREADMAKING PROCESSES
STRAIGHT DOUGH
SPONGE AND DOUGH
CONTINUOUS PROCESS
Preparation of ingredients for dough
Preparation of ingredients for sponge
Preparation of ingredients for brew
Weighing
Flour blending and sieving
Water tempering
Yeast dispersion
Salt
Other additions
Weighing
Flour blending and sieving
Water tempering
Yeast dispersion
Salt
Other additions
Weighing
Water
Milk solids
Salt
Yeast
Yeast foods
Other additions
Dough mixed salt excepted in salt delayed process
Sponge mixed
Brew mixed
Chorleywood Process
Sponge fermented
Brew fermented
Sponge broken down and mixed with other ingredients
Brew. flour and emulsified fat metered in continuously and mixed
Dough fermented
Dough fermented
Dough developed
Dough knocked back (salt added in salt delayed process
Dough knocked back (if necessary)
Dough divided or scaled
Dough extruded into pans
Dough pieces handed up
Intermediate proof
Dough pieces moulded
Final proof
Total fermentation time
Baking
Cooling
Total production time
Slicing and wrapping
Bread for sale unsliced and unwrapped
Dispatch and sales

11

Bread Improvers: Mineral Additives; Enriching Agents; Yeast Foods

BREAD IMPROVERS (1)

THE finest bread improver is a good craftsman. It is only the person who understands raw materials and their inter-actions in the baking processes, who can assess the comparative merits of various improvers, and above all who will know how and when to use them.

Flour is always of variable quality, depending on the grade, which in turn is affected by the weather and soil conditions in the country of origin. It becomes necessary, therefore, at times, to add something to the dough in order to bring the product to a predetermined standard. These additions should be used with knowledge and discretion, otherwise the quality of the loaf, far from being improved may be actually worsened.

Bread improvers may be divided into three main classes:

(1) Those of a mineral nature, mainly used by the miller.
(2) Those of an organic nature, mainly enriching agents.
(3) Those which, while coming under headings 1 and 2, are also valuable yeast foods, helping the yeast to work more vigorously.

Those under the first heading could more correctly be termed flour improvers. Mineral improvers are popular because they increase the yield of bread by necessitating the use of extra water; this does not necessarily improve the bread. Some mineral improvers have a slight drying effect on the crumb.

If the flour is of good quality, and fermentation is controlled, with the formula in balance, then there should be no need to add mineral improvers in order to produce good bread. The most important mineral addition to bread is common salt (sodium chloride), and the adjustment of the salt content can often be effected in order to correct a slight fault that may be the excuse for using a more expensive improver.

Persulphates

These are fairly widely used by the miller. The persulphates used are potassium and ammonium. Persulphate is used at the rate of ¼ to ½ oz. per sack (280 lb.) by the miller. Flours treated with persulphates will take more water to allow for the tightening which takes place as fermentation proceeds; in this way increased yield is obtained. The toughening effect is considered to be due to the effect of the nascent oxygen on the structure of the gluten.

Potassium Bromate

Bromate has a remarkable effect on gluten, conferring stability to a marked degree. It is used by the miller at the rate of approximately $\frac{1}{10}$ oz. per sack. Bromate has an astringent action on gluten, necessitating the use of more water in the dough. It improves the gas retaining properties of the gluten, thus increasing loaf volume.

It is the principal effective ingredient in several well-known bread improvers used by the baker, and in view of the powerful action even $\frac{1}{10}$ oz. has on a sack of flour, the student will readily understand the reason for care in the use of bread improvers in the bakery, for bromate may already have been used by the miller. If bread improvers are used, the utmost care should be exercised in weighing carefully according to the manufacturers' instructions.

Sulphates

Sulphates have a marked astringent action on gluten. Alum (potassium aluminium sulphate), and copper sulphate, were once used by the baker in the days when long fermentation processes were usual. The addition of these sulphates seemed to delay ripening, have a bleaching effect, and because of their effect on gluten, produced a bold and well volumed loaf. They are both prohibited by law nowadays because their use is considered injurious to health. The student may find the word 'hard' contained in a bread recipe in books of the last century; this was the term used for alum by the bakers of that time.

Both magnesium sulphate (Epsom salts) and sodium sulphate (Glauber salts), have an astringent action, together with a bleaching effect. Magnesium sulphate also has a stimulating property on yeast action; the effect of this salt being more noticeable in the oven than at the dough stage. It is considered advisable to adjust the salt content when using magnesium sulphate, e.g. 4 lb. of salt and ½ lb. of magnesium sulphate.

Phosphates

Acid calcium phosphate and ammonium phosphate both have a tightening action on gluten, and since phosphates are a necessary constituent of yeast food, they are both fermentation stimulants. A.C.P. is used at the rate of 1 lb. per sack, which can be increased to 2 lb. per sack to inhibit the development of rope. Ammonium phosphate is used at the rate of 8 oz. per sack.

Lime Water

In the days when long process doughs were usual, lime water was used to retard fermentation in hot weather and in addition it had an astringent action on gluten. As lime is alkaline it reduced the acidity of the dough, and thus slowed the speed of fermentation. Lime water was used at the maximum rate of 1 quart per sack.

Organic Acids

Lactic and succinic acids are natural constituents of a fermenting dough, so that an addition, within limits, can be made with perfect safety. They are both very efficient with flours containing a tough tenacious gluten, producing a better conditioning. Lactic acid can be used in amounts up to 8 oz. per sack, and succinic acid from 2–4 oz. per sack.

Nearly all of the bread improvers offered to the baker contain one or more of the above, together with a suitable filler, such as a mixture of starch and salt. It is therefore easy to see that in wrong or careless hands, there is a distinct danger of over chemical treatment, if added to flour by both miller and baker.

BREAD IMPROVERS (2)

Malt

The student will now know that of the various forms of malt used by the baker there are two distinct types—diastatic and non-diastatic. Diastatic malt serves four purposes, it adds flavour, it increases the sugar content of dough immediately, and provides diastatic enzymes which break down starch, thus ensuring a steady supply of sugar for the fermentation process. Diastatic malt also contains proteolytic enzymes which help to modify gluten. Non-diastatic malt serves the dual purpose of providing sugar and flavour.

Sugars

Sugars, with the exception of lactose, are fermentable by yeast.

Lactose (milk sugar) is only sparingly fermentable. Flour contains natural sugar—principally sucrose—in varying amounts; normally it is about 2·5–3%. This is sufficient, during controlled fermentation over a reasonable period, to provide a steady source of sugar for gassing purposes. Sometimes flour with a low sugar potential is met with, this is known as low maltose flour. With this flour, fermentation proceeds normally for a time and then begins to fail towards the end, that is, during final proof, producing a small volumed loaf with little or no crust colour.

High maltose flour also can be a problem to the baker. It is caused by the chemical changes that take place when the wheat grain begins to sprout while still in the ear, consequent upon wet, humid weather conditions during harvesting. Doughs made with this flour gas excessively, partly because of the high sugar content, but also because of the increased diastatic activity, which still further adds to the sugar content by the production of maltose from the breakdown of starch.

The result is a loaf of large volume and with a high crust colour; the structure of the crumb is weak causing, in tin bread, a collapse of the sides, and because of the dextrin (a gum that is a by-product of the breakdown of starch) and the excessive sugar present, the crumb is dark, showing streaks, and the loaf is difficult to bake out.

For low maltose flours, it follows that sugar in some forms is necessary, and in this case diastatic malt is the best improver, for it adds sugar to the dough and the diastatic enzymes that will keep up the supply. It may be found that additional sugar is also necessary, in which case, glucose is advised up to 1 lb. per sack.

In automatic plant production, sugar at the rate of 6 to 8 oz. per sack may be the means of assisting recovery from the mechanical action of the machines, by increasing the gassing rate. For sweeter varieties of fermented goods, 1 to 8 oz. of sugar per quart of liquor is advised, and up to 10 to 12 oz. per quart for bun goods.

It must be remembered that yeast functions differently according to the density of the sugar solution in the dough; with doughs containing a sugar solution of up to 10% (12 to 15 lb.) per sack, the fermentation rate increases. Above these figures it is retarded. A good quality bun dough contains a 30% solution, hence the desirability of an initial ferment. Nevertheless a 10% solution in white bread would seriously degrade and weaken the structure of the loaf, because sugar has a solvent action on gluten. This could be counteracted by a short process dough and the use of mineral improvers and extra salt to effect an increase in gluten stability. This is seen in the American type of bread made by the continuous method, where a 13% sugar solution is used.

Sugars may be graded into two groups:

Solids	*Semi-solids*
1. Granulated	1. Fondant
2. Castor	2. Glucose
3. Icing	3. Invert sugar
4. Barbadoes	4. Golden syrup
5. Demerara	5. Honey
6. Nib sugars	6. Treacle

The second group act also as anti-staling agents. In addition they are more easily assimilated by yeast because of the high percentage of mono-saccharides (simple sugars) that are present. All sugars are sweetening agents.

Icing Sugar.—The use of icing sugar in the production of bread and fermented goods is limited to the dusting or glazing of fancy tea breads, buns and Danish pastries.

Barbadoes and Demarara.—These sugars because of their colour, are useful brown bread improvers, adding a characteristic flavour to brown breads. The recommended usage is 2 oz. to 14 lb. of meal. The original Chelsea bun contained either of these sugars, which was spread over the dough with the currants before rolling up.

Nib Sugars.—These are used for decorating tea breads and for use in, and on bath buns.

Fondant.—This is used for the decoration of some types of bun. It is an exceptionally good bread improver used at the rate of up to 4 lb. per sack in very short process white doughs.

Glucose, Syrup and Invert Sugars.—These all have the same effect as fondant, but as they are more immediately fermented by yeast, they should be used only in the shortest process doughs. The reccommended usage is 1½ lb. per sack.

A new commercial sugar known as E.C. glucose is now available to the baker. It is a product of the enzymic conversion of starch and is sweeter and less viscous than ordinary acid converted glucose (see Chapter 23).

It is recommended that E.C. glucose can replace the cane sugar content of breads and rolls resulting in a more ready dough relaxation during the moulding stages.

For sweeter tea breads, 50% of the total sugar content can be replaced by the new glucose and, for bun goods, 25% can be replaced.

Treacle.—In brown breads treacle is excellent both for imparting flavour, and as a moisture retainer.

Honey.—This is used in special fancy tea breads. A mixture of honey and lard rubbed into dough at the knock back stage is an excellent improver for exhibition breads.

BREAD IMPROVERS (3)

Fats

Fats have a physical rather than a chemical effect on dough. As fat is a shortening agent, that is, it reduces toughness, thus conferring a mellowness, it is particularly valuable for use with strong flours with a tough harsh gluten. Because fat confers moistness on bread, its inclusion is advisable in very short process doughs, particularly emergency no-dough-time doughs, where fermentation time is not sufficiently long for natural gluten softening.

Fat is also considered to have a lubricating effect on the fine gluten strands which, together with its shortening action, results in an increased volume. The crust is rendered more thin and biscuit-like.

It is considered that butter and lard are by far the best fats to use, a mixture of both being ideal, for they add their distinctive flavours to the bread as well as their physical properties. Neutral fats and oils having no flavour only improve physically.

Fermentation is retarded according to the amount of fat used, so that an increase of yeast may be necessary.

Fat can be added by rubbing it into a portion of the flour, by pouring it into the dough in the form of oil, or melted fat, or by introducing it in the form of an emulsion. By using an emulsion, a greater degree of fat dispersion is effected. Fat is used generally at the rate of from 2 to 4 lb. per sack. It is considered than even 1 lb. per sack has a beneficial effect on the resultant bread.

Amounts up to 10 lb. per sack can be used for specially enriched bread; it is advisable, however, that with the larger amounts milk should be added, because its tightening effect on gluten offsets the excessive shortening action of the fat.

Fats used excessively, will result in a loaf with a small volume, and a close 'cheesy' crumb. The crust will be soft and short with very little colour; in addition, both crust and crumb will have a certain greasy feel. Here, in summarized form, are the effects of fat in bread.

(1) Increases the food value.
(2) Reduces elasticity, softens the crust and crumb, thus making the bread more easily digestible.
(3) Confers moistness on bread, thus retarding staling.
(4) In normal amounts it increases volume. Used excessively, volume is seriously reduced, because the extensibility of the gluten is largely destroyed.
(5) Butter and lard add flavour to the loaf.
(6) In larger amounts, fat retards fermentation.

Milk

When milk is added to a dough, fat, sugar, protein and mineral salts are added, because milk contains all these essential food factors; thus the bread is enriched and the food value increased. Skim milk powder is the form of milk mainly used for bakery products; its inclusion in dough being accompanied by the use of more water. The amount used is generally calculated to ensure that of the total liquid content, 50% is milk (provided that the bread is not sold as milk bread.)

The effect of milk in dough is mainly physical. The milk fat, if full cream milk is used, has the same effect as added fat, tending to increase volume by its lubricating and shortening action on gluten; this, however, is largely neutralized by the action of lactic acid in milk which tightens and increases the stability of gluten.

Milk sugar (lactose) is only slightly fermentable by yeast and remains in the dough, this in addition to the natural sugar still present at baking time. This increases the crust colour, due partly to the caramelization of the sugars during baking. An excess of milk powder in a dough, unless adjustments are made, will result in a small bound loaf with an extremely close crumb and with a dark crust colour.

Plate II shows the effect of reconstituted skim milk powder on loaf volume. Loaf No. 1 contains water only as the moistening agent. Loaves 3 to 5 contain increasing ratios of milk to water as follows: 25/75: 50/50: 75/25. Loaf No. 5 contains milk as the sole moistening agent. In loaves No. 6 and No. 7 the milk concentration is the same as for No. 5, but they contain in addition, fat at the rate of 1 lb. and 4 lb. to the sack respectively. It will be seen that fat will restore the loaf volume when skim milk powder is used.

Further investigation has taken place into the reasons for the tightening effect of milk in bread. While the mechanism of this depressant effect is still not fully known, it is found that the whey protein fraction is responsible. It is also found, that certain heat treatment during the drying of milk, or by bringing reconstituted milk to the boil, will neutralise this effect.

When used as an enriching agent, the following points should be observed for it is only in the observance and the knowledge behind it that enriched bread of good quality can be made.

(1) Check whether the milk powder has been heat treated.

(2) Increase the water content, and to " free " the dough, diastatic malt, or fungal enzymes or more yeast can be used. Skimmed milk powder used commercially contains little fat, therefore fat should be added.

(3) It is important that the dough temperature is maintained, because the effect of chilling is more pronounced in a milk dough than in ordinary doughs.

(4) More yeast and water means that the fermentation time should be reduced.

(5) Because of the tendency to take on more crust colour, the baking temperature should be lower. It follows therefore that to bake the bread properly, the baking time should be increased.

The Bread and Flour Regulations, Statutory Instrument 1963 No. 143, has laid down the standard for genuine milk bread as follows:—

" No claim whatsoever can be made for the addition of milk to bread unless it contains a minimum of 6% whole or skimmed milk solids, calculated by weight on the dry matter of the bread.

Milk bread may not be described as "milk bread" unless the 6% is *whole* milk solids. Bread containing the minimum amount of skimmed milk solids may be described as "milk bread" provided that such words as "containing skimmed milk solids" or "containing separated milk solids" are added.

A formula and the instructions for making bread that may be sold as milk bread, are on page 194.

12

Combustion: Heat Transference; Ovens: History; Firing; Types; Construction; Principles of Heating; Turbulent Heat; Care and Maintenance of Ovens

OVEN FIRING

OVENS may be heated by coal, coke, gas, oil or electricity; in fact, anything that will generate heat can be used as a fuel, depending of course on the heating system of the oven. Again, bearing in mind the type of oven to be heated, the cheapest fuel is not always the most efficient, for it may be the least economical.

The combustion of fuel is a chemical process in which the carbon of the fuel combines with the oxygen of the air to form CO_2 (carbon dioxide) and the hydrogen combines with the oxygen to form H_2O (water), the reactions generating a great amount of heat. The student should understand that the substance to be burned is a fuel and the process of combination with oxygen and with the generation of heat is combustion.

Most fuels contain the elements carbon and hydrogen in varying quantities, and if it is borne in mind that carbon and oxygen will produce CO_2 and 8,080 heat units, and hydrogen and oxygen will produce H_2O and 32,000 heat units, the student will readily understand that a fuel that contains a greater amount of hydrogen will have a higher calorific value; for this reason coke has a lower calorific value than either oil, gas or coal. The residual ash after combustion is complete, is also of great importance, for it follows that the greater amount of ash means that the proportion of combustible material is less with a corresponding lowering of calorific value.

The student will know that without oxygen there can be no combustion. He has only to put a lighted candle into a jar and cover the top; when the oxygen in the jar is used up the flame will go out.

If the firing of an oven is not carried out properly, the reaction is not completed, for one gram of carbon will combine with less oxygen to produce the poisonous gas, carbon monoxide, with only 1,934 calories. This carbon monoxide with sufficient oxygen, can be burned to produce carbon dioxide with the balance of the calories, i.e. 6,146 to bring the total to 8,080.

The following essential points to be observed when firing a solid fuel oven should always be studied by the student:

(1) Understand the construction and the working of the oven. In this way a greater measure of control can be gained.
(2) Understand the nature of the fuel that is being used.
(3) Keep the fire bars clear so that a plentiful supply of air is available for complete combustion. The flues must be cleaned out regularly so that there is sufficient draught. With an adequate supply of air, clinker formation is less and the amount of residual ash is reduced.
(4) Plan and give time for obtaining the desired baking temperatures.
(5) Replace as soon as possible all burned fire bars and furnace fittings. Failure to do this may result in all the bars buckling and all metal fittings deteriorating, so that all will need replacing.
(6) Take care in regulating the draught or the maximum calorific value of the fuel will not be obtained.
(7) The quickest way to cool an oven is to close the ash-pit doors, open the damper and the furnace doors. In this way cool air is drawn into the furnace and not through the fire.
(8) Study at all times the recommendations of the makers, their advice is always available.

Many of the points emphasized for the care and maintenance of solid fuel ovens are equally applicable to ovens fired with gas oil or electricity. Here are some additions to the above.

Gas

(1) Keep a careful check on the air supply, avoiding excessive draught.
(2) Burners, jets, valves etc., must be frequently inspected, kept clean, and in efficient working order.
(3) All burners should be correctly adjusted to maintain heating efficiency.

Oil

(1) The flame should be inspected at short and regular intervals. A smokeless flame indicates heating efficiency. Smoke shows an excess of oil in the mixture, while the presence of flying sparks indicates an excess of air.
(2) Keep all burners clean and properly adjusted.

Electricity

(1) Have internal elements checked regularly by a competent electrician to ensure maximum safety and efficiency.
(2) Pay attention to the use of the switches controlling top and bottom heat for the maintenance of even heating and economic fuel consumption.

The efficiency of an oven or of the fuel used depends on correct firing and oven maintenance. Economic efficiency, however, depend to a large extent, not only on the cost of fuel and maintenance, but on another important factor and that is the intelligent use of the oven.

Here are some important points that the student should bear in mind:

(1) The oven hand should be trained in the operation of the oven or ovens under his charge. This should not only include the points already listed but correct baking procedure.
(2) The oven should be loaded to its maximum capacity in relation to efficient baking.
(3) Baking should be continuous throughout each shift.
(4) Oven doors should be kept closed as much as possible. There should be a minimum of partly filled baking-sheets.
(5) Stand-by heat losses should be reduced to a minimum. All stored heat in the oven should be maintained as far as possible by the avoidance of draughts.
(6) Accurate records of fuel consumption and baking output should be kept.
(7) Regular servicing is essential.
(8) The baking costs of an oven mean nothing unless they are related to the value of the products baked in a stated working period.

HEAT TRANSFERENCE

Having gained some knowledge of the principles of combustion and oven heating, the student should understand something concerning the transference of heat, from the point of fuel combustion to the baking chamber. Heat can be transferred in three ways, by conduction, radiation and by convection.

Conduction

If one end of a metal rod is heated in a flame it will be found that the other end will quickly become hot also; thus the heat is conveyed from the flame and along the whole length of the rod. This transference of heat is known as conduction. The particles that make up the substance of the metal are packed closely together and on heating, the particles vibrate very slightly, the rate of vibration being regulated by the amount of heat applied. The particles knock against each other setting up a vibration all along the metal. In time the whole of the substance vibrates and so becomes hot.

Generally speaking, all metals, especially copper, are good conductors of heat; fabrics, asbestos, wood, air and glass are some of the materials that are poor conductors of heat; that is why in the bakery, hot trays and tins are handled with cloths, and why the insulating packing materials in ovens are either asbestos or glass wool.

When a cake or a loaf is placed into the oven, heat is conducted from the oven bottom, through the tray or baking-tin until it reaches the centre of the cake or loaf.

Radiation

When heat is transmitted without it being in contact with any conducting material it is said that the heat is radiated. The sun is an example of heat radiation. All fires and radiators, whichever way they are heated, are other examples. The heated object is continuously giving off heat in the form of rays which are absorbed by any other objects in the vicinity which have a lower temperature.

Black or roughened surfaces absorb heat much more quickly than polished surfaces; that is why there are reflectors at the back of gas and electric fires; these polished surfaces reflect the heat radiated by the fires. Light coloured clothes are worn in hot climates, and in bakeries, because they do not absorb heat so readily as dark clothing.

If two pieces of metal of equal weight and size, one polished and one blackened, were put in the sun, the dull or blackened one would become hot much more quickly than the polished one. It is for the reason that a blackened metal will absorb heat more quickly than a polished one, that new baking tins are 'baked off' by placing them for some time in a cool oven. This darkening of the tin or 'seasoning' as it is called, must be carried out with care for the tin that covers the steel will melt at about 450° F. running down into blobs and spoiling the baking tins.

The 'top heat' of an oven is radiated from the crown and sides on to the bread and cakes being baked and this gradually penetrates to the centre, meeting the conducted heat from the oven bottom.

Convection

This is the actual movement of liquids and gases consequent on heating. This movement in water can be shown by placing a beaker of water over a bunsen burner and dropping in a crystal of permanganate of potash. As the water gets hotter and the crystal dissolves, the coloured convection currents will be seen to move upwards and outwards, then down the sides and again to the bottom of the beaker.

Heat is first conducted from the bunsen through the bottom of the beaker and heats the centre of the bottom layer of water, which, expanding and becoming less dense, is forced upward displacing the cooler and denser water which drops to the bottom of the beaker.

In this way the water is kept moving as long as heat is conducted to it. The draught of a furnace or fire is produced by the rapid rising of warm convected air and waste gases. The same principle is applied also to the hot water systems used in houses and factories, and to systems of ventilation.

The transference of heat by convection is part of the system of heating steam tube ovens. This will, however, be explained when the subject of ovens is reached.

A completely new principle of baking is now in use involving what is known as turbulent heat.

For centuries bread-baking has been effected in static heat, whether the bread remains still, as in a normal oven, or whether it moves, as in a travelling oven. During baking, bread dough, which is not a good conductor of heat, forms a cushion of its own vapour immediately next to its surface, which insulates it from the surrounding atmosphere thus making heat penetration difficult. The scientist would say that the dough piece has assumed the spheroidal state.

This can be explained by two examples. If water in drops enter a vessel of oil of suitable density and heated to a temperature of about 120° C., the water drops take on a spheroidal shape and do not immediately boil away. If the spheres are touched with a needle, violent boiling occurs at once, because heat has penetrated through the vapour insulation which is broken.

If a drop of water falls on a heated plate well over the boiling point of water, it assumes the shape of a slightly flattened ball. Evaporation is comparatively slow because the vapour film insulates it from the heat, which only penetrates as the vapour slowly disperses, when evaporation is slowly completed. If the water globule is ruptured evaporation is rapid.

The principle of the application of turbulent heat to baking, is that by violent agitation of hot air, the insulating vapour film is broken, so that the heat is constantly in contact with the dough, thus penetration becomes more quickly effective.

This principle of baking is now applied to large travelling ovens and has also been developed in ovens for the small baker. One such small oven has unique features in that the bread to be baked is placed on to metal racks which are wheeled straight in to the oven in a matter of seconds. The baked products are removed with the same expedition.

OVENS

There are many centuries between the earliest form of baking and the modern oven. The first bread in primitive times was probably baked on a hot stone after the ashes were pushed aside. From this it is easy to imagine the next stage when something was built over the hot stone to trap the heat, and so the first oven was made.

Soon something more permanent was needed, and ovens were built of stones and clay. These were heated by a fire being burned inside them, the ashes being swept out after the oven was thoroughly hot. The ancient Roman loaves in Naples museum were baked in ovens that can still be seen in the ruins of Pompeii.

Many stone ovens can be seen in old houses and palaces in this country. Visitors to Stratford-upon-Avon can see the stone bread oven in Mary Arden's cottage. Mary Arden was the mother of William Shakespeare. In London, the stone ovens in the Tudor kitchens of Hampton Court Palace, built in the time of Henry VIII, can still be seen. It was not until the early eighteenth century that it became the custom to build ovens with chimneys and larger ovens became the rule.

For many years wood was the fuel invariably used and this continued until the introduction of coal as a fuel for commercial use. Even so, wood or faggot ovens are still used all over the world in places where wood is cheap and plentiful. It is held by bakers who use them, that bread baked in wood ovens has a sweeter and better flavour; this is claimed also by those who use coal fired ovens. There seems no doubt, however, that both wood and coal fired ovens do produce bread with a crisp and well flavoured crust.

Towards the end of the eighteenth century ovens were being built with flues fitted with dampers to carry away the smoke. To save some of the trouble of removing the ash from the oven, the fuel, either wood or coal, was burned in a metal basket on wheels known as waggons; these could easily be removed when the oven was sufficiently hot. Later, furnaces were built into the side of the oven for the combustion of coal, these being known as side-flue ovens, many of which are still in use in this country today. Wood and coal ovens, while efficient in their day, due to the fuel and ash having to be dealt with in the bakery itself, are a source of dust and dirt.

Towards the end of the nineteenth century, Perkins perfected the steam tube oven, the heating system of which operated on a new principle. This type of oven was a great advance, both in efficiency and cleanliness. It can be heated by coke, gas or oil fuel.

Ovens heated by gas, oil or electricity are gradually superseding those fired with solid fuel. Ovens can be classified under two headings. Internally heated and externally heated. The internally heated ovens can be subdivided into those burning solid fuels, where the combustion takes place within the baking chamber itself. In this category are wood or side-flue ovens; side-flue ovens adapted to gas or oil burning, and those where gas or electricity is used internally.

With internally heated ovens, in which solid or liquid fuel is burned within the baking chamber, baking cannot take place while the oven is firing. With gas or electric ovens, or where the oven is externally heated, the oven remains clean, so that baking is continuous, that is, while firing is still taking place.

Side-flue ovens

With an elementary knowledge of combustion and with some knowledge of the evolution of the baker's oven, the student will need to know a little more on this subject, not only because the oven is the most important item of equipment in the bakery, but because a question on ovens is a certainty in an examination paper sooner or later.

Built strongly of brick, the side-flue oven will give excellent service for many years, in fact they have been used on many occasions by three generations of the same family. They are internally heated with

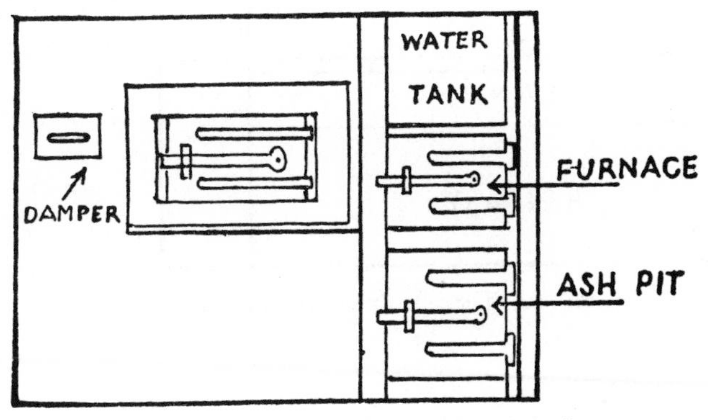

FIG. 7.—The side-flue oven. Front elevation.

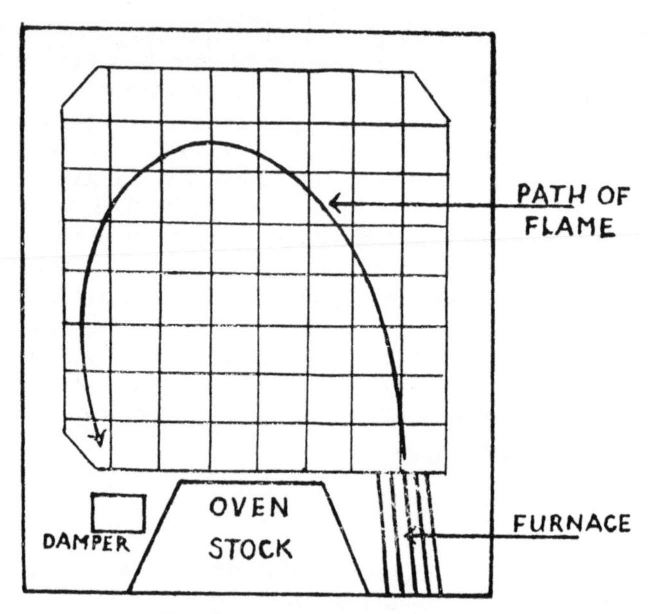

FIG. 8.—The side-flue oven. Plan.

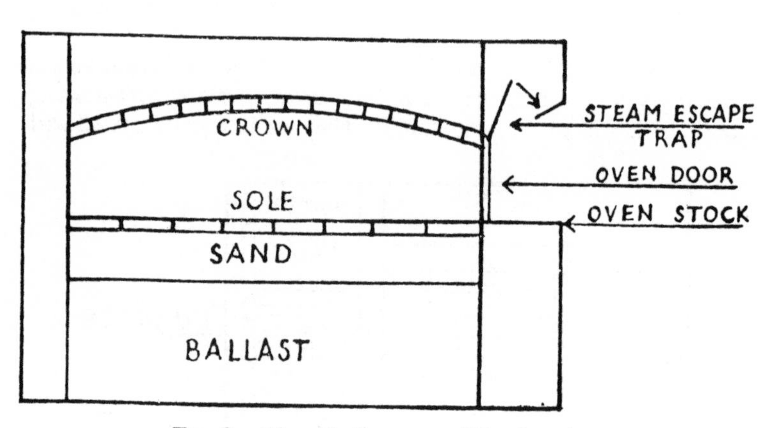

FIG. 9.—The side-flue oven. Side elevation.

a flue on one side, and a furnace on the other, in which the fire is burned; combustion taking place in the baking chamber itself, with the by-products escaping by way of the flue and up the chimney. Figs. 7, 8 and 9 show the construction of the side-flue oven.

These ovens have a damper built into the flue which is closed when firing is finished, so that the draught is stopped and no heat can escape by way of the chimney. This type of oven is not fitted with a thermometer, so that much depends on the skill and experience of the baker for correct baking temperatures; this is generally and fairly accurately assessed by the clearance of soot from the brickwork along the back and sides of the oven chamber.

The side-flue oven has been a popular and comparatively cheap oven to use for the small baker, but they are gradually being superseded by the small gas or electric oven. There are, however, a considerable number of side-flue ovens still in use, some of them converted to oil or gas firing. Where there is mixed production, there is generally enough heat left in the oven after breadmaking at night to bake all the cakes required during the day, provided that cakes are made in correct sequence according to the diminishing heat. The ovens are inclined to be dirty in use when coal is used, because both fuel and ash are of necessity in the bakery. A long pole with a damp sack tied on one end, known as a 'scuffle', is used to wipe the oven sole clean of ash before baking commences. A typical oven sole construction would be of tiles, generally a foot square, resting on sand.

Firing is timed to be finished a short time before setting commences, so that an opportunity is given for the heat to become 'solid', i.e. evenly distributed. To protect the bread from the rather fierce radiation of heat, wooden 'upsets' are laid along the search, the name given for the back and sides of the baking chamber. The red-hot furnace is screened by the use of strong water pots which also provide humidity.

Firing a side-flue oven is simple. A draught is effected first of all by opening the ash-pit door, pulling out the damper and closing the steam escape trap over the oven stock; after this, the furnace bars are cleared of ash and clinker. A fire is built up of paper, wood and coal.

When the fire has burned clear, the furnace is again loaded with coal. The number of times that the furnace is loaded depends entirely on the initial heat of the oven; generally three is the maximum at the start of bread-baking, reduced to two and then one—known as a 'flash'—as the batches of bread are baked.

It is important when loading the furnace, to push sufficient white-hot coal to the oven end of the furnace, to act as an ignition to the combustible gases released from the roasting coal in front. In this

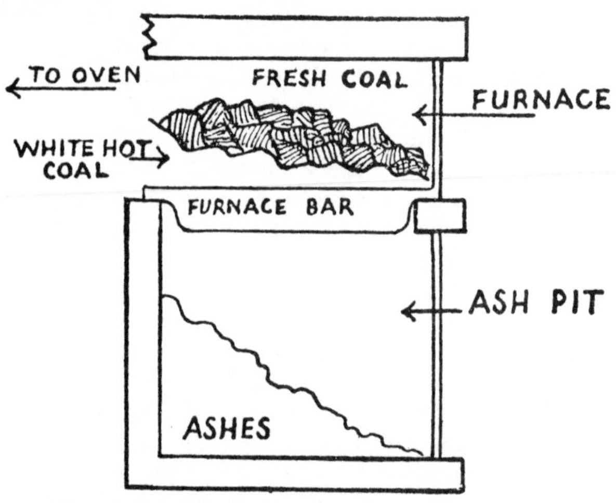

FIG. 10.—The side-flue oven. Furnace loading.

way excessive smoke from the chimney is avoided, and more efficient use of fuel is effected (Fig. 10).

Steam tube ovens

This type of oven was invented by the Englishman, Perkins, in 1851, and was the first oven built on this principle. It was a great advance on the side-flue oven, firstly because it was externally heated, and so baking was continuous, and secondly because it was much cleaner in use, with the furnace outside the production centre of the bakery.

The principle of heating is by an induced pressure on a water surface which raises the boiling-point and thus the temperature. This is done by a series of tough cold drawn steel tubes, approximately $1\frac{5}{16}$ inches in diameter and with a bore of about $\frac{15}{16}$ inch. Each tube contains about 40% of internal volume of distilled water, and is hermetically sealed.

The tubes, evenly spaced, are placed in rows, one row under the sole and the other just under the crown of the oven. The tubes are tilted back a little so that the lower ends are in the furnace. When the fire is lighted or the heat applied, the heat is conducted through the metal of the tube to the water. Convection currents are set up and the water soon boils at 212° F. The steam from the boiling water cannot escape and the pressure on the surface increases; this raises the boiling-point still further.

As the heat is still being applied it continues to boil at a higher temperature. More steam increases the pressure and the boiling-point. Eventually the pressure becomes so great that the water boils at 500° F. and over. This heat is radiated into the oven and is recorded on the thermometer. The heat is almost the same along the whole length of the tube, even though the heat is applied at the furnace end. When the temperature of the tube is 250° F. there is a pressure within

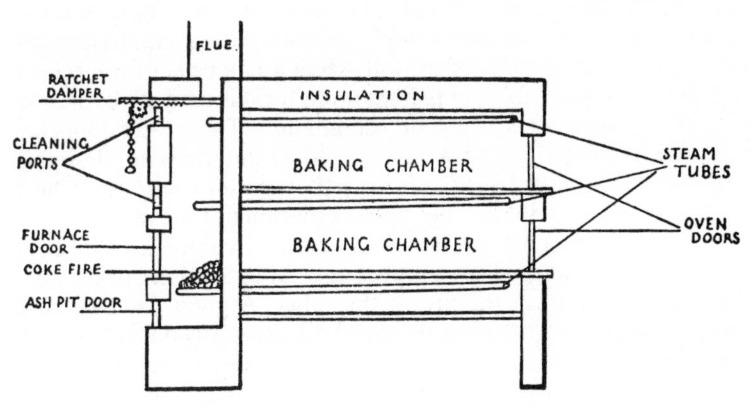

FIG. 11.—The steam tube oven. Coke fired.

the tubes of 15 lb; at 400° F. it is 235 lb. and at 500° F. it is about 700 lb. The student will understand from this that care is necessary in maintaining and firing this type of oven; a burst tube can be very serious indeed.

Generally the tube ends extend the whole length of the furnace at the back of the oven. In some ovens the tube ends are bent to fit compactly into a smaller furnace, resulting in a more evenly heated oven and a greater fuel efficiency. Fig. 11 shows the construction of a steam tube oven. Here are the advantages and disadvantages of this oven.

Advantages

(1) Continuous baking, hour after hour.
(2) Clean.
(3) No fumes in bakery.
(4) No fuel or ash in the bakery.
(5) Can be used with either coke, gas or oil as a fuel.

Disadvantages

(1) Higher capital outlay.
(2) There is a danger of burst tubes when not under efficient control.
(3) Regular examination necessary.
(4) Time needed in raising or lowering the temperature.

Firing

If coke is used, the fire is lighted on the bottom row of tubes with the ash-pit doors and the dampers opened initially until the fire begins to burn red, when the ash-pit doors are closed and the damper partly pushed in. If the student will watch a competent furnaceman he will note that the damper is important, for it is used at all times to regulate the speed of combustion within limits. The ash-pit doors are not used so much during baking, for a white-hot fire is not desirable —not only does it damage the furnace, but creates oven 'pull' which results in distorted shapes and possible burning of bread.

It is most important that the fire be free of accumulated clinker at all times. This will cling to the tubes and act as a barrier to the conduction of heat from the fire to the tubes. A good ovenman will quickly note this by the effect on the bread, especially if it is baked on the sole of the oven, for along the line of the tube, or tubes affected, there will be a tendency for the bread to 'flow' and there will be little bottom crust.

Whether the ovens are coke, gas or oil fired, the flues and tubes must be kept clean or the efficiency of the oven is lowered. Cleaning is even more important with coke fired ovens because of dust which soon accumulates on the upper rows of tubes and in the flues. The best practice is to clean at regular intervals, for instance, once a week.

These ovens are subject to periodic examination by the Home Office and insurance company's inspectors, it is therefore imperative for this reason and for reasons of safety that the furnace, the furnace brickwork and the tubes are kept in good condition. Properly maintained and efficiently worked, these ovens will give excellent service for many years.

Drawplate Ovens

These ovens are externally heated, usually by steam tube fired by coke, gas or oil. This type of oven was designed to speed up oven loading and unloading, which could be done much more speedily by several men working together. This was not possible on a peel oven which could only be worked by one man and an assistant.

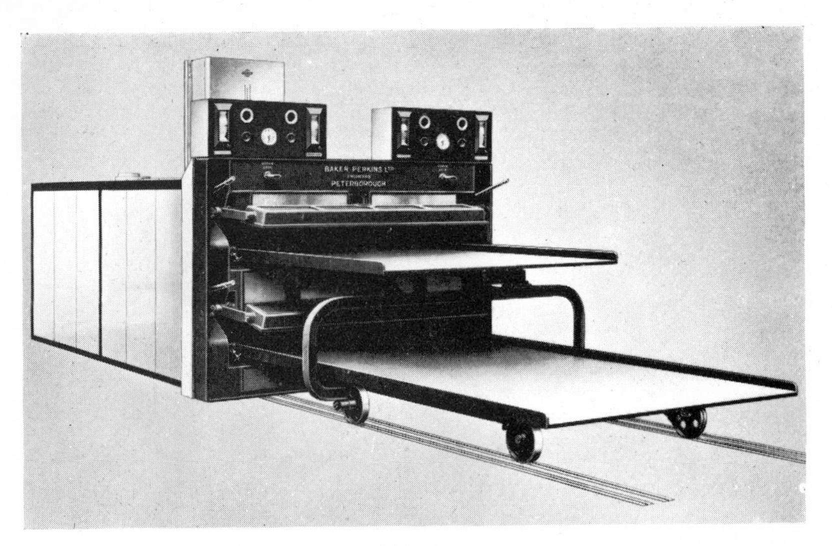

VIII An electric drawplate oven

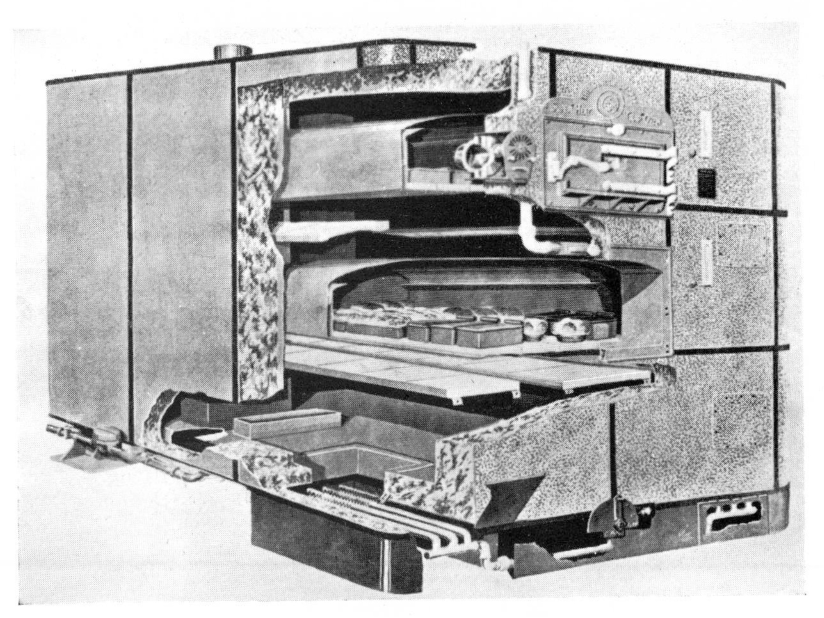

IX Cut-away drawing of a Cox 'Heat Trap' Hot Air oven

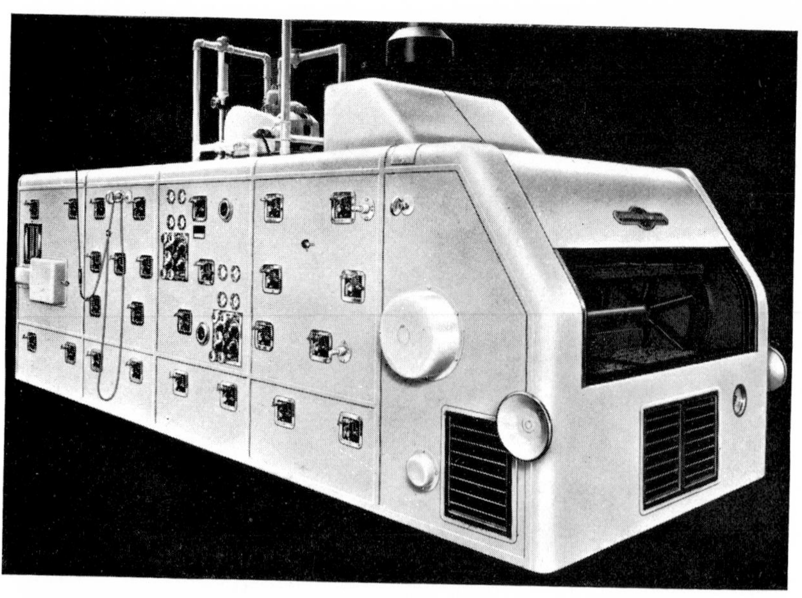

X The 'Uniflow' controlled tray travelling oven

XI The 'Uniflow' swing tray travelling oven

XII The 'Kneeda' reel oven

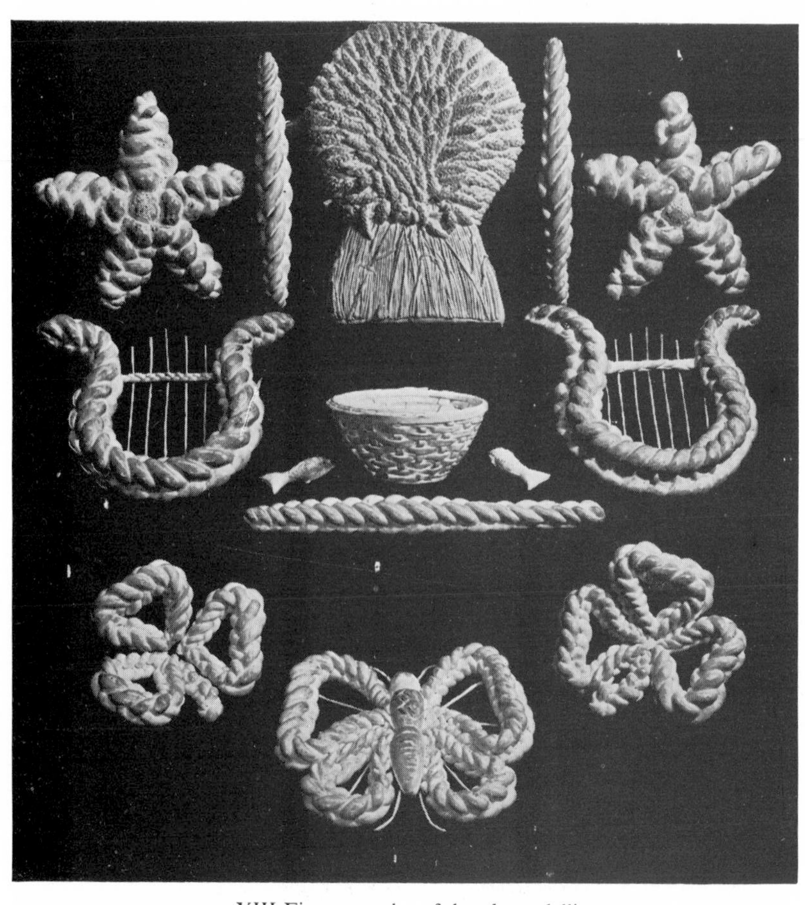

XIII Fine examples of dough modelling

This speeding up is effected by drawing the plate or oven sole out into the bakery, hence the name. In this manner the baked bread is quickly pushed on to metal lined tables and wheeled away. In a similar manner the unbaked bread is wheeled to the plate in provers and the oven quickly loaded. All bread, whether tin or baked on the oven bottom, is placed on 'setters' the width of the oven, these are placed into the provers. It is then a simple matter for two men, one on either side of the oven to tilt the setter, so that oven loading takes place a row at a time.

The plate rests on a wheeled carriage. The wheels, which are grooved, fit into metal runners fitted flush with the floor. The plates are easily pulled out and pushed in, passage being effected by counter-weighted doors which are easily manipulated. Single- or double-deck ovens are installed if desired or even a single-deck drawplate with a peel oven on top.

As a result of the introduction of the drawplate oven, two important points must be recognized.

Firstly, the ovenman with his skilled precision and speed in setting and drawing bread from the oven was no longer needed, the work being done by semi- or even unskilled labour.

Secondly, it is true to say that with the introduction a turning point in baking history was reached for it became possible, with a battery of these ovens, to initiate large-scale bread production, thus opening the way for automation. The standard rate of baking was estimated as a round an hour, that is, that within that time, each oven was loaded, unloaded and given a heat recovery time of approximately 10 min.; baking time was 40-45 min.

The drawplate oven is still popular for the large-scale baking of slab cakes and malt bread.

Plate VIII shows an electric two-deck drawplate oven.

Hot-air Ovens

These ovens are externally heated, burning gas, oil or solid fuel, the furnace in some types being some way from the oven itself. The principle of heating is by hot convection currents which circulate in flues and ducts between the baking chambers. There is very little flue 'pull' so that hot air circulates slowly.

The newer types, heated by gas, have the burners at the bottom of the oven; they are therefore much more compact and take up less room. In addition there is a greater heat efficiency, for the hot air on cooling is returned and released at a low level, not as in the older system, at the top before the heat is fully exhausted. There is no flue pull, only the movement of convection currents from the burners, round the oven and back to the low level flue. The new ovens of this type are heavily insulated with mineral wool; this is clearly seen in the cutaway drawing of a Cox 'Heat Trap' oven, Plate IX. Hot-air

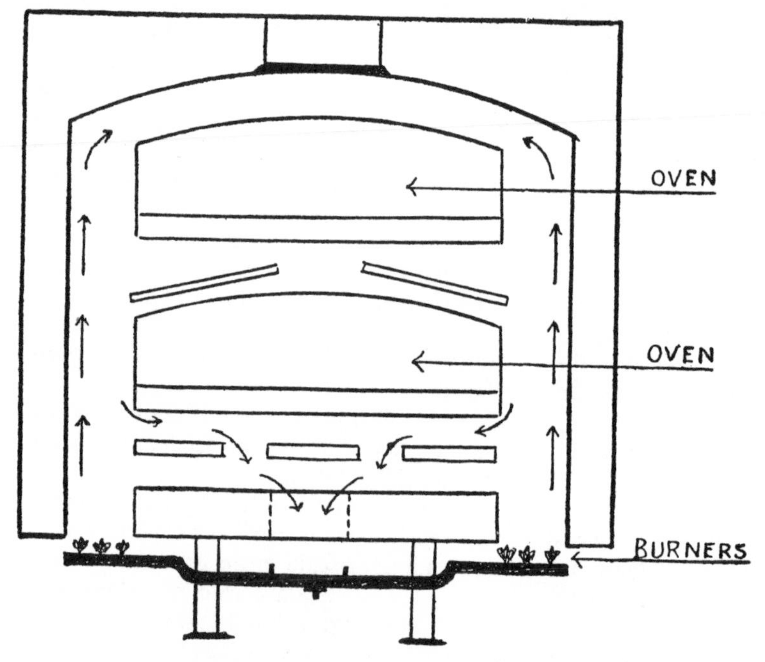

FIG. 12.—The hot-air oven. Cross section.

ovens are clean in operation, baking can be fairly continuous, more so in the later types, and they are safe. Fig. 12 is a line drawing of a hot-air oven in cross section. The arrows indicate the path of hot-air currents.

Electric Ovens

Electric ovens are coming more and more into common use, although the fuel cost is a factor that demands some consideration. These ovens are extremely popular in countries served by cheap hydro-electric power.

The electric oven is handy, efficient, easy to handle and maintain, clean and hygienic and has excellent baking qualities. It is practically steam tight, reducing evaporation in baked goods to a minimum. The oven is heated by elements enclosed within metal tubes placed in rows in a similar manner to those in a steam tube oven. The oven is well insulated against heat loss by radiation, so that it is negligible. Most of the ovens in use have tiled soles, are portable and of the peel type, although larger units such as the drawplate and the travelling oven are in use.

Vienna Ovens

Vienna bread and rolls must be baked in a steam-saturated atmosphere; for this reason, the Vienna oven is built on a different principle from the ordinary oven. Steam is lighter than air and it therefore rises; it is this fact which is the basis for the construction of this type of oven.

The oven sole slopes upward and is in two sections, the first at a more acute angle than the second. This first section is not used for baking, but merely to give better access to the baking sole on which the bread and rolls are placed. It will be seen that the beginning of the baking sole is approximately at the same level as the bottom of

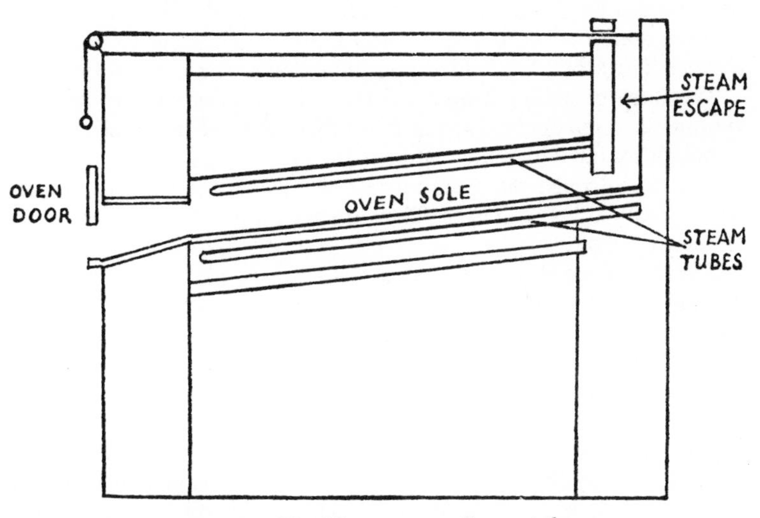

FIG. 13.—The Vienna oven. Steam tube.

the opened oven door, so that all injected steam is trapped within the baking chamber. Fig. 13 shows the construction of a steam tube Vienna oven.

There is a flue at the upper end of the baking chamber, in which a damper, operated from the front of the oven, can be opened towards the end of baking time, to allow for the escape of steam. In this way the bread and rolls can finish baking in a dry heat, giving the crisp, dry crust, characteristic of well made Vienna bread.

The ordinary oven with a level sole can be adapted to bake good Vienna bread, simply by fitting a steam trap inside the door frame. This trap which is of sheet metal, is designed to block most of the door aperture, giving a clearance at the bottom sufficient only to allow for the bread and rolls to be set into the oven. In this way the steam escape line is lowered, and the oven is reasonably full of steam, which is injected under pressure from a steam spray pipe.

Travelling Ovens

The step from the drawplate oven, with its movable sole, to the large travelling oven was but short. With the introduction, uninterrupted continuous baking in one oven became possible. There are three main types, the swing tray, the tunnel or travelling plate oven and the controlled tray oven.

The swing tray oven contains an endless chain on which cradles or trays are fixed, into which the bread is placed. The trays move upward and downward and around the oven chamber to complete a cycle. Thus they are loaded and unloaded at the same point.

They are generally heated on the hot-air principle i.e. hot air running through ducts, using as fuel either coke, oil, gas or electricity, although by far the greater number today burn fuel oil or gas.

The tunnel oven occupies more floor space, for the sole travels horizontally along its length. They are generally internally heated by either gas or oil.

The controlled tray oven has the trays held in a horizontal position during their journey through the oven. This is important for confectionery such as tarts, custards and light sponge goods which would be distorted by a swinging motion. Plate X illustrates this type of oven and Plate XI the swing tray oven.

Basically, both types of travelling oven are the same; new systems of heating, however, now make them far more economical to operate. This is done by the re-circulation of heater flue gases; in this way the fuel is made to yield its maximum heat and heat losses are thus reduced.

Reel Ovens

A comparative newcomer to the number of travelling ovens is known as the reel oven, although a similar type was first produced in 1892. It is now becoming increasingly popular, particularly in smaller bakeries where space is at a premium, for no peel is necessary for loading or unloading.

The reel inside the oven is fitted with metal plates on which is placed bread or cakes, the whole rotating in a vertical plane around a horizontal axis, taking two minutes to complete the full cycle. The number of plates depend on the size of the oven. Stopping and starting is electrically controlled by means of a push button.

The oven can be fired by gas, electricity, oil or solid fuel; firing is internal with gas and electricity and external—on the hot-air principle—when using oil or solid fuel. The gas-fired oven is fitted with an electronic flame failure control, an efficient safety device which ensures that the gas is cut off immediately should the flame be accidentally extinguished.

The oven is quickly heated and the heat is remarkably flexible; working temperatures being easily and quickly attained. The heating efficiency is high, particularly with the internally heated type, for heat losses are at a minimum.

The reel is chain-driven by an electric motor of low horse-power. All types of bread and cakes can be baked and the movement is so smooth that it is claimed that slab cakes, even high-ratio types, can be successfully baked in these ovens. Steam, which is usually needed in large amounts, can be injected for bread-baking, the resultant product possessing a fine crisp crust. Plate XII shows the reel oven.

13

Enzymes: Fungal Enzymes; Fermentation Tolerance; Gassing Power; Gas Retention; Staling: Anti-Staling Agents; Flour Improvers: Bleaching Agents; Batter Process of Breadmaking

ENZYMES

FROM time to time in previous chapters the student has been introduced to substances known as enzymes, and the time has come to know what they are, what they do, and why they are so important.

Enzymes are nitrogenous compounds produced by living organisms. In the past they have been described as unorganized ferments, as opposed to organized ferments such as yeast, bacteria, etc., which have life. They are best described as organic catalysts. In the human body, enzymes are ever active in changing the food we eat, into simple compounds so that in the latter condition they can be dissolved in the fluid of the digestive tract and so assimilated by the body. Without enzymes we could not live.

As catalysts they are capable, in relatively small quantities, of speeding up or depressing the rate of a reaction, without themselves being permanently changed. All this may be a little confusing to those who have no great knowledge of catalysts so that a little story may make it more easy to understand.

The story concerns an old Arab chief who, knowing that he was about to die, made his will and appointed another chief as his executor. He directed that his eldest son should have one-half of his estate, his second son, one-third, and his youngest son, one-ninth. When he died, the executor found that the estate consisted of 17 camels, and he was faced with the problem of dividing them into the proportions directed. When at the point of giving it up as impossible he suddenly saw a way out of his dilemma, and he did this by adding a camel from his own herd, making the total 18.

He was now able to carry out the provisions of the will, the first son receiving nine camels, the second son six camels and the youngest son got two. These added together made 17, so the executor took his camel back. This camel could be described as a catalyst, for it effected a change without itself being changed in any way.

The story merely illustrates. The student must not be tempted to answer a question on an examination paper concerning enzymes or catalysts in this way. At the same time it can be recommended as an interesting story at a bakery students' function.

Enzymes are highly selective and specific in their nature, initiating and accelerating one type of reaction and no other; for instance, the yeast enzyme invertase will speed up the changing of sucrose and water to dextrose and levulose; maltase will do the same with maltose and water to produce dextrose; they will take part in no other reaction.

Enzymes are active only under certain conditions of temperature and *p*H, these conditions varying with different enzymes. It can be considered that most enzymes are destroyed at 190° F., although they will tolerate higher temperatures under perfectly dry conditions. The optimum active temperatures are between 120–130° F., the temperature range extending to 170° F. Since all enzymes are proteins they are destroyed by coagulation on contact with strong acids and alkalies. They can be frozen without damage.

It will help the student at this stage to remember that the chemistry term used for the various carbohydrates (sugars and starches) all end with 'ose', i.e. sucrose, dextrose, glucose, amylose, etc., and the enzymes in panary fermentation all end with 'ase', i.e. maltase, invertase, zymase, protease, etc. It will interest the students also to know that the word 'enzyme' was first introduced in 1878, and is from the Greek, meaning 'in yeast'.

The enzymes concerned in panary fermentation can be described under four headings.

(1) The amylolytic group which dissolves the starch membrane and so releases the soluble starch. The starch so released, together with the soluble starch readily available from the starch cells fractured in the milling, is then changed to maltose and dextrin. The means by which these changes occur are not clear.

The enzymes concerned are the alpha- and beta-amylases, which combined are sometimes referred to as the diastatic enzymes, or part of the activity of a diastatic group. This group is found in flour and diastatic malt. The scientist knows three types of alpha-amylase: fungal, cereal and bacterial, each having a different thermal inactivation point. Of the three, bacterial alpha-amylase has the highest, and fungal amylase the lowest, which makes fungal amylase ideal for the baker as a flour improver because it is inactivated at a lower temperature in the baking loaf than cereal amylase natural to the flour, or added in diastatic malt, thus there is little or no danger arising from any excess.

(2) The zymogenic enzymes convert dextrose and levulose (the former much more readily) to CO_2, alcohol and other by-products.

The enzymic group, the zymase complex, is found in yeast.

(3) The inversive enzymes, of which there are two in panary fermentation, both found in yeast. Invertase which inverts sucrose to dextrose and levulose, and maltase which change maltose to glucose. The process is known as hydrolysis, because a molecule of water is taken into the chemical change.

(4) The proteolytic enzymes break down proteins to simpler nitrogenous compounds. In panary fermentation they are found in flour and diastatic malt. They are responsible for the conversion of some insoluble proteins to a state of solubility when they can be broken down to peptones, polypeptides and amino acids. Fungal proteases can be used as an additive to flour to assist in modifying tough, tenacious glutens.

FUNGAL ENZYMES

The maltose figure of flour has been considered to be of the greatest importance to both miller and baker. It is the measure of the diastatic capacity of the flour, i.e. the sugar producing power.

The maltose test was first introduced by Rumsey in 1932, and the diastatic capacity of the flour under test is calculated as a percentage after it has been incubated at 27° C. for an hour.

If the figure is below 2·0 then the gassing power is seriously retarded, particularly at the final proving stage of the dough, when the naturally occurring sugars in flour have been exhausted. Bread made from low maltose flour is small in volume with a close 'cheesy' crumb, and with little crust colour.

If the figure is high, then there is an excessive production of sugars and dextrins from starch, and the resultant loaf will have high crust colour, a dark, streaky, gummy crumb and show signs of partial collapse at the sides due to the effects of the highly activated proteolytic enzymes, and the effects of excess sugar on the gluten structure. The student can produce this for himself by making up a small dough with an excess of diastatic malt, and baking the loaves in tin shapes.

Coinciding with the importation into this country towards the end of the last century of strong American flours, malt products were introduced to the baker, becoming the ideal corrective for flours with a low maltose figure and with tough tenacious glutens. Malt provided both the diastatic enzymes for the breakdown of starch to sugar, and the proteolytic enzymes for the modification of gluten, rendering it more extensible.

Cereal diastatic enzymes, however, have a high thermal inactivation figure, they are not destroyed until the temperature within the baking loaf has reached to about 165–170° F., during which time, they are extremely active on a starch rendered more sensitive by gelatinization, producing sugars and dextrins within the loaf.

The introduction of the bread-slicing machine has focussed attention on crumb stickiness and stability and has posed the question of the diastatic corrective without adversely affecting the tensile strength of the crumb, that is, a sufficient supply of sugar from the breakdown of starch without the dextrins. The challenge has been met by the cereal chemist and a new type of diastatic corrective is available to the miller and the baker.

As cereal research progressed, it was discovered that in the diastatic group of enzymes there were two, which became to be known as alpha- and beta-amylase. Of the two it was found that low maltose flour was never short of beta-amylase so that attention was turned to alpha-amylase.

The scientist knows three types of alpha-amylase:

(1) Fungal alpha-amylase, which is manufactured from the growth of the mould, Aspergillus oryzae.
(2) Bacterial alpha-amylase produced from the growth of certain bacteria.
(3) Cereal alpha-amylase found in flour and diastatic malt.

Bacterial amylase has a high thermal destruction point and if added to flour would be active in the baking loaf over a longer time and would produce within the loaf, dextrins that would cause serious damage to the clarity and elasticity of the crumb.

Fungal amylase has a lower inactivation point than cereal amylase and thus is ideal for the baker, for little or no danger could arise from an accidental overdose as could happen with an excess of diastatic malt.

Another fugal enzyme isolated from mould, is a protease. This enzyme is extremely helpful in modifying and rendering more extensible, tough glutens which cause what is known as 'bucky doughs'. By its use a much better volume and shape is assured in the finished loaf. This is particularly so in protein enriched breads.

Fungal enzymes are used in small amounts per sack, usually in grams if in powder form, or in tablets of regulated dosage. Amylase and protease is available in combined form. To facilitate more accurate weighing the powders are available in different strengths.

It is advised that fungal enzymes should be suspended in 4 to 5 times its own weight of water and added to the yeast liquor. It is advised also that a test bake is the best means of assessing the amount required for different flours, although the makers of fungal enzymes are always ready to advise if requested.

Here is a summary of the differences between diastatic malt products and fungal enzymes as correctives of certain flour variabilities.

Malt	*Fungal enzymes*
Diastatic malt provides sugar, diastatic and proteolytic enzymes together, according to the amounts used and the diastatic value of the product.	Provides in controlled amounts a specific enzyme or enzymes only. It can be added strictly in accordance with the flour deficiency.
The diastatic group is not inactivated within the baking loaf until a figure of about 170° F. is reached.	Alpha-amylase is destroyed at a much lower figure.
Provides flavour according to the amount used.	Provides no flavour.

FERMENTATION TOLERANCE

The whole art of breadmaking is to get the gassing power and the ripened dough structure parallel at the optimum period. In other words, there should be sufficient gas being produced during final proof, and the initial stages of baking to aerate, and the dough structure should be in such a condition that it will give to the expanding gases and yet retain them.

There is a period before and after the desired optimum is reached, when gassing and dough ripening run parallel, before gas production slows down and the dough structure begins to weaken. This period is known as the fermentation tolerance, for good bread can be produced during this time.

Here is an explanatory graph (Fig. 14) for a dough with a bulk fermentation time of 3 hr., going to the oven in 4 hr. In this example there is a fermentation tolerance of about 50 min.

Flours will differ in the period of tolerance; in some, the gluten will quickly become degraded after the optimum is reached, the dough showing the signs of over-ripeness. Other flours will have glutens that will remain stable for some time after the desired fermentation time has been reached, in consequence they will be said to have a good fermentation tolerance.

This tolerance is closely bound up with gluten quality, gas production and retention, the resistance of the gluten to the softening effects of water and acids, the action of the proteolytic enzymes, the

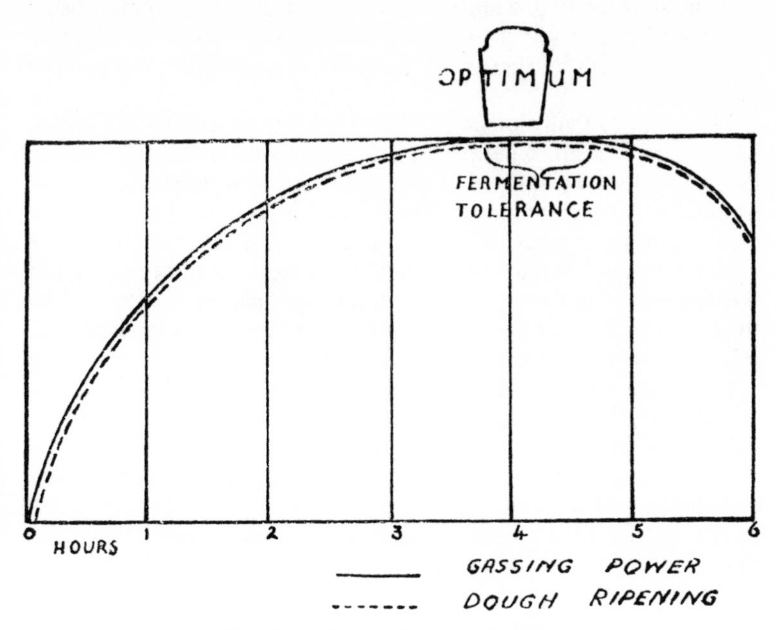

FIG. 14.—Fermentation tolerance.

results of diastatic activity, the use of additives and lastly, the temperature of the dough.

GASSING POWER

Gas (CO_2) is not produced solely by yeast; it depends on yeast and many other factors, the whole of which are responsible for panary fermentation. Some of these factors are understood, while others more complex are less so; many others are still not known.

Broadly the factors affecting gassing power are as follows:

(1) Quality of the flour.
(2) The sugar present and produced.
(3) The amount and quality of the yeast.
(4) The control of fermentation. This includes the balance of basic raw materials, additions, temperatures, etc.

Number two is dependent on the available starch that can be converted to maltose, that is, the available soluble starch from the mechanical fracture of starch cells during milling. The average figure of available soluble starch is from 7 to 10%.

In flour there is a quantity of natural sugar, the average being about 2·5%. The greater percentage consists of sucrose, of which there is about 1·5%. There is a little dextrose and from 0·5 to 1·0% of maltose.

The maltose figure of flour is of great importance to the miller, whose aim is keep it between 1·5–2·3%. To ascertain the figure a laboratory test is employed in which flour to be tested is mixed with water in controlled amounts. The mixture is incubated at 27° C. for exactly one hour, after which a precise test is given and the maltose figure calculated. It must be noted that this figure must be in excess of the amount of maltose in the dry flour, for maltose is increased by the action of diastase, when flour is mixed with water and allowed to stand (see page 225—Hagberg Number).

If the maltose figure after test is found to be below 1·5% then there is a danger that the dough produced may generate insufficient gas during the final proof, which is the critical fermentation period. If the figure is above 2·3% then there is the danger of a sticky, dark crumb and a collapse of the crust at the sides when the loaf is baked.

The quality of the flour in relation to fermentation has a great bearing on gas production, because fermentation is simply the result of the action of enzymes, and it is therefore dependent on the potential activity of certain enzymes in flour which will determine the suitability of a flour for breadmaking. The most important of these enzymes is the amylolytic or diastatic group. This group gets its name because it deals specifically with amylose, which is the chemist's name for starch. The two main members of this group are the alpha- and beta-amylases.

It is considered that the release of soluble starch is associated with the activity of alpha-amylase, while beta-amylase is concerned with the production of maltose. Maltose and water is further changed by the enzyme maltase to dextrose, which is assimilated by yeast and changed to CO_2. This breakdown is dependent on, and regulated by, the temperature and *p*H of the dough. A certain amount of diastatic activity in the dough is therefore assential; excessive alpha-amylase activity is, however, not desirable for it will produce the faults associated with high maltose flour.

The amount and quality of the yeast is also important, because more yeast of good quality means more gas from the sugars available. The student will note that more yeast with the sugars available, means a greater gassing potential, so that it becomes clear that the balance is of great importance.

Sugars are not fermentable unless they are in solution and it becomes apparent that the amount of water in a dough also has an effect on gassing power, a tight dough slows up fermentation, which is speeded up by the addition of more water.

The use of yeast foods such as sugar, fondant, honey, malt or syrup will increase the gassing power, always provided that they are not used in excessive quantities. The amount of salt used also has a bearing on the speed of fermentation.

Finally, temperature and the *p*H figure have a controlling effect on fermentation. Alterations in *p*H can be the results of using acid improvers or the development of acid fermentation. All this emphasizes the necessity for control over every stage of fermentation.

GAS RETENTION

The generation of CO_2 would be useless unless it is retained in the dough fabric. Gas retention then becomes of equal importance to gas production. For the gluten to hold the gas, it must be so conditioned by the fermentation process and by manipulation, that it is resillient enough to extend to the expanding gas pressure, and strong enough to retain the gas produced.

The suitability of the gluten for the task is seen to be of critical importance, and it is only gluten of good quality that is resilient and extensible enough when ripe, in holding the gas within the dough structure. There are, of course, other factors concerned.

(1) The amount of yeast used, and its speed and quality. This has a bearing on the pressure of gas on the dough structure.

(2) The action on gluten of the proteolytic enzymes, for these enzymes are considered to have a modifying action on insoluble protein.

(3) The mill grist and the extraction rate. These are important, for in the case of the mill grist, the mixture of wheats contained in the grist must be so balanced that the resultant flour will produce good bread. In regard to the extraction rate, the student will now know that the higher the rate, the greater the proportion of bran snips there will be present. The bran particles will break down the coherency of the gluten structure, weakening the gas retaining quality of the dough. Further, as bran contains no gluten, then the gluten percentage in the dough is lessened. In addition, with the longer extraction rates there is a greater possibility of excessive proteolytic activity, which will rob the gluten of its resiliency and gas retaining properties.

(4) The water content of a dough has a part to play, firstly in the hydration of the insoluble proteins to form gluten. Here the

importance of the correct mixing time in dough-making becomes apparent, for it is by this means that the gluten becomes sufficiently hydrated. Secondly water has a softening effect on gluten. This is, of course, dependent on the bulk fermentation time.

(5) Salt and mineral improvers have a stabilizing effect on gluten and will increase its resistance to undue expansion and this is useful in the case of weak glutens. Excess of some improvers may, however, break down the gluten structure of dough completely.

(6) Time and temperature, both have an effect on gas retention. An excessive period of fermentation will so degrade gluten strength that it will be incapable of retaining the gas. Temperature is import-and, for the colder the dough, within limits and provided that there has been no compensatory increase of yeast, the greater is the potential strength of the gluten. A hot dough will have the reverse effect, for the gluten will quickly become degraded, partly as a result of the excessive temperature and partly because of the speed of fermentation.

(7) Finally, manipulation is an important factor in gas retention, for knocking back, handing up, and moulding, assist to a large degree in the ripening of gluten.

With the knowledge of gas production and retention, it becomes clear that overall control of the breadmaking process is a vital necessity in the making of good bread. The intelligent use of raw materials and methods will mean even better bread.

Here, for the student, is a chart showing alterations in the potential strength of flour by various adjustments.

Increase	*Potential Strength*	*Decrease*
−	Water	+
−	Yeast	+
+	Salt	−
−	Temperature	+
−	Time	+
−	Malt	+
+	Mineral improvers (if necessary)	−
−	Organic improvers	+
+	Milk (if used alone without fat)	−

Where the minus sign comes under the heading 'Increase', then a decrease of the material or condition will increase the potential strength of the flour. A plus sign under the same heading will mean that an increase will also increase the potential strength. Under the heading 'Decrease', the exact opposite will obtain.

After a study of all the aspects of fermentation, the student will begin to understand, and appreciate, the skill and knowledge necessary in the production of good bread, day by day from the variable materials and conditions that beset the baker.

STALING

It is often thought that the staling of bread is caused simply by the evaporation of moisture from the loaf. This is not so, for although bread does lose moisture from the crust and crumb under certain conditions, it is known that evaporation of moisture is not the sole cause of staling.

The whole picture is not at all clear, although research into staling has been going on almost continuously for many years. It was probably the toasting of bread that first set the scientific mind to its study, for, as everybody knows, if a slice of stale bread is toasted, it rapidly takes on colour on the surface, which becomes crisp, but the interior crumb softens, even though some moisture is driven off during toasting.

Krunitz, a German scientist, found that if a loaf is heated again for a short time, it will, for a limited period, have most of the qualities of a new loaf. The French scientist, Boussingault, investigated the phenomenon and found that it was only necessary to heat the loaf to 158° F. to bring about a considerable freshening. He proved that staleness is not dependent on the quantity of moisture present. He did this by sealing a piece of new bread in a glass tube so that the evaporation of moisture was impossible; nevertheless the bread went stale. He found also that by heating the bread in the tube, the appearances and quality of newness was recreated. Provided that the bread was not spoiled by moulds, he found also that the operation could be repeated over and over again, with the same results.

Staleness in bread has been defined by Whymper as the dryness and crumbliness felt by the palate, requiring an increased amount of saliva to soften it. The flavour, too, gets more insipid as the bread gets more stale.

There have been many attempts to make bread that will not stale, but so far they have not been successful. A measure of success, however, has been achieved by additions to the dough, some of which retard staling, while some have a softening effect on the crumb, thus giving the quality of newness over a longer period. Boiled potatoes, scalded flour or gelatinized potato starch have been used, sometimes with the inclusion of malt. Malt alone in varying quantities, within limits, has also been used to offset staling. Fats and milk have also been used for the same purpose. All these ingredients, because of their hygroscopic nature or other moisture retaining or crumb softening properties, have been used with some success. Many of them have also enriched and added to the food value of bread.

During all this research, one thing has been confirmed without any doubt, and that is, that good quality flour, properly fermented, baked, cooled and stored, will produce bread, not only with a soft crumb, but with moistness that will endure for a reasonable time.

The results of investigation into bread staling carried out by the British Millers' Research Association in 1937, have been published in a special report. The report states that bread can be kept fresh at a temperature at or over 120° F. This, however, apart from the cost, which would be uneconomic, would invite the development of rope (unless inhibitors were used) and the growth of moulds.

After dealing with the characteristics of stale bread and the effects on the keeping quality as a result of staling, the report subdivides the chief aspects of staling into two parts: (*a*) crust staling; (*b*) crumb staling.

Crust Staling

The control of crust staling is seen to be largely as a matter of adequate ventilation during bread storage. Bread crust is hygroscopic, attracting moisture, so that in the evaporation of water from the crumb towards the atmosphere, some of it is retained in the crust, resulting in a tough leathery condition, with an unpalatable flavour. This flavour is taken up in turn by the crumb from the crust. Excessive humidity in the bread store, therefore is not desirable, neither should there be violent changes in temperature, for sudden cooling may bring about condensation of moisture on the crust surface.

Crumb Staling

Katz, the Dutch scientist, whose work on bread staling is outstanding, found that crumb staling to a certain extent, is dependent on changes in the starch, which releases water which is taken up by the protein, so that, broadly speaking, staling is a shift of moisture within the loaf rather than its loss.

If the student will gelatinize some starch, he will notice that after a time it will harden and contract; moisture will be seen on the surface of the gel which has been exuded from the gelatinized mass. This process of the exuding of water is known as syneresis, and it goes a long way in explaining what happens within the loaf, bringing a hardening and drying of the starch cells with the consequent crumbliness characteristic of stale bread.

In new bread the starch cells are elastic, holding the maximum of water. In this form the starch is known as alpha starch, and as the temperature is lowered becomes unstable, slowly changing to a mixture of alpha and beta starch. Beta starch holds less water, some of which is exuded and taken up by the protein. Thus the change takes place in two parts, firstly a chemical change in the starch and secondly the physical change consequent on it. The student will now understand the conclusions of investigators, that if bread is kept at a comparatively high temperature, staling will be retarded. In view, however, of the cost and possible undesirable results of this method, it seems that any addition and/or method, that will inhibit the chemical changes in the starch, will go a long way in solving the problem of staling.

For the student, two things will stand out clearly, first the necessity for extensive practical and theoretical knowledge on fermentation, and secondly, the necessity for the scientific background gained by the study of bakery science, for with knowledge of both, he may be able to make important contributions to research into the many problems concerning breadmaking still to be solved. Here is a summary in diagrammatical form:

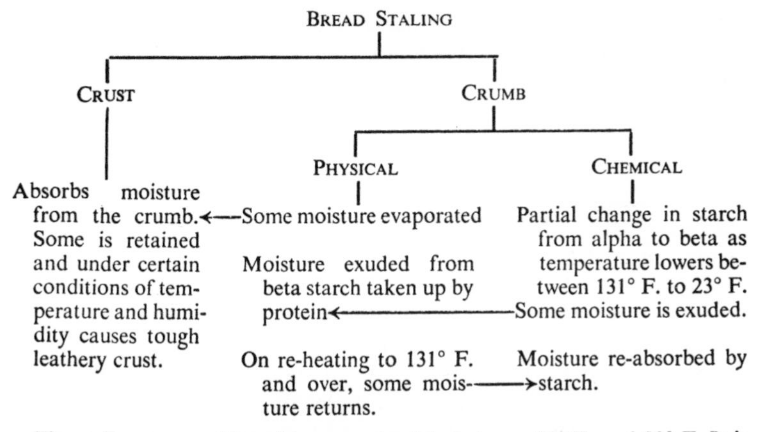

The staling range of bread is approximately between 75° F. and 23° F. It is particularly rapid about 40° F. If bread is rapidly reduced in temperature to below 23° F., then staling is practically suspended.

ANTI-STALING AGENTS

The wrapping of bread has, to a certain extent, prolonged the keeping quality of the loaf, but this has been only accomplished by a loss of some of the essential characteristics of good bread. The aroma of freshly baked bread in the baker's shop is now becoming rare; the crisp, crackly crust and the flavour of the crust and crumb of well-fermented, and well-baked bread is becoming a thing of the past. It is also becoming a debatable point as to whether the community has lost rather then gained by the change in bread standards.

It seems now that dough is made to suit a variety of machines culminating in the slicer and wrapper, whereas in the past, the craftsman-baker made dough to produce bread to the standard demanded by his customers. It is even becoming more difficult to buy a crisp crusted well-baked roll. All this is something for the student to ponder on.

A good deal of research and experimentation has been going on in recent years on additives to bread, designed to prevent or retard staling, or to so soften the crumb that the phenomenon of staling is less pronounced.

Emulsifiers as anti-staling agents have, during the past decade, been the subject of investigation for possible toxicity by committees both here and in the United States, for the effect on public health could be serious, if there were chronic poisoning over several generations. It is readily understood, that the authorities concerned must be satisfied that no present or future danger can exist by the use in foodstuffs of these additives. There are several types of anti-staling compounds used in breadmaking the most popular of which are the superglycerinated fats.

Glycerol Mono-Stearate

Chemically, G.M.S., as it is more generally called, is one of a group of substances known as monoglycerides, and these are found in a wide range of natural products. Animal and vegetable fats and oils contain monoglycerides; they are also formed in the cooking and digestion of fats and so form a part of the normal diet.

All edible fats, whether of animal or vegetable origin, are mixtures of esters of glycerol (commonly known as glycerine) and fatty acids. They are known as glycerides. A molecule of glycerol can combine with three molecules of fatty acids and a triglyceride is formed. When a molecule of glycerol reacts with two molecules of fatty acids, the result is a diglyceride, and if one molecule of fatty acid enters the reaction a monoglyceride is formed.

There are many fatty acids that can take part in these reactions. Amongst the more common are oleic acid and stearic acid. A monoglyceride formed from oleic acid becomes glycerol mono-oleate. A monoglyceride with stearic acid in its composition becomes glycerol mono-stearate, better known as G.M.S.

G.M.S. has excellent emulsifying properties because it has an affinity for both fat and water. A monoglyceride contains two to three times as much glycerol as a normal fat and glycerol mixes readily with water. G.M.S. is thus a valuable emulsifying agent and because of this it has been used as a 'fat extender' during the period of fat shortage, but since bakery fats are now readily available, G.M.S. has become to be recognized as a valuable bakery raw material in its own right because it is capable of producing results in bread and cakes which cannot be obtained from any other substance.

An analysis of commercial G.M.S. would show that it would contain between 32·5–35% monoglycerides, the remainder being a mixture of unreacted shortening and diglycerides. The product is an excellent bread improver. For use in breadmaking, G.M.S. is made into an emulsion by whisking 1 part with 5 parts of near boiling water; the gel is used at the rate of 8–12 oz. per sack. It is also used in combination with shortening, the mixture being made by beating together 2 lb. of shortening with 6 lb. of cooled emulsion. The mixture is used at the rate of 3–4 lb. per sack.

A concentrated G.M.S. is available to the baker and is prepared from the commercial mixture by a process of molecular distillation, giving a product of not less than 90% monoglycerides. It is emulsified with near boiling water in the same way as for 35% G.M.S. and used at the rate of 3–4 oz. per sack as a bread improver. This gel is excellent for sponge goods because of its power of emulsifying the fat in egg yolks; the G.M.S. and the lecithin in the yolks, both being emulsifying agents, combine to confer a greater stability on the egg/sugar foam.

A plastic G.M.S. is now available to bakers which does not need emulsification. It is in the form of a texturized plastic fat and is used at the rate of 8 oz. per sack for bread and 1–2 lb. per sack for fermented bun goods.

Provided that G.M.S. is used in the correct amounts, it not only confers crumb softness and stability on bread and fermented goods, but increases the volume and improves the texture to a marked degree.

The term 'super-glycerinated fats' is used to cover 'Any mixture of mono-di- and triglycerides of fat forming fatty acids'. G.M.S. is therefore a superglycerinated fat. Shortenings containing G.M.S., manufactured for use in high ratio cakes are also super-glycerinated.

Lecithin

This valuable emulsifying agent is a phosphorized fat. Commercially it is produced from the soya bean. It is also a valuable constituent of egg yolks. Lecithin has marked stabilizing properties and exerts a physical action on gluten. The combined action being more marked in soft doughs, modifying the gluten and conferring an increased stability on the dough structure. Crumb stability and the keeping qualities of the loaf are improved and the volume increased. It is used in emulsified form at the rate of about 1 lb. per sack.

Soya Flour

Soya flour is a natural food with a high protein content. The fat is extracted to improve the colour, giving a fine white flour which is easily dispersed in the dough.

Soya flour is a yeast food and increases the absorption of water which, being held in the dough confers crumb softness and helps to retard staling. The recommended usage is 2½ lb. per sack with the water content of the dough increased by the same weight as the added soya flour.

In 1962, Regulations came into operation prescribing certain emulsifying agents and stabilisers, prohibiting the importation and sale of foods containing those not on the permitted list.

Where bread is concerned, only stearyl tartrate and partial glycerol esters will be permitted, emulsifying agents which include glycerol monostearate (G.M.S.) and the diacetyl tartaric esters of monoglycerides (T.E.M.S.).

CHEMICAL FLOUR IMPROVERS

All through history man has sought to improve, whether it be his dress, his habitation, his weapons or his learning. His food has been no exception to the rule, for since time immemorial improvement has been going on in methods of agriculture, and in the processing and cooking of food. Mostly his improving has not been at fault, for the results are evident and so easily proved: sometimes they are definitely and obviously at fault and experimentation has stopped.

Occasionally time has proved an error and the 'improvement' is discarded. It is in between these extremes, when improvement seems obvious, but is not fully proved, that discussion and controversy is at its fiercest.

The subject of what may be termed the chemical additions to flour is a case in point, for results seem to prove the wisdom of using them, yet all the time there has been doubt. In the case of the treatment of flour with nitrogen trichloride, better known as agene there is no doubt that there is a pronounced physical improvement in the nature of the flour so treated and in consequence an improvement in the bread made from it.

The fact that a toxic substance has been isolated from agenized flour, and this has been proved to be the cause of hysteria in highly bred dogs, has set off a display of journalistic pyrotechnics that has caused damage to the goodwill of the baking industry. One side in the controversy says, that as it has not been proved harmless to human digestion, it should not be used; the other side say that as it has not been proved harmful to human digestion then there seems no reason why its use should be prohibited. British millers have agreed to discontinue the use of agene.

Adulteration to bread and flour in medieval times meant that the baker or miller had to spend a period in the stocks or the pillory, or was drawn through the streets on a hurdle. To make perhaps a better target he was sometimes nailed by his ear to his bakery door. History does not record the lives of honest bakers and millers who were legion. During the last 50 years, the reports of inspectors show that the miller and baker deserve well of their fellow men. If any additions were made, they were made in good faith. Such an addition is alum which has an astringent effect on gluten giving an increased stability to the flours of the particular period when it was used, so improving both the volume and the crumb of the loaf. Old textbooks have many references to 'hard' as alum was called by the bakers of the time. Alum was prohibited as an addition to bread at the beginning of the century, to the disgust of the craftsman baker of that era.

The history of flour bleaching shows clearly that the search has been for a substance that will whiten the colour of flour, and at the same time confer stability on the gluten, in fact, a bleach and an improver combined. Jago, who has been called the father of bakery science, first investigated in this country, the possibilities of bleaching flour; he was successful with flour milled from Oregon wheat which was quite yellow in colour; for this he used ozone. Unfortunately the flour became tainted so that the treatment had no commercial value.

Nitrogen peroxide next became a subject for a patent, for in 1901, John and Sidney Andrews found that it had a pronounced bleaching action on flour. Two years later, Alsop was granted a patent, again for the use of nitrogen peroxide, but unlike the Andrews who produced the gas chemically, Alsop generated it electrolytically, by means of an electric arc, through which air was passed in controlled amounts. Chlorine was next introduced as a bleaching agent by Wesener. The use of nitrosyl chloride, nitrogen trichloride, benzoyl peroxide and chlorine dioxide followed later.

All bakers know that flour is better for breadmaking after a period of storage; the baker of the past invariably put his hand into a bag of newly delivered flour to find out whether it was 'hot off the mill' as it was termed; if it was, he would not use it until it had aged in the store for some days. He knew that this ageing not only improved the colour, but gave an increased stability to the gluten so that a better and bolder loaf could be produced.

Kent-Jones (1924) found that flour kept in a vacuum neither bleached nor improved, so that the changes taking place during storage are undoubtedly related to the absorption of oxygen. The miller also knew that the storage of flour brought an improvement in quality, so that stocks of flour were kept at the mill and despatched only after a period of storage.

When it was discovered that, by the addition of certain chemicals, flour could be artificially aged in a short time, then the expense of storing flour for the purpose of maturation was found to be unnecessary. Agene (nitrogen trichloride) was found to be ideal for the purpose of conferring this immediate maturity to flour and for the last 25 years, by far the greater percentage of flour has been bleached and strengthened by this gas.

One of the criticisms in the past concerning bleaching, was that it became possible to pass off, after treatment, low grade flours as flours of higher quality. This is not so, for high grade flour has a bloom and brightness that is unmistakable when compared with a lower grade bleached flour that is white merely because the natural yellow colour has been removed.

A further criticism has been that the yellow colouring matter, carotene, which is closely related to vitamin A, is destroyed by bleaching. Further research has revealed that the yellow colouring matter is not biological active carotene.

Nitrogen Peroxide

It was the introduction of nitrogen peroxide as a flour-bleaching agent that established the advisability, and to a certain extent, the legality of flour bleaching as a means of removing the excess of yellow colouring matter in flour, for in this country and in the U.S.A. test cases in the courts settled the issue between those who would improve flour by bleaching, and those who insisted that bleaching had a deleterious effect on flour.

In the legal battle which went on from 1909 to 1919 in the U.S.A., a compromise was reached, when it appeared that, provided the American miller labelled the flour as bleached, then the Government departments concerned would take no action. In this country, in 1909, the legal conclusion, after thorough investigation, was that nitrogen peroxide had no deleterious effect on flour and thus the general principle of flour bleaching was established, subject to investigation into each type of flour bleach used subsequently. After this case, it appeared to be generally realized that bleaching was carried out not for the purpose of disguising faulty flour, but for the purpose of improving the colour.

Nitrogen peroxide in gaseous form is used in very small amounts, a pound being sufficient to bleach 250,000 lb. of flour. An investigating committee was concerned with the fact that nitrites were formed in the flour, but decided that the amount was so small that it could not be regarded as serious.

Chlorine

This bleaching agent was popular at one time for the treatment of flour. It is a dangerous gas and great care must be exercised in its use. Used at the rate of from one to two ounces per sack it is an efficient bleach; in addition it has a maturating effect on the protein; for this reason exact treatment is necessary, for an excess will break down the coherency of gluten, rendering the flour completely unsuitable for panary fermentation.

Because of this effect on gluten, heavy chlorine treatment is used in the manufacture of special cake flours, where it is necessary to destroy the normal characteristics of gluten. In addition, heavy treatment increases the acidity, which is required in this type of flour.

The bleaching action of chlorine is not clear; it is suggested that it is not by oxidation, but by the formation of a colourless compound with the colouring matter in flour. An investigating committee dealt fully with the action of chlorine on flour protein, for it was suggested that the nutritive value of some of the constituent parts of protein were affected by chlorine. Tests have proved inconclusive.

Nitrosyl Chloride

At one time this gas was used with chlorine, but its use is largely discontinued.

Benzoyl Peroxide

This is used in powder form, being mixed with a neutral substance and introduced to the stock during the milling; one part of benzoyl peroxide being sufficient to bleach 30,000 parts of flour; its bleaching action is the oxidation of the colouring matter in flour.

Nitrogen Trichloride

Not only is nitrogen trichloride an efficient bleach, but it also has a strengthening action on gluten. In its commercial form it bears the well known name of agene. It has an oxidizing effect on the colouring matter in flour. It is used at the rate of from one to twenty grammes per sack according to the grade of flour being treated; the higher the grade, the lighter the treatment.

The opinion of the committee investigating the use of nitrogen trichloride was similar to the view expressed on the use of chlorine. Now after many years the use of agene is to be discontinued.

With the use of agene discontinued, alternative methods of bleaching and treating flour, so that good bread can be produced, are occupying the minds of the miller, the research worker and the baker. Chlorine dioxide, ascorbic acid and the 'batter' process of breadmaking seem to be the general alternatives, apart from the mineral improvers already discussed. These include ammonium persulphate, potassium bromate and calcium phosphate.

Chlorine Dioxide

This gas has a similar bleaching and maturing effect on flour, as nitrogen trichloride; because it is more powerful in action, less of it is necessary compared with agene.

Its bleaching effect is not only on the colouring matter in flour, but also on the bran snips, particularly if the flour is moist. It is suggested that its bleaching action on bran is similar to that of sulphur dioxide, but unlike this bleach, which lowers the baking quality of flour, chlorine dioxide definitely improves the dough and the quality of the resultant bread.

Ascorbic Acid

Ascorbic acid (vitamin C) has assumed a greater importance as an improver since the application of the Chorleywood Process of breadmaking, wherein it is used at the rate of 9.5 g. per sack ($\frac{1}{3}$ oz.).

The action depends on two enzymes present in flour, ascorbic acid oxidase which together with atmospheric oxygen converts ascorbic acid during mixing to dehydroascorbic acid. This acid is an oxidising agent which, with the help of another enzyme, dehydroascorbic acid reductase, bleaches the dough protein. The dehydroascorbic acid is reconverted to ascorbic acid as the oxidation proceeds. Ascorbic acid is largely destroyed during baking.

Batter Process

To prepare for the possibility of a general prohibition of the use of chemical additions to flour, and because, as was stated earlier, man will always seek to improve, a great deal of research and investigation has been undertaken into the possibility of using physical methods for improving flour, so that the resultant bread would be comparable with bread made from chemically treated flour. Out of this research has come the batter method of breadmaking.

It is important for the student to have some knowledge of this system for the purpose of answering a possible question dealing with modern trends in breadmaking, quite apart from the possibility of using the method in commercial practice. The method has been covered by patent, but the patentees have now released the whole process for general use.

Briefly the system is to take about three-quarters of the untreated flour and make it into a sponge with nearly all the water, the yeast, salt, malt and fat (if used), some unprocessed soya flour, leaving it to ferment for about an hour. The balance of the flour and water is added, and the resultant dough, after thorough mixing, is given the normal bulk fermentation time according to the yeast content and the temperature of the dough. Knocking back is carried out in the normal manner.

The essential difference between this method and the normal sponge and dough system, is the increase of mixer speed at sponge making, the doughmaking speed being normal. This increased speed is the means whereby the mixture takes up atmospheric oxygen which has a bleaching action on the flour, while the beating has a developing effect on the gluten. Unprocessed soya flour has the natural enzymes intact, one of which, lipoxidase appears to be an additional factor in the bleaching action.

The student interested in the subject of 'Flour Improvers' and desirous of further information on the subject, should have available 'Modern Cereal Chemistry' by Kent-Jones and Amos.

14

Barms: History; Use of Barms in Breadmaking

BARMS

THE old-time baker was a highly skilled craftsman, even although he had very little technical knowledge. The fact that bread was produced day in and day out without yeast, as we know it today, being delivered to the bakery, gives some idea of the practical skill that was necessary in the preparation of what was called barm and patent yeast, with which the baker fermented his bread.

It was known that if a liquid yeast food or wort was prepared and then left, it would eventually start to ferment, and it could, after a suitable time be used to make bread. This was known as 'spon' or spontaneous barm. What was not known was that fermentation was started by airborne yeast spores which alighted on the wort, where they multiplied rapidly.

It was known also that if the wort was prepared in the same ferment tub that had been used before, fermentation commenced much more quickly. A bottle of beer or some draught stout, both of which contain yeast, was sometimes used to effect quicker fermentation. An old bakery book suggests that the best time to start making a 'spon' barm was after the week's baking was finished, and that it be made in the end of the trough, where a previous barm had been stirred. It was certain that there were enough yeast cells present to start immediate fermentation.

The same book suggests as a starter, the following: 'Get a large champagne bottle and put a quart of brewed yeast in it, with a couple of ounces of brown sugar and a little raw flour. Cork it up and let it stand on a warm shelf where it will not be disturbed. This will be a veritable virgin yeast, but it will take about 60 hours before it will show signs of life. It must stand until a head forms in the neck of the bottle and the cork rises out. Then it will be ready as a starter.'

When compressed yeast came on the market, it was not immediately used, the tradition of barm-making being hard to break down. It was advised, somewhat regretfully, however, as an emergency starter. As an insurance against complete stoppage, some bakers smeared a stick liberally with barm and let it dry; in an emergency the stick was used to stir a new barm, so that fermentation was speeded up.

Compound barms were general at that time and consisted of malt and hops liquor, which was started by a quantity of barm from a previous brewing. Here is a very old formula for a compound barm:

Put 4 gallons of water and 3 oz. of hops in a large boiler and put it into the oven for about 3 hr.

After that time strain it into a ferment tub. When the reflection of the face can be seen clearly on the surface of the liquor, add 3½ lb. of crushed malt and stir. Cover with a sack and leave for 4 hr., when the liquor should be about 70–80° F. Stir in vigorously 3 pints of a previous brewing and 2 lb. of flour; cover with a clean sack and put it in a place free from draughts and where the temperature can be maintained. It should stand undisturbed for at least 6 hr., when it is strained and stored in casks or earthenware jars until required.

It is essential that the stock be changed from time to time or the yeast will deteriorate in strength. To delay this deterioration bakers of the day added their favourite 'strengtheners' or 'correctors', such as brown sugar, ginger or caraway seeds, the last securely tied in a cloth.

Here is a recipe for compound barm given by the Ministry of Food on the outbreak of the last war to be used in an emergency:

Compound Barm

lb.	*oz.*		*lb.*	*oz.*	
40	0	Water	7	8	Malt flour *or*
	2	Hops	10	0	Crushed malt
	½	Salt			Starter at the rate of one of starter to eight of malt liquor.

The hops are boiled in a gallon of water for 3 min. At 166° F., the crushed malt or malt flour is added. The temperature should be now between 150–154° F. It is covered and left for 3½ hr. It is then strained and cooled to 80° F. in winter and 70° F. in summer. The starter is then added, together with the salt and both are well stirred in. It is kept at a uniform temperature for 36 hr., and will remain in good condition for breadmaking for a further three or four days. For the first starter one ounce of yeast is used. For subsequent barms a half-gallon of matured barm is set aside from each previous brew.

Bread from Compound Barm. First set a sponge with:

lb.	*oz.*		*lb.*	*oz.*	
3	12	Compound barm	35	0	Water
	8	Salt	70	0	Flour

Temperature of sponge 75° F. Mix for 4 min. only. Stand for 15 hr.

Make into a dough with:

lb.	*oz.*		*lb.*	*oz.*	
110	0	Water	4	8	Salt
1	0	Fat	210	0	Flour

Dough temperature 82° F. Bulk fermentation time, 3 hr.

A barm should always be mature before it is used either as a starter for a fresh barm or for making bread. The student will understand that a barm is a media for growing yeast. It therefore becomes obvious, that if it is taken before sufficient yeast has been reproduced, then each subsequent batch must become weaker and weaker until at last it is practically useless for fermentation purposes.

It must not be supposed, however, that a greatly extended period will result in a greater accumulation of yeast; this is not so, for the food will be exhausted and conditions will inhibit growth.

Barms (2) *Malt Extract Barm.* This is a variation of the compound barm and is prepared as follows:

lb.	*oz.*	
10	0	Water (70° F.)
1	8	Malt extract (preferably of low diastatic value)
	5	Yeast

This barm is allowed to stand for 18–48 hr. For starting subsequent barms, 3 lb. is saved, but before use it should be 48 hr. old. Make a dough as follows:

lb.	*oz.*		*lb.*	*oz.*	
280	0	Flour	5	0	Salt
150	0	Water	10	0	(1 gallon) Barm

Dough temperature 82° F. Bulk fermentation 6 hr.

Parisian Barm. These are the barms into which flour is introduced. They are made in four stages—mash, scald, batter and storage (the term used for the addition of the ripe barm for inoculation). Here is an example.

(a) *Mash*

lb.	*oz.*	
20	0	Water (160° F.)
7	0	Crushed malt

Cover and leave for 3 hr. Then strain. Make up the wort to 2 gallons. Temperature 126° F.

(b) *Scald*

lb.	oz.		
30	0	Flour	Run in boiling water a gallon at a time, stirring vigorously.
40	0	Boiling water	

(c) *Batter*

When the scald has cooled, it is added to the wort. At this stage the gelatinized starch of the flour is changed to dextrose by the action of the diastatic enzymes in the malt. The batter is allowed to cool to 80° F.

(d) *Storage*

The batter is now stored with 1 gallon of barm from a previous brewing. The barm is ready in 3 days and should not be disturbed during that time.

Here are two different formulae using Parisian barm. Both are for 1½ sacks using two different systems.

QUARTER SPONGE PROCESS

Quarter

lb.	*oz.*		
28	0	Water	Temperature of quarter 80° F.
70	0	Flour	Time 13 hr. The quarter is made into a sponge.
	10	Salt	

One gallon of barm.

Sponge

lb.	oz.		
160	0	Water	Temperature of sponge 78° F.
126	0	Flour	Time 1½ hr. The sponge is then incorporated into a dough.
2	8	Salt	

Dough

lb.	oz.		
20	0	Water	Temperature of dough 78° F.
224	0	Flour	Time 1½ hr.
5	8	Salt	

HALF SPONGE PROCESS

Sponge

lb.	oz.		
100	0	Water	Temperature of sponge 80° F.
185	0	Flour	Time 13 hr.
1	8	Salt	

Two gallons of barm.

Dough

lb.	oz.		
105	0	Water	Temperature of dough 78° F.
235	0	Flour	Time 1¾ hr.
6	8	Salt	

Potato Barm. Another source of gelatinized starch is the boiled potato Here is the formula and the method for making potato barm.

lb.	*oz.*		
3	8	Potatoes	The potatoes are boiled in the 7 lb. of water until soft. Potatoes and liquor are sieved on to the flour, leaving the skins behind. A dough is made with the flour, potato pulp and water, covered and left for 5 min. Add 15 lb. of water, break up the dough and bring the mixture to 80° F. Stock the mash with the yeast and sugar and leave for 20–24 hr. at an even temperature.
7	0	Water	
3	8	Flour	
	2¼	Yeast	
	6	Sugar	

Straight Dough from Potato Barm (1½ sacks)

lb.	*oz.*		
210	0	Flour	Dough temperature 78° F. Knock back at 2 hr. and again at 3 hr. Scale at 4 hr.
115	0	Water	

Two gallons of potato barm.

The student will note that the essential principle of barm is that it contains the foods necessary in solution for the growth and multiplication of yeast cells, whether they are added initially as a starter from a previous brew, or directly with compressed yeast. Temperature and fermentation conditions must be such that optimum activity is maintained. Barms made from malt and hops contain the necessary sugars, nitrogenous material and diastatic enzymes from the malt.

The flour or Parisian barms provide the essential constituents in the natural sugars and diastatic enzymes in malt, together with the natural sugar and the soluble starch in the flour, while the nitrogenous food is available in both malt and flour. Potato barm contains soluble starch from potatoes and flour; nitrogenous food from both; sugar in flour and from the amount added.

Bearing all this in mind, the student will understand that other materials can be used in an emergency for the construction of a barm, provided that the finished barm contains all the materials necessary for the growth of yeast and that conditions are favourable for optimum activity. Dates for instance are rich in sugars and where they are plentiful they can be used to make a barm if no other sugar is available, or if the sugar available is to be used for other purposes.

Date Barm. Simmer 6 lb. of dates gently for 20–30 min. in 9 gallons of water. During the simmering, 4½ lb. of flour is scalded with sufficient of the date liquor to make a batter. After sufficient time the rest of the liquor and the dates are put through a sieve, stirring the whole time. When the brew has cooled to 85–90° F., it is stocked with 3 oz. of compressed yeast. The barm will be ready for use five or six hours later.

15

Nutrition: Constituents of Food; Nutritional Value of Bread: Constituents of Bread; Enrichment of Bread

NUTRITION (1)

We eat and drink to live. What we eat and drink may have a profound effect on our lives, by the nature of the food itself, by the way in which it is prepared and by the way in which it is served. Some foodstuffs have a greater nutritional value than others, because weight for weight they contain more of the necessary constituents, or a greater percentage of the more valuable substances necessary for health. Quantity and quality are both important.

The constituents of food that are necessary for growth, activity and reproduction and the maintenance of healthy life are water, protein, carbohydrates, fat, mineral matter, vitamins and other necessary food factors.

When food is eaten, it is broken down by the digestive system into simpler chemical compounds, a process known as digestion. These compounds are taken from the digestive system by the blood to the body tissues, where they are either further broken down to very simple compounds releasing heat and energy, or they are built up into more complex substances for the growth, maintenance and repair of the body tissues, and to provide for the necessary regulation of these functions, and the establishment of food stores. The breakdown of the chemical compounds by the tissues is catabolism. The build-up of necessary materials is known as anabolism. Catabolism and anabolism together comprise the process known as metabolism.

Fats, carbohydrates and protein can all be used by the body to provide heat and energy, and the measure of their value in this respect is in heat units or calories. A calorie is the amount of heat required to raise one gram of water through one degree centigrade, from 15–16° C. For the purpose of assessing the calorific value of a food a kilo-calorie is used, this is a thousand calories. It is known better as the large Calorie, although in the work of diet and nutrition at the present time the capital letter is dropped.

The calorific value of a food can be obtained by burning a known quantity in a bomb-calorimeter in an excess of oxygen, and then observing the increase in temperature of the known amount of water surrounding the combustion chamber into which the liberated heat passes. The amount of heat produced is given by the product of the mass of water and its temperature rise expressed as calories.

The generally accepted calorific values of the constituents of food are as follows:

One gram of protein	= 4·1 calories
One gram of carbohydrate	= 4·1 calories
One gram of fat	= 9·3 calories

When the heat-giving constituents of food have had their calorific values assessed by the bomb-calorimeter method, a more convenient method of obtaining the calorific value of food is followed. Here is an example:

1 lb. of wheatmeal bread contains 179·2 grams of carbohydrates, 9·6 grams of fat and 49·6 grams of protein.

Carbohydrates will yield 179·2 × 4·1	= 734·72 calories
Fat will yield 9·6 × 9·3	= 89·28 calories
Protein will yield 49·6 × 4·1	= 203·36 calories
The calorific value of wheatmeal bread per pound	= 1027·36 calories

Here is an example taken from Intermediate Domestic Science (Rankin and Hildreth):

1 lb. of pork contains 67·6 grams of protein and 111·1 of fat.

The protein will yield 67·6 × 4·1	= 277·16 calories
The fat will yield 111·1 × 9·3	= 1033·23 calories
The calorific value of pork per pound	= 1310·39 calories

It will be seen that protein and carbohydrates are equal in calorific value; proteins, however, are generally more expensive and are required for the purposes of nutrition that cannot be carried out by carbohydrates. It is for this reason that dietically, carbohydrates are advised for the production of heat and energy in a balanced diet.

People differ in their calorific requirements, according to age, sex and to the amount of energy which they expend. A man doing very heavy manual work may need each day 5,000 calories against the 3,000 needed by the man whose physical work is much lighter. The average figure for calorific intake per day according to age, is as follows (these figures are conditioned by the amount of energy expended):

	Years	*Calories*
Children	0–6	1,650
,,	6–10	2,300
,,	10–14	2,750
Females	14 and over	2.750
Males	14 and over	3,300

Here is a table of calorific values expressed as calories per pound.

White bread	1,036·9	Rump steak	2,006·3
Wholemeal bread	1,012·4	Sirloin	1,748·5
Wheatmeal bread	1,027·3	Leg of mutton	1,501·0
Butter	3,502·9	Leg of pork	1,262·4
Margarine	3,570·9	Herring	686·8
Cheese (full cream)	2 011·3	Chicken	359·7
Milk	303·0	Cabbage	192·3
Eggs	659·1	Apples	159·9

If the student will compare the price of bread per pound with the price per pound of other foodstuffs, he will note that the cheapest way of purchasing calories is in the buying of bread.

NUTRITION (2)

To understand more of the subject of nutrition and to relate it to bakery products, the student must study in greater detail the various constituents of food.

Water

Life without water is impossible. Over one half of the weight of the human body is water. Of the total body, the muscles contain about 50%, the bones 13% and the blood, 5%. Most of the water is in the combined state, that is, as a constituent of proteins which form most of the nervous, muscular and connective tissues. The rest of the water is in the free state providing the fluid basis of blood, lymph and glandular secretions and excretions.

About 75% of food ingested is water. The adult body needs on an average 5¼ pints each day, either as a liquid or in food. Most of it is discharged by way of the kidneys, the lungs and the skin. Water is a great solvent and is essential for the breakdown of foodstuffs in the digestive system, where at the end it acts as a carrier of waste products.

White bread contains about 40% water.

Protein

Proteins are complex substances containing the elements carbon, hydrogen, oxygen and nitrogen; many contain sulphur, and a few phosphorus also. Proteins have a calorific value in that they produce heat and energy; they are more valuable in diet, however, for the making and maintenance of muscle and the repair of worn tissue.

Proteins are a build-up from fundamental units—the amino acids—of which there are at least 22 known. If the student will consider each amino acid as a brick, he could then build up hundreds of patterns, some simple and some complicated. With this as an example it becomes clear that the nature of a particular protein, and there are many of them, depends essentially on the amino acids present, and how they are built up.

Diet to be satisfactory must contain protein, not only in quantity, but in quality. Of the amino acids, 10 of them are termed 'essential' as they cannot be synthesized by the body at all, or a sufficient supply cannot be synthesized rapidly enough. These amino acids must be supplied to the body in food protein in adequate quantities. The other 12, the 'non-essential' amino acids, can be synthesized and need not be present in food protein although they are required by the body tissues.

When one or more of the essential amino acids is missing from the diet, or present in insufficient quantity, some form of malnutrition results.

Animal proteins, except gelatine, contain all the essential amino acids in sufficient quantity for human requirements, but most vegetable proteins are deficient in one or more of them. Gluten, although containing all of the essential amino acids, is rather deficient in one of them, lycine. In addition gluten contains a high proportion of the non-essential amino acids.

In enriched breads, containing eggs and milk, and in cakes, the baker provides the essential amino acids. Furthermore one should note that bread and butter, and bread and milk form valuable dietetic combinations.

Carbohydrates

One of the simplest forms of carbohydrate is glucose, which is most valuable in nutrition, for it provides heat and energy almost at once, for it is directly assimilated by the bloodstream and oxidized. All other sugars, except fructose, and the starches are broken down to glucose by the digestive system. Bread and cakes are cheap and attractive sources of carbohydrates in the general dietary. Bread in particular is probably the cheapest of all energy foods.

Fats

Whether they are of animal or vegetable origin, fats are another source of energy. They are compounds of glycerol and fatty acids. The natural fats and oils are triglycerides, that is, they are composed of three fatty acids on a glycerol base. The composition of the triglyceride determines the melting point of the fat.

Animal fats such as suet, lard and butter have a higher melting point and are hard or plastic; vegetable fats, having a lower melting point are mainly oils. In the diet, the melting point of fat is important, for the content of the fat cells must be fluid during life, therefore the solidification point of fat must be above blood heat.

In the digestive system, fat is finely emulsified and some of it is split into fatty acids and glycerol. The fat that is split is absorbed into the blood, and the greater part of that which is not split is absorbed into the lymphatic system and delivered into the bloodstream near the heart.

The liver uses the fatty acid in the blood, while the fat from the lymph is probably stored under the skin and around internal organs until required for use by the liver. In the liver, fatty acids are prepared for breakdown to release energy.

Fat is the vehicle by which the fat soluble vitamins are taken into the body.

The baker supplies dietary fat in small quantities in bread, although as a vehicle for further fat intake, for example, bread and butter, bread is ideal. Cakes provide a greater dietary source of fat, depending on the type and quality of the product used.

Minerals

Mineral substances are required continuously by the body if the diet is to be balanced and healthy life maintained. They are required for many purposes, although the necessary intake is relatively small. Without them life would be impossible.

If the body is reduced to ash, it is found to contain the following mineral elements, many in the form of compounds: calcium, iron, potassium, phosphorus, sodium, iodine and chlorine, together with traces of the elements copper, zinc, arsenic, fluorine, cobalt and manganese. The bones contain five-sixths of the mineral matter, and the soft tissues the remaining sixth. The skeletal structure needs calcium, and magnesium phosphates and carbonates. Minerals also play their part in digestion, respiration and the general metabolism of the living body.

Practically all bakery raw materials provide minerals, and this includes water. One important raw material is itself a mineral and that is common salt (sodium chloride). In addition, the calcium intake of the consumer of bakery products is increased by the addition of calcium carbonate (creta preparata) to flour at the rate of 14 oz. per sack of 280 lb. Iron is added to white flour, not as an enrichment, but as a restoration, otherwise all flours of an extraction rate of less than 80% would be deficient in this element. Milk, eggs and dried fruits when added to bread are enriching agents and add greatly to the mineral salts, available in the dietary of the consumer.

VITAMINS

The whole history of the work and investigation into what were first known as accessory food factors is fascinating, and the interested student will do well to study the story of the painstaking efforts of those who, over many years have brought knowledge of this subject to a high level. A book well recommended for study is *Intermediate Domestic Science*—Part I, Rankin and Hildreth. Nevertheless constant research is still going on, for there is yet much to learn.

It was known in the fourteenth century, at the time when Chaucer was writing *The Canterbury Tales* that scurvy, a disease caused by vitamin C deficiency, could be cured by the addition to the diet of fresh fruits and vegetables. Investigation in 1734 and again in 1735, described and demonstrated that certain diseases were due to an insufficient dietary intake of fresh fruit and vegetables. A British naval surgeon, James Lind, confirmed in 1741, observations made earlier, that dried vegetables were useless against scurvy and that fresh milk was beneficial in the treatment of that disease.

It was Lind who recommended that lemon juice should be an addition to the diet of naval personnel. This advice, however, was disregarded by the Admiralty, although at the time the deaths from scurvy exceeded the number of those who died from the hazards of war. In 1793, Lind's recommendation was officially tried when H.M.S. *Suffolk* made a voyage of 19 weeks without a case of scurvy. History reports that Captain Cook made certain that his crews had fresh fruits and vegetables with the result that they were free of this disease. It was not until the beginning of the nineteenth century that lemon juice was issued at the rate of 1 oz. per man for each day, although scurvy remained a scourge in the mercantile marine until the middle of the nineteenth century.

A further advance into the causes of what were beginning to be called the deficiency diseases, was made by a Dutch army doctor, Eijkman, who in the Dutch East Indies, discovered that beri-beri was caused by the consumption of the staple food of the region, polished rice. His investigation proved that the discarded skins contained a substance essential to health; we know it now as vitamin B. In 1911, Funk carrying on further experiments into the actual deficiency causing beri-beri, used the word 'vitamine' instead of the more cumbersome 'accessory food factor'. The final 'e' is now dropped and the word vitamin is used.

It was the Englishman Gowland Hopkins, of Cambridge, later knighted and awarded the Nobel prize for medicine, who after painstaking experiment proved the presence in natural foods, especially fresh milk, of substances necessary to life and health—in fact the vitamins. Later, scientists in the U.S.A. isolated some of the vitamins and proved that they were in two groups, some water soluble and the others fat soluble. After 1919, as a result of world investigation, the isolation of vitamins continued, their chemical composition ascertained, after which they were synthesized on a commercial scale. There are over 15 vitamins known at the present time, some classified alphabetically. Vitamin B, however, consists of at least twelve factors, which originally began to be classified numerically. Now most of them are known by their chemical names.

Vitamin A.—This vitamin is found in animal fats, milk, butter and especially in fish liver oils. Eggs, green vegetables, carrots, and tomatoes are a rich source. Table margarine has an addition of 760–940 international units of vitamin A per ounce. It is a fat soluble vitamin; lack of it is the cause of a generally lowered resistance to disease and can cause hardening and cracking of the skin and the front of the eye sometimes leading to blindness. Vitamin A is essential for the young. Without it growth is impossible.

It was discovered first during investigation into cod liver oil, although it was not until 1925 that it was found that the original fat soluble vitamin A was in fact two separate vitamins, A and D. The vitamin is closely associated with beta carotene found in chlorophyll, the green colouring matter in plants. Biologically active carotene is converted into vitamin A in the body. If heated for six hours at 100° C., vitamin A is destroyed.

Vitamin B.—The original 'water soluble B', discovered by McCollum and Davis in 1915, is now referred to as the vitamin B complex. In 1920 it was discovered that the vitamin contained one part that was affected by heat, while the other was thermo-stable. The former was termed vitamin B_1, the other B_2. In 1933, vitamin B_2 was found to contain two factors, one riboflavin and the other nicotinic acid. From time to time other factors have been distinguished, until now it is known that there are at least twelve in this group.

Vitamin B_1 is found in yeast, meat (especially pork), and cereals (particularly the scutellum of wheat). The B_1 content of flour decreases with the extraction rate. Vitamin B_1 is the anti beri-beri factor; in a lesser degree, a deficiency will cause loss of appetite, nausea, nervousness and general lack of efficiency. The chemical name for vitamin B_1 is aneurin (thiamine in the U.S.A.) and is synthesized commercially on a large scale.

Vitamin B_2 is found in milk and milk products, cereals, yeast, beer and tea. A deficiency will cause eye troubles, cracked lips, digestive disturbances and an increased liability to infection. The chemical name for vitamin B_2 is riboflavin. Like vitamin B_1, riboflavin is found naturally in greater quantities in the higher extraction rate flours.

The next member of the B complex is nicotinic acid (niacin in the U.S.A.). It is fairly widespread in foodstuffs, particularly in meat and cereals. Lack of it will cause dermatitis and, in extreme cases, the deficiency disease, pellagra, the symptoms of which are skin eruptions, muscular weakness, digestive derangement, and possible insanity.

Pantothenic acid, another of the group, is found in minimum quantities in most foods, especially cereals. Why it is needed in man, and the results of its deficiency are at present not known.

Inositol, *p*-aminobenzoic acid, folic acid, pyrodoxin and biotin are also members of this group. The part taken by these vitamins in human diet is not clear.

Vitamin C (Ascorbic acid).—This is the anti-scurvy vitamin, a deficiency of this vitamin being particularly serious in the past among seamen. Crews on long voyages, deprived of fresh fruit and vegetables suffered from bleeding gums and loosened teeth, subcutaneous bleeding and loss of appetite, death ensuing if the deficiency was prolonged. Less acute symptoms are a low state of health, poor resistance to infection and diminished growth.

For growing children vitamin C is essential. This explains why the Health Services encourage the distribution of orange juice, rose-hip syrup and blackcurrant purée, the last two of which are particularly rich in this vitamin. Ripe tomatoes are another excellent source. Seeds are lacking in this vitamin but they become a rich source, if allowed to germinate for five days.

Vitamin C is water soluble and easily destroyed on heating therefore green vegetables are best eaten raw. If cooked the operation should be done as quickly as possible. The use of soda in the cooking of green vegetables will destroy the vitamin. Chemical preservatives in fruit and in fruit juices will do the same.

Vitamin D.—This is the anti-rachitic vitamin. It is fat soluble and is closely associated with vitamin A. It is found in milk, animal fats and in fish liver oils, particularly cod and halibut. A deficiency is responsible for rickets in children. There is also a failure in the development of bone and teeth, all of which points to a disturbance of the calcium phosphate metabolism of the body.

Vitamin D is synthesized in the body by the action of sunlight and by exposure to ultra-violet rays. At one time it was thought that a lack of sunlight was the cause of rickets. It is known now, that either a lack of sunlight or vitamin D will cause rickets, and a sufficiency of one or both will prevent the disease. Table margarine has an addition of 80–100 international units of vitamin D per ounce.

Vitamin E.—The germ of wheat is rich in this vitamin which occurs also in some green vegetables. It plays an important part in reproduction. Knowledge of the part played by this vitamin, is still far from complete.

Together with iron, both vitamin B_1 and nicotinic acid are required to be added in controlled amounts to flours less than 80% extraction, to bring them to the nutritional value of flours of higher extraction.

NUTRITIONAL VALUE OF BREAD (1)

Reams of paper have been used on the subject of the nutritional value of our daily bread. The student will find it interesting to collect and collate the many reports on the subject, written by nutritionists, dieticians, doctors, neurotics, faddists and politicians, from the well informed, to the ill informed in all countries, and from all strata of society, excepting those perhaps suffering from hunger.

The answered prayer, 'Give us this day our daily bread', has also given food for thought, and a farinaceous ammunition, both white and brown, that has been tossed backwards and forwards in friendly debate, heated discussion, and on occasions when violent verbal pyrotechnics have been the rule.

One aspect alone has been repeatedly ignored, and that is the aesthetic value of the individual enjoyment of bread: the satisfaction of eating a piece of well made, well fermented, fully flavoured crusty bread, be it brown or white, natural in its nutritional value or synthetically reinforced. Nobody seems to remember or quote the dictum of that great bread craftsman, J. R. Irons, who once said that most of the flavour in bread is in the crust. Human teeth and crusty bread seldom meet nowadays in this country, for modern bread is devoid of that lovely, golden flavoursome armour that was so well enjoyed in the past.

The student will know that excellent bread can be made with flour, yeast, salt and water. He will know the composition of all four and their nutritional values. Of the four ingredients, flour is the only variable, and the nutritional value of that will change according to the extraction rate or by additions during milling.

The nutritional value of bread can be increased by such additions as fat, milk, sugars, malt fruit and nuts. Bread is rarely eaten alone, so that dietetically speaking, bread and milk, bread and butter, bread and cheese, etc., are valuable. Any dietetic deficiency in bread can be made good by other foods in combination with it.

In many cases bread is the ideal vehicle for a combination; for instance, one would not eat butter or jam alone, but good butter and good jam on good bread is a delight.

Bread can be made from wholemeal, wheatmeal or white flour. The meals vary in composition; wholemeal can be bought as 100% extraction in which case it is generally stone ground, containing no additives whatsoever. What may also be legally termed wholemeals are the old established brands containing over 95% of the wheat grain; these contain creta preparata at the rate of 14 oz. per sack. The legal definition of wheatmeal is any flour with an extraction rate in excess of 85%; these also contain creta preparata at the same rate.

Proprietary germ meals are a mixture of white flour, salt and cooked wheat germ and also contain creta preparata. White flours, according to grade, vary in their extraction rates between 40–70% and these must be brought up to the required nutritional level to ensure a minimum content of iron, vitamin B_1 and nicotinic acid. All white flours contain creta preparata.

The recent report of the Medical Research Council on 'The effect of variations in the extraction rate of flour on the growth of undernourished children' is particularly interesting. The authors Dr. E. M. Widdowson and Professor R. A. M. McCance, fed bread and other foods made from flours of different extraction rates to undernourished German children.

The experiment seems to prove that no difference, either in growth or in health could be detected in the groups of children eating food made from the flours of different extraction rates. The authors, however, emphasize that the greatest caution must be used in coming to any general conclusions on the basis of the results.

An independent panel of persons representing scientific and medical opinion has now been formed to examine the differences in composition and nutritional value of flours of different extraction rates, and those to which the three token nutrients have been restored.

In the meantime the student may draw three conclusions in the light of his technical and practical knowledge:

(1) That all breads are nutritionally valuable.
(2) That the balance of nutritional value varies according to the extraction rate of the flour and/or, additions made to the flour by the miller and to bread by the baker.
(3) That the largely ignored aesthetic value of the individual enjoyment of bread, is of the greatest possible importance. It may be the greatest asset of the craftsman baker.

NUTRITIONAL VALUE OF BREAD (2)

Quite apart from the aesthetic value in the enjoyment of good bread and the fact that bread of all types is a valuable food, the student will be expected to have further knowledge of its nutritional value.

Carbohydrates

Carbohydrates are the energy producers. Bread is particularly important as an energy food, providing 20–30% of the total energy requirements of the people. The figures vary in different countries according to the average consumption per head of the population. The endosperm of wheat contains about 70% carbohydrate in the form of starch and 2–3% in the form of sugars provided that the wheat is sound. The bran coatings contain a small amount not used by the body to provide energy, its function in digestion being to provide roughage to assist in the final elimination of bodily waste.

The student will readily understand that the lower the extraction rate, the greater is the percentage of starch. It follows then, that the energy value of white bread is greater and more readily available than that of the meals of greater extraction rate.

Protein

Protein is necessary in diet as a body builder. Bread has an approximate protein content of 8 %. This is a valuable contribution to nutrition, for bread is a basic food and is eaten more or less abundantly. About 20% of the protein intake of the people is provided by the bread baker. It is also the cheapest source of protein.

The scientist places protein into two classes. Animal protein generally is considered first-class and vegetable protein second-class. First-class protein contains all the essential amino acids in correct proportion and in sufficient quantity for human requirements. Gluten as a vegetable protein is included in the second category, although the protein contained in the germ, the scutellum and the aleurone layer, are all considered first class. It will follow, therefore, that flours of high extraction rates will have a higher protein content, and a proportion of it will be of a higher class.

It is interesting to note that scientific investigation has shown that where proteins of different values are eaten, then all the protein may be considered, dietetically as first class. Bearing this in mind, the student will readily understand the increased nutritive value of bread in combination with other food containing first class protein; bread with meat, butter and cheese are excellent examples.

Minerals

Minerals are absolutely essential for life and health, even although the amounts required are small. Bread contains calcium, potassium, phosphorus, iron and of course common salt. By far the greater mineral content of the wheat grain is found in the bran coatings, therefore, wholemeal and wheatmeal bread are a better natural source of mineral matter than white bread. In the higher extraction flours, however, some of the phosphorus is contained in phytic acid which combines with calcium and produces phytates which are not used by the digestive system. This is the reason why the miller was obliged by the Ministry of Food to include calcium carbonate (creta preparata) to all flours except wholemeal. Bread and flour provide 26% of our total calcium intake and 30% of our total intake of iron.

Vitamins

Bread contains vitamins of the B group-vitamin B_1 riboflavin and nicotinic acid. The bran coatings and the germ providing the greater proportion of these vitamins, the scutellum yielding nearly 60% of the total vitamin B_1.

It will be seen that flour of high extraction rate and germ meals are valuable in this respect. As the extraction rate is lowered so also is the vitamin content. Some of the vitamins are destroyed in baking. In soda bread more are destroyed.

When studying the nutritional value of bread, the student must always bear in mind the reinforcement of flour of an extraction rate below 80%, details of which have already been given.

BREAD ENRICHMENT

Bread is enriched to increase the food value, add to the flavour, to produce a softer and finer crumb and to retard staling. All these points have sales value.

Excellent bread can be made from the four basic materials: flour, water, yeast and salt. When the salt content is lowered and fat and sugar added, within limits, then a bun is produced. The difference between a bun and a loaf of bread therefore is in the balance of salt and enriching agents. The dividing line, of course, cannot be defined arbitrarily, although it can be said that when the product loses its characteristic, although neutral flavour, and cannot be eaten and enjoyed with savoury food, then it ceases to be bread.

The student must always remember that the finest bread improver is a good craftsman; the mere addition of enriching agents will not necessarily produce better bread, in fact used without technical knowledge, bread of poorer quality may well be produced. The student must always have in mind, and seek to study, national and regional tastes.

In France and Scotland, for instance, excellent, although totally different bread is produced, neither being particularly enriched. Again, English bread and that of the U.S.A. are totally different and although much of the bread of the U.S.A. is heavily enriched, it may not please the British public. It is possible that a reversion to the old English standard of well made and fermented crusty bread will increase sales, while heavily enriched bread may tend to lessen them. Changing tastes, experimentation and trial will, of course, provide the answer.

The addition of fat to bread will give better volume due to its shortening action on gluten, thus lowering resistance to the expanding gas. It will also help to retard staling. Soya flour because of its fat content will act in a similar manner; it also contributes to the protein content and provides enzymes that are active in fermentation. Sugar and malt increase the gassing power of yeast, which in turn assists in the creation of an increased volume. In addition they confer sweetness to both crust and crumb. Milk counteracts the action of fat and sugar in increasing volume, because of the tightening effect of milk casein on gluten. Lactose (milk sugar) however is not fermentable by yeast and is retained in the loaf to sweeten the crust and crumb. The student can examine the physical differences for himself, simply by comparing a piece of ordinary bread with a piece of bun. Better still he will do well to make and bake two small batches of bread as described overleaf.

If no dried egg is available add four ounces of shell or frozen egg and deduct three ounces of water.

The student should study the doughs carefully at dough-making and during the bulk and final fermentation. When the baked bread is cold it should be cut and further studied. In this way a great deal

English tin bread

lb.	*oz.*	
1	14	Flour
	¾	Yeast
	½	Salt
1	1	Water (approx.)

Dough temperature 80° F.
Bulk fermentation 2 hr.
Yield three loaves weighed at 1 lb.

U.S.A. enriched bread

lb.	*oz.*	
1	2	Flour
	1	Yeast
	½	Salt
	1	Fat
	1½	Sugar
	1½	Milk powder
	1	Dried eggs
1	1	Water

Dough temperature 76° F.
Bulk fermentation 2 hr.
Yield four loaves weighed at 12½ oz.

can be learned of the action on dough, fermentation and on the finished bread by the addition of enriching agents.

A further type of enrichment, better known as reinforcement or fortification, is carried out by introducing into white flour, a sufficient amount of vitamins and minerals to remedy the nutritional defects of these low extraction flours. In this way it is possible for consumers to have the white bread they desire without sacrifice of nutritional standards.

This policy was first introduced by British millers shortly before the last war, when vitamin B_1 was added to white flour. This was continued during the war until the enforcement of 85% extraction flour made it unnecessary. The principle of reinforcement is still adhered to, for on the decontrol of flour in 1953, it was laid down that flour of under 80% extraction should be reinforced. The fortification of flour in the U.S.A. is much greater than in this country. Here is a table of comparison.

	Britain	*U.S.A.*
	milligrams per 100 grams	
Thiamine	0·24	0·44
Riboflavin	—	0·27
Nicotinic acid	1·60	3·56
Iron	1·65	2·90

Vitamin D is an optional additive in the U.S.A.

According to Dr. Amos, the well-known cereal chemist, the whole policy of fortification should be subject to certain rules. Nutritional values should not be indiscriminately increased, and the nutrients should not be foreign to the food. Vitamin A, for example, should not be introduced into bread, and the addition of vitamin D to flour as is done in the U.S.A. should not be approved. Dr. Amos suggests that the decisive consideration should be whether a nutrient is insufficient in a normal diet, and not the fact that it is lacking in one particular item of food.

16

Vienna Bread: Basic Formula; Manufacture; Action of Steam; Fancy Rolls; Fancy Tea Breads; Plaiting; Harvest Bread; Cholla Bread; Hot-Plate Goods; Chemically Aerated Breads; Milk Bread; Fruit Breads; Stollen

VIENNA BREAD

VIENNA bread is essentially an enriched bread in contrast to French bread which can be termed a water bread. Vienna bread is not ordinary milk bread that has been well baked or baked in steam. Vienna bread is something entirely different and its manufacture can be termed a specialist craft.

At one time it was considered impossible to make it without special imported flour and baking it in a Vienna oven. With the advance of technical knowledge, it is possible to bake excellent Vienna bread in an ordinary oven adapted for the purpose and fitted with a steam generator. Flours suitable for the making of Vienna bread can be blended by the baker himself.

The most important thing is a knowledge of the standard for Vienna bread, how it is achieved and the principles and technology behind the manufacture. Here is what can be considered a standard for this type of bread.

External Characteristics.—The crust should be thin, highly glazed and with a bright golden colour. The crust should break with a snap and should possess a crunchy biscuit-like quality. This type of crust is known in the baking industry as an 'egg-shell' crust.

Internal Characteristics.—The crumb should be soft and silky, with an open structure showing relatively large gas holes. It should not have the structure of ordinary bread. The colour should be a sparkling creamy yellow. Plate IV shows a fine Vienna loaf.

Materials.—These should be of the finest quality. The flour should be mellow, of top quality and of medium strength, blended with a strong Canadian flour, which generally speaking should not exceed

50% of the blend; in many cases 10% is enough to give strength, stability and volume. Craftsmen, however, will blend their flours to their individual tastes and according to the method of manufacture employed.

The yeast should be fast working, and one producing good flavour. Malt should be used, especially if the proportion of strong flour is high. Any fat of good quality is suitable, although many craftsmen consider the best fat addition to be a mixture of butter and lard because of the flavours both of them confer.

Vienna Doughs.—The dough should have a high water and yeast content, and be made cold at a temperature below 74° F. It is considered that the best temperature is between 65–70° F. Ice can be used to get this low initial temperature. The dough should be well developed at the mixing stage. As the temperature of the bakery is usually higher than the dough temperature, the speed of fermentation increases as the dough temperature rises (bearing in mind also the high yeast and water contents which speed fermentation).

In view of this it is important that doughs should be of such a size that the number of workers employed on it can handle and control it. It is important to have vigorous fermentation at the last stages before the bread goes to the oven. This is helped by frequent 'knock backs' which, however, should not be too thorough, in fact a gentle turning and stretching without the expulsion of too much gas is all that is necessary.

It is of the utmost importance that during proving the dough piece is not allowed to 'skin'. To prevent this, bread and rolls are proved upside-down on cloths. An alternative method is to prove in boxes that can be nested, that is, stacked one on another so that the dough pieces can prove in humidity and freedom from draughts. It is important also that the dough pieces shall not touch during proving or structural weaknesses will be evident in the baked bread or rolls.

Baking.—Vienna bread and rolls are baked in a steam-saturated atmosphere. (This had already been explained in Chapter 12 under the heading Vienna Ovens.) As the dough pieces are set in the oven, the steam immediately condenses on the cool dough surface, gelatinizing the surface starch which is dextrinized by heat, giving the characteristic high glaze of the properly baked Vienna loaf.

The student will now understand the necessity for a cold dough. A short time before the bread or rolls are drawn from the oven, the steam is allowed to escape, and baking is finished in a dry atmosphere. This gives the necessary crispness to the crust.

BASIC FORMULA

Questions relating to the making, baking and glazing of Vienna bread often appear on the final written examination paper of the City and Guilds on breadmaking, and the student may also be required to make Vienna bread or rolls in the course of his practical examination.

He will do well to study with care, both the principles and their application to practical work. He will know now that Vienna bread is different from ordinary bread, in that it is enriched, carries more water and yeast, is made cool, and is baked in steam.

Skinning must be avoided both during the recovery period after handing up, and during final proof. If skinning takes place during the latter stage, glazing will be adversely affected during the initial baking period, and in consequence the crust of the bread will be dull. The dough should be fermenting vigorously with plenty of 'life' in it when it is set into the oven.

Formulae for Vienna bread can be found in bewildering variety in bakery textbooks, and the student may find it difficult to memorize, for the purpose of answering a possible question in a written examination, a formula that can be considered basic. The variety of formulae is due to the differing techniques and methods of worthy craftsmen, quite apart from variations in flour qualities, dough temperatures, and fermentation times. Here is what can be considered as a basic formula given on a quarter sack basis, together with a student's batch taken to the nearest quarter of an ounce.

Vienna Bread

	lb.	*oz.*	*lb.*	*oz.*
Flour	70	0	3	8
Fat	2	0		1½
Salt	1	4		1
Sugar	1	0		¾
Milk powder		12		½
Yeast	1	8		2
Water (approx.)	42	8	2	2

Dough temperature 72°F. Fermentation time 2 hr. Fold back every 30 min. Yield—220 loaves weighed at 8½ oz. Students' batch yield—11 loaves. The bread will be approximately 7 oz. when baked.

After scaling, the dough pieces are handed up and covered during the recovery period, after which they are moulded to the usual Vienna shape and proved in one of the ways already referred to; the essential point of either method being the prevention of skinning.

When ready for baking, the loaves are cut five or six times diagonally with a sharp blade, each cut being in the form of a nick which opens to a leaf shape during baking. If the loaves have been proved upside down, then the cutting is done on the slip immediately before setting.

Setting is done by means of slips, which are flat wooden blades about four or five inches wide, the longest being about two feet longer than the oven. Shorter slips are used as necessary. Both bread and rolls are set in a steam saturated atmosphere in rows radiating from the mouth of the oven, steam injection going on the whole time, ceasing a few minutes after setting is completed.

Before the bread or rolls are drawn from the oven, the steam is allowed to escape so that the baking is finished in a dry atmosphere.

The Action of Steam.—The action of steam on the crust of bread is interesting and a knowledge of it is essential if the student is to produce Vienna bread and rolls with the characteristic crisp and shiny crust.

With ordinary bread, oven humidity is essential if a well-shaped loaf is to be produced, always bearing in mind the importance of correct fermentation, manipulation, timing, oven loading and—if used—the size of baking-tin. With correct humidity, the loaf expands evenly during baking, has an even break, a healthy crust colour, with the vivacious sparkling quality that we know as bloom.

To study the effects of baking in an oven without humidity, the student can experiment for himself by placing several loaves in a dry oven, allowing one or two to skin badly before setting. The loaves will expand in the oven to a degree depending on the initial resistance. In a dry atmosphere a skin is formed immediately; as expansion takes place within the loaf the skin breaks at the weakest point, usually near the side at the top of the baking tin, producing a more or less badly shaped loaf with a pronounced break, and with a crust lacking in bloom.

If the loaf skins badly before baking, then there is a thicker crust that resists expansion for a longer time, until at last it manifests itself more as a burst than a break, with, in consequence, a greater distortion in shape and with the crust showing the original skinning in the form of grey patches. There is no crust sparkle; this is due to an absence of light dispersion from starch that has not been gelatinized because of the lack of surface moisture.

If the oven atmosphere is sufficiently humid, then the surface of the loaf remains moist longer; expansion is even, and for a time unrestricted until at last, just before activity within the loaf ceases, a slight even break occurs and the structure of the loaf is shapely and symmetrical.

Moisture, both in the skin and condensing on it, allows the starch cells to swell and the soluble starch, sugars, gums and other breakdown products of fermentation in the presence of heat, produce the healthy sparkle and colour in the crust that is associated with the well fermented and processed loaf.

If a loaf is washed with water before setting, or is proved in an excess of steam, a glaze is effected that is quite different from the natural bloom of unwashed bread baked in a humid atmosphere. Depending on the degree of fermentation, the amount of water used, or moisture present on the skin of the loaf from the prover, the crust is more or less toughened and the glaze has an artificial look.

Vienna bread is different, for it is baked initially in an excess of steam, resulting in a symmetrical loaf, without oven break, and with a thin, crisp and highly glazed crust. This is effected by sufficient condensation of moisture on the loaf surface in the first few minutes of baking.

The student will now understand the reason for the continual insistence on the necessity for a cool dough, for it is only on a cool dough that the injected steam will condense; further, if the condensation is to be effective then there must be no skinning or the condensed steam will be useless.

Condensation continues until the crust temperature is above the dew point of the baking atmosphere, then evaporation takes place. In the meantime the starch cells on and near the crust take up moisture and under the influence of heat swell considerably, some of them bursting and liberating soluble starch.

Pressure within the loaf keeps this on the crust surface, producing a fine translucent glaze under which can be seen the true crust which has remained stable and elastic enough to prevent oven break. Cutting, which in ordinary bread determines the oven break, is in Vienna bread, seen merely as a decoration, for the cuts should not break up the continuity of the smooth surface.

With the steam removed during the last stage of baking, the crust dries out and becomes crisp. This is absolutely necessary, for excess moisture retained in the crust will be joined by moisture evaporating from the crumb, and the crust becomes 'leathery', and uninteresting.

FANCY ROLLS

When a piece of dough is taken and shaped it has, provided that the shape is pleasing, been given a form of decoration that improves the general appearance and it at once becomes of greater appeal to the potential customer. At the same time a great deal of pleasure is given to the craftsman, for the dough becomes a media for creative work.

The student no doubt would like to emulate the craftsman and share his pleasure by manipulating dough into various shapes. For the budding craftsman, there is no better start in dough manipulation than by shaping fancy rolls; furthermore it is necessary if he aspires to City and Guilds qualifications. In the intermediate examination in breadmaking he may be required to produce half a dozen simple shapes. In the final examination the types required are generally more complicated.

For the intermediate examination, the student is advised not to try and be too clever unless he is sure of himself and his ability; rather to concentrate on simple shapes and make them really well.

In all the following examples, the weighed dough pieces are moulded round and covered with a damp cloth during the necessary recovery period. Unless baked in steam, all rolls are carefully washed with diluted egg.

Round Rolls.—These are the most simple of all rolls. The dough piece is merely re-moulded into a round shape and placed on to baking sheets. They may be given a single cut before baking.

Batons.—These are moulded from the round pieces in a similar manner to a swiss bun. They may be baked uncut, or given a series of oblique cuts. An excellent effect, and added flavour, can be given by dusting with flour after washing, and before cutting. The dusting should be done before placing on to the baking sheets.

Points.—The rounded dough pieces are simply moulded into long shapes with rounded points at both ends. These rolls can be left uncut, given a single cut down the centre or given a series of oblique cuts. The last two forms of cutting can also be given after a dusting of flour.

Other roll shapes, each of which is illustrated, appear opposite.

Knots.—The dough piece is rolled into a rope about 9 inches long and folded as shown in the illustration Fig. 15*a*, being careful that neither end shall extrude unduly. The baked roll is shown in Fig. 15*b*.

Double Knots.—These are similar to the simple knots except that the dough pieces are rolled out about twice as long then folded into double strands. Both ropes are folded as in illustration Fig 16*a*. The baked rolls will look as in illustration Fig. 16*b*.

Staffordshire Knots.—The dough pieces are rolled into ropes about 12 inches in length and manipulated as shown in illustration Fig. 17*a*. The finished roll is shown in Fig. 17*b*.

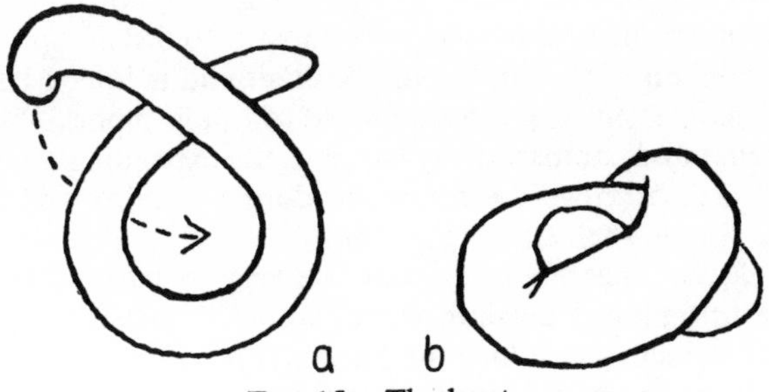

FIG. 15.—The knot.

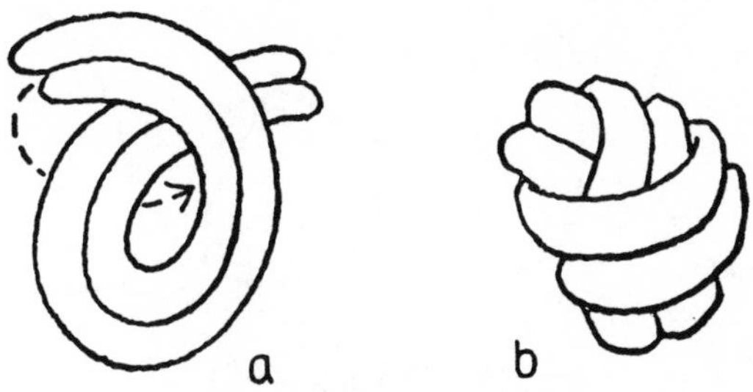

FIG. 16.—The double knot.

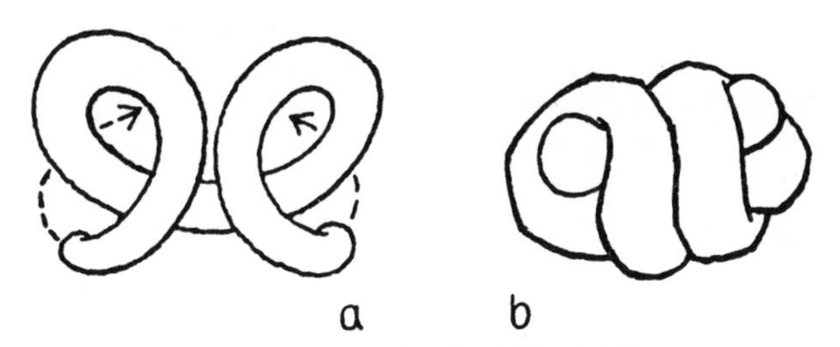

FIG. 17.—The Staffordshire knot.

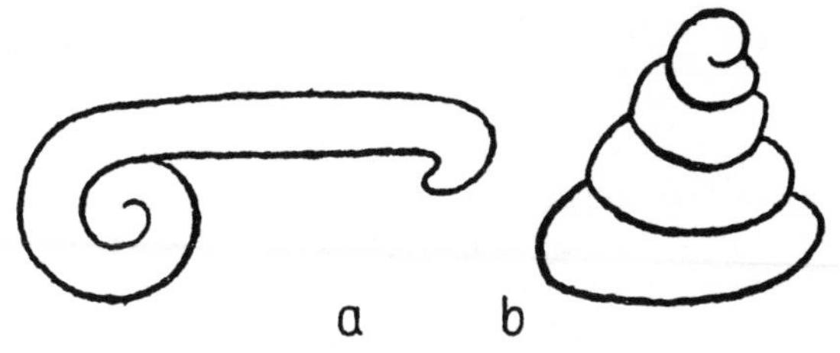

FIG. 18.—The winkle.

Winkles.—These are made by extending the dough pieces to about 12 inches in length. They are loosely folded in spiral form from one end Fig. 18*a*. The tip of the other end is folded back and tucked under the centre of the completed roll. It is important that the spiral is loose and comparatively flat. It is the expanding double end underneath, that brings the centre up during proving and baking, giving the winkle shell effect (Fig. 18*b*).

Cheese Rolls.—These unusual rolls are easy to make. The dough pieces are first pinned out into circles about 6 inches in diameter (Fig. 19*a*), which are folded in halves (Fig. 19*b*) and then into quarters. It is important when folding that the rounded edges are not

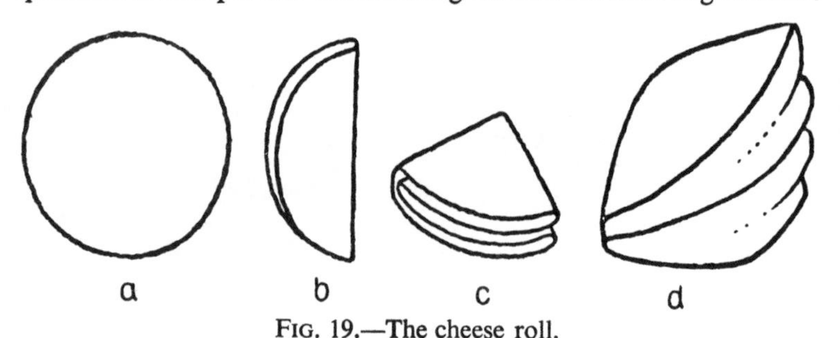

FIG. 19.—The cheese roll.

directly one above the other, each layer receding back from the bottom one (Fig. 19*c*). Care in this will result in the shape as illustrated in (Fig. 19*d*). Made properly these are delightful rolls. They are easily opened, buttered and finished with a slice of cheese.

'C' Rolls.—The illustration (Fig. 20) shows the formation quite clearly.

'S' Rolls.—These again are shown clearly in illustration, Fig. 21.

FIG. 20.—The 'C' roll.

FIG. 21.—The 'S' roll.

The Wedge.—The dough piece is rolled to a rope about 12 inches long, thicker in the middle and pointed at the ends. The ends are brought together and twisted until the wedge shape is formed. The illustration shows this quite clearly (Fig. 22).

Rosettes.—Again a rope is formed but this time about 15 inches

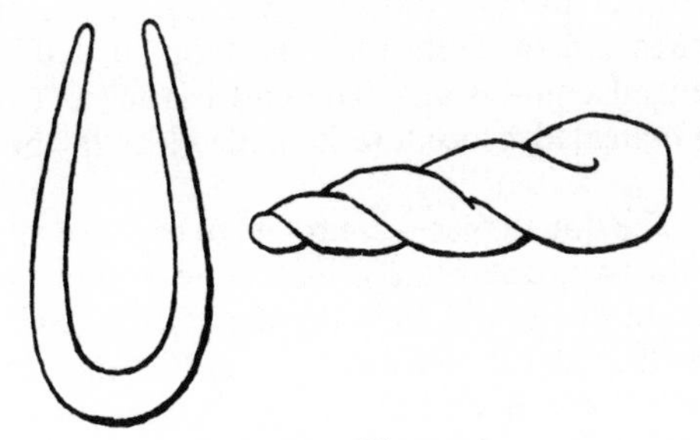

FIG. 22.—The wedge.

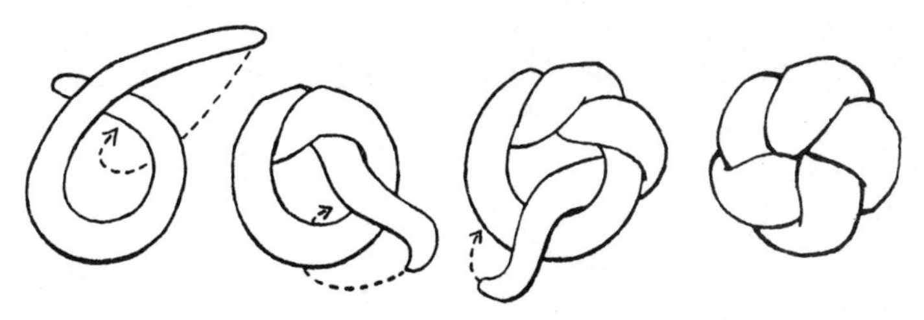

FIG. 23.—The rosette

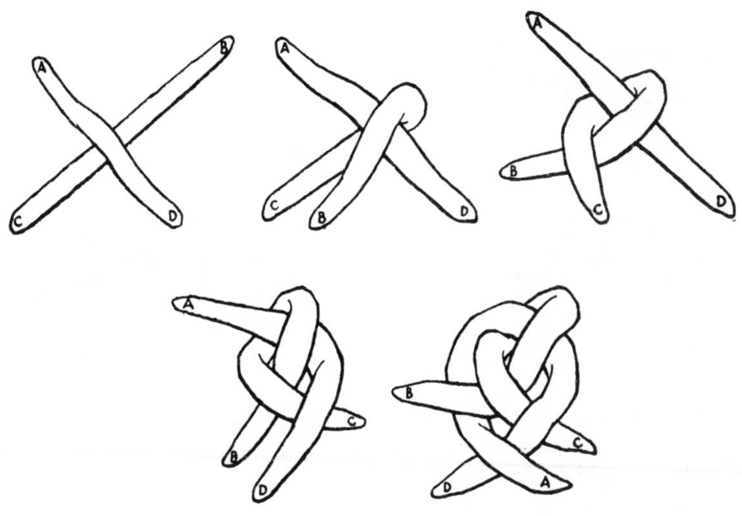

FIG. 24.—The peardrop and button.

in length. A loop is made at one end, and the operation consists of putting the other end twice through the loop so that there are five segments arranged equi-distant. The end is tucked under the roll. The rather complicated procedure is made clear in the illustrations (Fig. 23).

Peardrops.—The dough pieces are rolled to ropes of about 13 inches and divided into two, one piece a little longer than the other. The longer piece is put down first as in the illustration (Fig. 24), and the smaller piece laid across it to form a cross. B is then brought down over D, C is taken over B, and D. over C. A is brought under B and over D. Then C is taken over A. The last two sequences are repeated until the plait is finished. The roll is then turned over and put on to the baking sheet. The student will find that all dough-plaiting is very satisfying, but he is advised not to go on too long. The plait will look much better if, after the general formation, the ends are

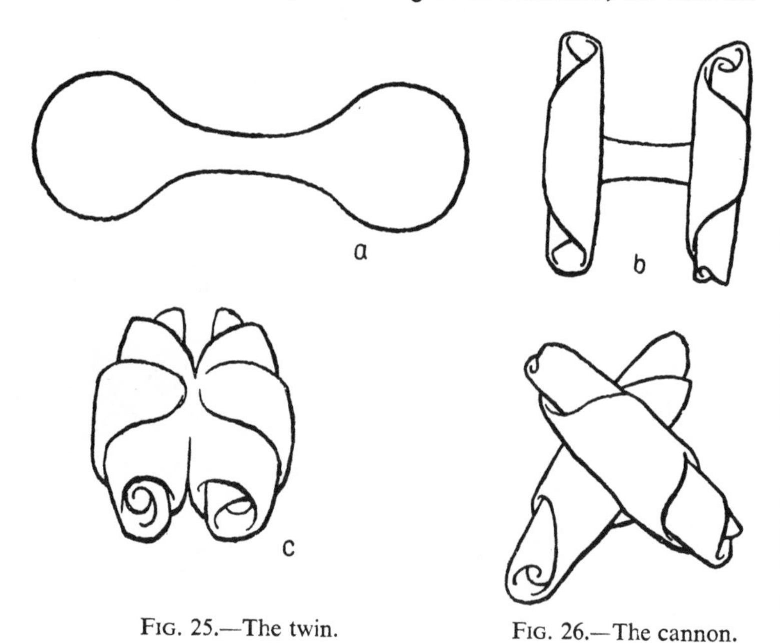

FIG. 25.—The twin. FIG. 26.—The cannon.

tucked under out of the way. Continuous plaiting of the ends, apart from being a waste of time, gives the roll a look of untidiness.

Buttons.—Proceed in exactly the same way as for peardrops, but before turning the roll over, take the point of the roll to the top, then turn it over.

Twins.—With the hands the dough pieces are shaped as illustrated (Fig. 25*a*). The ends are pinned or pressed flat. Using both hands, the ends are rolled up towards the centre. Tension is maintained the whole time to stretch the centre band (Fig. 25*b*). The rolls are turned over and the centre bands cut before the rolls are baked (Fig. 25*c*).

Cannons.—These are made exactly the same as for the twins, except that they are not turned over at the finish. Instead one part of the roll is arranged at right angles over the other as seen in the illustration (Fig. 26).

Crescents.—The dough pieces are pinned out into long oval shapes. Rolling up is commenced from the top while tension is maintained by pulling the tail piece with the other hand. The rolling should be tight, consistent with it not breaking the dough structure. When finished, the rolled piece should be cigar shaped, showing about seven folds, diminishing towards the ends on either side of the triangular shaped finishing flap. To finish, the rolls are then arranged into crescent shapes, the flaps coming over from the back.

Kaisers.—The rounded pieces are first flattened and the bottom edge of the circles turned up to form a straight edge. The thumb is then placed near the centre, and the far edge of the circle brought over it and fastened down with a light blow with the edge of the other hand. With the thumb still in position, the first finger is used to make the second fold, fastening down in the same manner. The third and fourth folds are also completed with the first finger, the thumb still in the original position. A small tail is left and this is inserted into the tunnel left after the thumb is removed, thus the last fold is effected, five in all.

FANCY TEA BREADS

The student will perhaps have seen a display of plaited tea breads in the windows of high-class bakeries especially those specializing in Continental goods, generally in the foreign quarter of our great cities. He will be struck by the symmetrical beauty of the shapes, which is enhanced by the shiny golden brown of the crust. If he aspires to such craftsmanship he will wish to practise and master the art of plaiting, especially as he may at some time be asked to make plaited shapes in the City and Guilds breadmaking examination.

There are some important basic rules that must be observed if the finished products are to be neat and attractive.

They are as follows:

(1) When the shape demands that the dough piece is sub-divided, then this must be done accurately, each piece being the same weight as the other.

(2) Each piece must be moulded to exactly the same length, unless otherwise directed.

(3) Each moulded strand must be of the same shape and thickness.

A moment's thought on these points and it will be clearly seen that it is virtually impossible to build a neat plaited shape with strands that are irregular in shape, length and size.

Here is a formula for rich tea bread with which the student may like to practise.

Rich Tea Bread

lb.	*oz.*		*lb.*	*oz.*	
1	4	Flour		¼	Salt
	9	Water (approx.)		2	Fat
	2	Egg		1	Yeast
	¾	Sugar			

Dough temperature 76° F. Bulk fermentation 1½ hr.
Baking temperature 450° F. Yield four at 8 oz.

One-strand Plait.—This unusual shape is quite simple to make, although it is not often seen in bakery windows. The dough piece is rolled to a fairly long rope, which is folded into a loop with a long

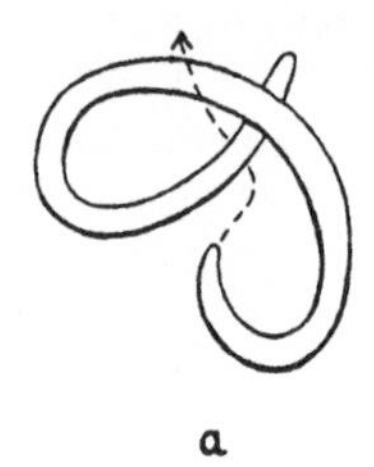

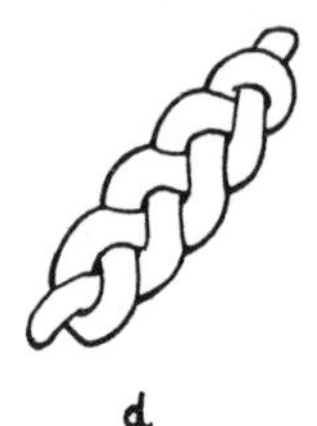

a b c d

FIG. 27.—The one-strand plait.

free end as shown in the illustration (Fig. 27*a*). The free end is then drawn through the loop (Fig. 27*b*). At this point the loop is given a twist to the right, before the end is threaded back (Fig. 27*c*). The loop is then given a twist to the left before the end is threaded back again. This sequence is repeated until the plait is finished (Fig. 27*d*.)

Two Plait.—Strictly speaking this is not a plaited shape. It is included partly to maintain a chronological order and partly because it is a good shape. The dough piece is carefully divided into two and each piece moulded into a longish torpedo shape, the two pieces being placed side by side (Fig. 28*b*). If the left hand is placed at one end and the right hand at the other and each end pushed simul-

FIG. 28.—The two-strand plait.

taneously in opposite directions, the shape will be formed (Fig. 28*a*). With this shape it is advisable to let the strands recover from the moulding before shaping, otherwise the plait will unwind.

Three Plait.—This plait is probably the oldest and most frequently used for fancy bread. Divide the dough piece into three and mould each into a not-too-long torpedo shape and place them side by side (Fig. 29*a*). Open out the bottom ends and commence plaiting by taking the right-hand piece over its neighbour (Fig. 29*b*), then follow

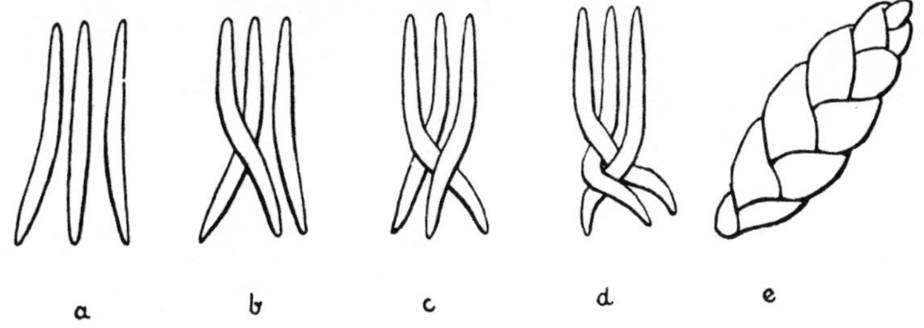

FIG. 29.—The three-strand plait.

with the left-hand piece (Fig. 29*c*), continue this sequence until the end is reached.

Turn the whole over to bring the unplaited ends to the bottom. After making certain of the right order, finish the plait in the same way (Fig. 29*e*). A much better plait is produced by starting in the centre and finishing at the ends. It is the method used by the greater number of craftsmen. The method of plaiting and the finished shape is illustrated.

Four Plait.—Shape four strands exactly as described for the three plait and place them with the four top ends fastened together (Fig. 30*a*). Proceed to plait in the following order: 2 over 3, 4 over 2, and 1 over 3. The sequence is repeated until the plait is finished (Fig. 30*e*).

The student must remember that after each move, the ends will

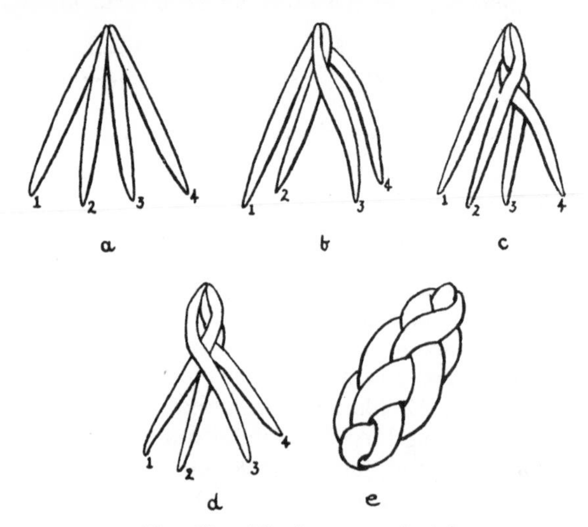

FIG. 30.—The four-strand plait.

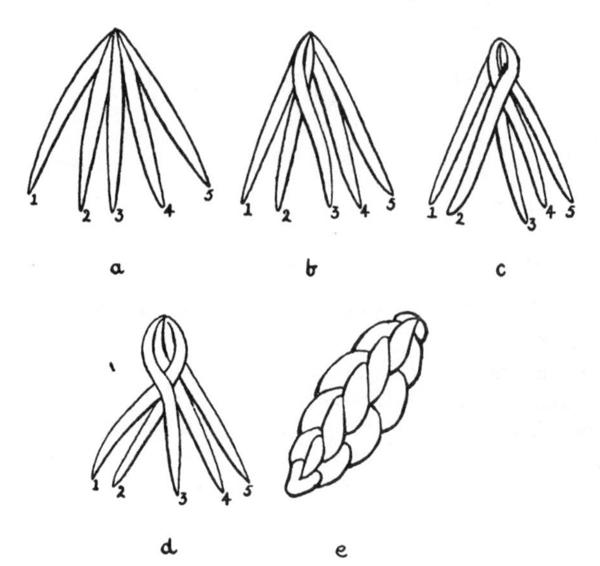

FIG. 31.—The five-strand plait.

bear the numbers one to four reading from left to right. For example, after the first move, 3 becomes 2 and 2 becomes 3. After the second move 4 becomes 2 and so on. This applies equally to the five, six and eight plaits.

Five Plait.—The dough piece is divided into five equal pieces and moulded as already described. They are arranged as shown in the illustration (Fig. 31*a*). The moves are: 2 over 3, 5 over 2 and 1 over 3, the sequence being repeated until the plait is finished (Fig. 31*e*).

Six Plait.—Divide into six equal size pieces and mould and

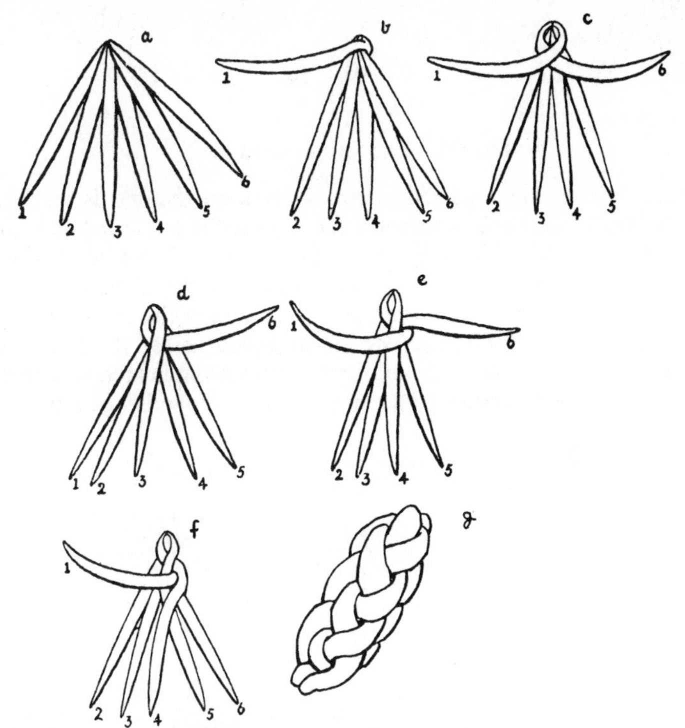

FIG. 32.—The six-strand plait.

arrange as for the four and five plaits (Fig. 32*a*). There is an initial move that is not afterwards repeated and that is 6 over 1. Then follows in turn, 2 over 6, 1 over 3, 5 over 1 and 6 over 4. This sequence is repeated until the plait is complete (Fig. 32*g*).

Seven Plait.—After dividing into seven, the pieces are moulded a little longer than for the previous plaits. They are placed side by side on the table and opened out at the bottom so that there are four strands at the left and three on the right (Fig. 33*a*).

Plaiting consists of taking the outside strand on the left and bringing it to the middle and pushing it to the right to lay beside the right-hand strands (Fig. 33*b*). The outside right-hand strand is taken to the middle and pushed to the left (Fig. 33*c*).

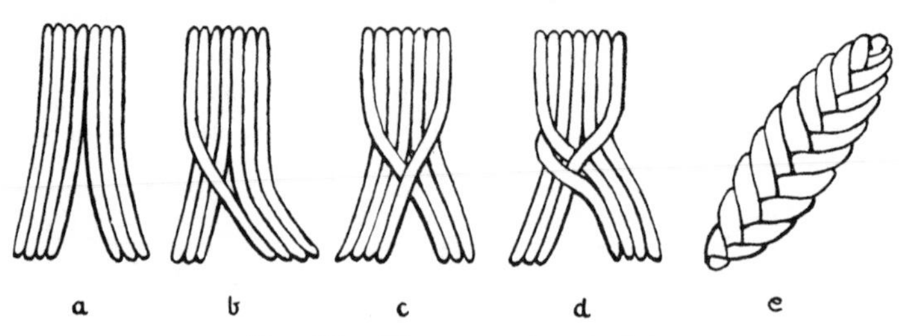

FIG. 33.—The seven-strand plait.

These moves are repeated alternatively until the end is reached. The half-plaited shape is turned over so that the unplaited ends are at the bottom. After making certain that the order is correct, plaiting is continued as before. Fig. 33*e* shows the completed plait.

Five, nine and eleven strands can be plaited in the same way.

Eight Plait.—The eight pieces are arranged as for the four, five and six plaits (Fig. 34*a*). The moves are more complicated and are as follows: 8 moves under 7 and over 1. This move is not repeated.

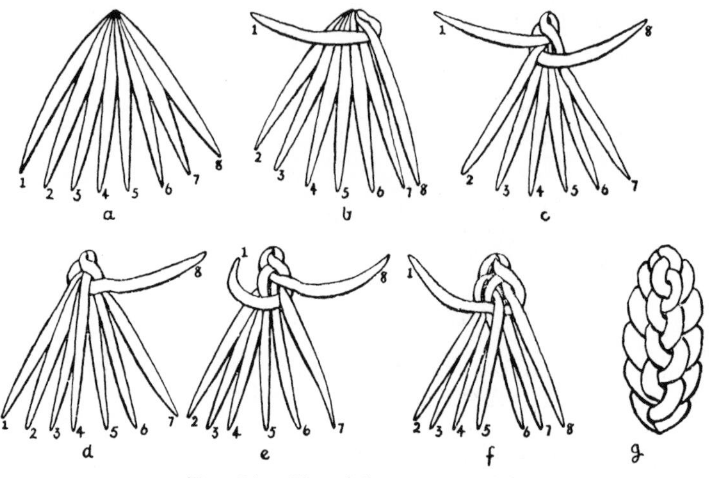

FIG. 34.—The eight-strand plait.

Four moves follow which are repeated until completion. They are: 2 under 3 and over 8, 1 over 4, 7 under 6 and over 1 and 8 over 5. The attention of the student is again drawn to the instructions given in the four plait and that is, the numbering of the strands are from left to right in chronological order, and these numbers remain after each move. Again as an example, after the first move in the eight plait, 8 becomes 1, 7 becomes 8 and 1 becomes 2. Fig. 34*g* shows the completed plait.

All plaits, unless baked in steam, are egg-washed and may be decorated with maw seeds which add to the appearance and flavour.

Most of these shapes can be used to enlarge the range of fancy rolls. In the same way some of the shapes given for fancy rolls can be applied to tea breads.

HARVEST BREAD

In the autumn of the year it is the custom to give thanks for the harvest. For centuries past, loving hands have garlanded and embellished the churches of town and country with the fruits of the earth, and it is fitting that wheat and the harvest loaf has almost always taken pride of place. Quite apart from the symbolism of the loaf, it has a particular interest, for it is nearly always an excellent example of the craftsmanship of the local baker.

Festival bread is an item on the syllabus of all bakery schools. In the final examination of the City and Guilds in breadmaking the student may be expected to make a loaf suitable for a harvest festival. Here are two formulae suitable for modelling any of the shapes described.

(1)	*lb.*	*oz.*	
	2	12	Flour
		1	Yeast
		¾	Salt
	1	6	Water

Dough temperature 75° F.
One hour bulk fermentation.

(2)	*lb.*	*oz.*	
	9	0	Flour
		2	Yeast
		2	Salt
	4	4	Water
		2	Milk powder
		½	Sugar

Dough temperature 78° F.
One hour bulk fermentation.

The Wheatsheaf.—This is probably the most popular shape for a harvest loaf, for not only is it a perfect example of the affinity of wheat to bread, but it is also particularly attractive. The dough is pinned out to about three-quarters of an inch in thickness. With a pointed knife, held at a slant so that the cut edge is bevelled, the shape illustrated (Fig. 35*a*) is cut. After placing it on a baking-sheet it is well washed with water and thoroughly docked. Long thin ropes are cut and rolled from the scrap dough and cut to a length approximating to *a* and *b* in the illustration (Fig. 35*b*). The strands are placed in as natural a position as possible. The rest of the scrap is weighed at 2 oz., each being divided into six pieces. These are rolled up into balls and then elongated to about 1½ in. The pieces are nicked with a pair of scissors, as illustrated (Fig. 35*c*), to form ears. These are arranged on the base (Fig. 35*d*) care being taken that the arrangement is not too formal—nature and the farmer in these matters are not interested in uniformity.

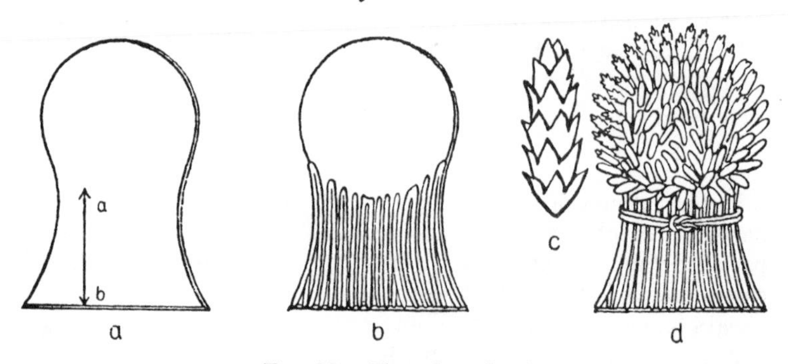

FIG. 35.—The wheatsheaf.

Finish with a few strands round the waist of the shape with a knot in the centre, the ends being tucked underneath. Wash carefully with egg, so that the fissures in the surface are not filled. Bake at 400° F. As an alternative to forming the ears separately, long ropes of dough, the thickness of the ear can be formed, which are nicked along the entire length with the scissors. These can be then cut into 1½-inch pieces, thus the formation of the ears can be effected with a great saving of time.

Loaves and Fishes.—An oval shape with bevelled edges is cut first, washed with water and well docked. A piece of scrap dough is rolled to a rope about 1 inch in thickness, which is then pinned out to a long ribbon about 2 inches in width. This is cut into three strips which are plaited to a length approximating to the circumference of the oval, on which it is fixed with a neat join.

The student will find that by rolling up each strand into spirals as illustrated (Fig. 36*a*) he will be able to plait the long strips quite easily. It will be found that by plaiting strips instead of ropes, the plaits will 'sit' on the edge more securely during baking. Plaited ropes are more likely to move and spoil the shape.

With the edging in position, five cottage loaves are made and notched and then arranged on the oval dish. The two fish are made from a piece of dough that has been pinned out fairly thin. The gills are marked and the tail scored with the point of a knife. The body of the fishes are nicked with scissors in the same way as for the ears of

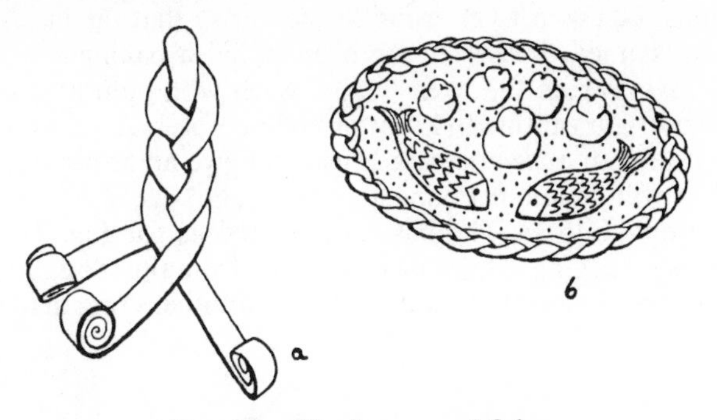

FIG. 36.—The loaves and fishes.

wheat. With the fish in position, the whole is carefully washed with egg and baked at about 420° F. Currants, pressed in firmly, are used for the eyes of the fish. Fig. 36*b* shows the completed piece.

Other Shapes. Illustration Fig. 37. A piece of dough is pinned out to about ½ inch in thickness, from which a circle with a bevelled edge is cut. This is washed with cold water and thoroughly docked. A rope of dough is placed round the edge of the circle and neatly joined. With a sharp pair of scissors the rope is carefully nicked all round. A wedge of dough is placed in the middle of the circle, on which small balls of dough are arranged to form a bunch of grapes.

FIG. 37.—Festival bread.

From the scrap dough the tendrils are formed and placed in position, together with two leaves cut out from dough that has been pinned out quite thin. The veining is marked with the point of a sharp knife. All but the grapes and leaves are carefully egg-washed before it is placed in an oven at 400° F. It is taken out when the shape is properly set and at this stage, the leaves are painted green, the grapes painted mauve and the tendrils picked out with chocolate colour.

Care must be taken when using the colour so that the base or the edge is not stained. Return to the oven to finish baking.

On removing from the oven finally, wash with gum arabic solution—½ oz. of gum arabic to 1 pint of boiling water. A very thin film of fat put on with a *clean* grease brush will give an attractive shine, although it will be less permanent.

Illustration—Fig. 38. The base is prepared as for Fig. 37 except that there is no edging. The wide cross is cut from thin dough, placed in position and washed with water. On this another cross made from

FIG. 38.—Festival bread. Another example.

thin ropes of dough, is superimposed, care being taken to do this neatly. The two small wheatsheaves, the cottage loaf and the baton are made and fixed. The whole is washed with egg and baked at 400° F. It is finished with gum-wash or with the grease brush.

Illustration—Fig. 39. The base is prepared in exactly the same way and edged as for the loaves and fishes. The two stalks are made and

FIG. 39.—Festival bread. A further example.

fixed as illustrated with the wheat ears placed in position. After the cross has been placed in the centre, the whole is finished as in Fig. 38. The designs illustrated (Figs. 37, 38 and 39) were demonstrated by Mr. John Scade, F.Inst.B.B., of the National Bakery School, London.

Large, well made bread shapes such as cottage loaves and fancy bricks or large plaited shapes are also suitable for harvest festival.

Modelling with dough is creative work, and the student may well like to try out some ideas of his own, not necessarily on the theme of harvest thanksgiving, but for other kinds of window showpieces. For instance, the arms of a town may be suitable for practice. Patience will be needed in experimentation, but that is a necessary preliminary to all good craftsmanship. Plate XIII shows some examples of plaited shapes.

CHOLLA BREAD

This interesting type of fancy bread is Jewish in origin. A three-strand plait decorated with maw seeds is sometimes called a cholla; it would appear, however, that the true cholla has a boat-shaped base superimposed on which is a thin string of dough or a thin plait.

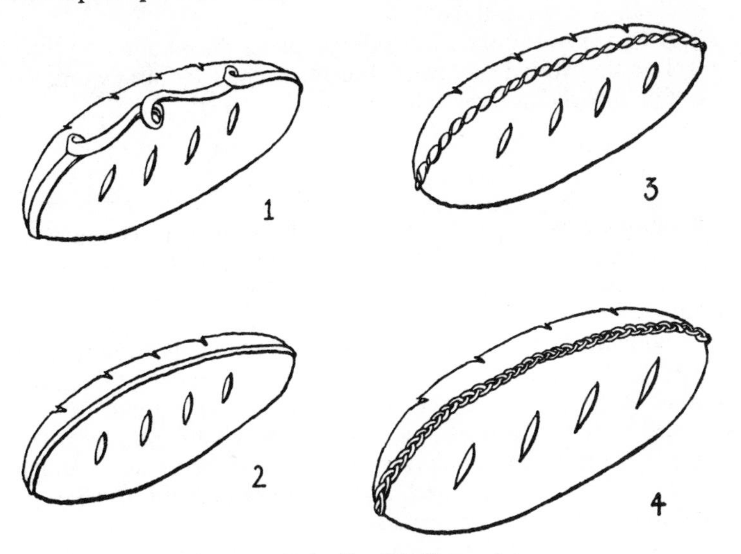

FIG. 40.—Chollas.

There are variations of these, some of which are illustrated (Fig. 40).

The dough from which chollas are made is generally enriched. When properly made the cholla is delightful in appearance and in the eating. In most bakery schools they are on the third or fourth year syllabus in breadmaking, therefore the student should perfect his skill in making them, for he may be called on to produce them in his final breadmaking examination, or more important still he may need to make them in industrial practice.

Here is a formula:

lb.	*oz.*		*lb.*	*oz.*	
3	8	Flour		1½	Fat
	2	Sugar		1	Salt
	1½	Yeast	1	10	Water (approx.)
	4	Egg			

Dough temperature 78° F.
Scale in 2 hr.
Knock back at 1½ hr.
Yield six at 15 oz.

After moulding, chollas are washed with diluted egg and proved in very little steam. Before baking they are given four or five small diagonal cuts on each side with a sharp knife or blade. They may be sprinkled with maw seeds.

The finish of the chollas illustrated is as follows:

(1) A thin strip of dough is placed on the moistened top of the cholla and given three twists.
(2) A thin single strand of dough completes this cholla.
(3) Two thin strands are twisted together and fixed firmly on top.
(4) For this cholla three thin strands are plaited.

HOTPLATE GOODS

The hotplate can trace its ancestry back through the centuries to prehistoric times, when men baked on hot stones, turning their rough cakes of bread over to finish baking when they were sufficiently set, so that they could be moved without breaking.

The hotplate, like the prehistoric stones, bakes only from the hot surface, unlike an oven where additional heat is radiated from the sides and the crown. This is the reason why hotplate goods have to be turned over to finish baking. Because the heat comes from the surface of the metal plate only, any tendency for the batter or dough to flow is immediately arrested. For this reason almost all hotplate goods must be softer in consistency.

It is advisable to have two plates, one for muffins and crumpets which must be baked on a burnished surface free from grease, and one for goods containing sugar, when the plate must be greased. If there is only one plate available, it becomes necessary to clean off the greasy plate thoroughly, before attempting to bake crumpets. To effect this a bath brick can be used for scouring or a furnace brick can be used with a mixture of salt and fine sand. In both cases the plate is given a final polish with either paper or a clean cloth. The work is hard and hot, but necessary especially for crumpets, for grease will result in heaviness rather than in the beautiful honey comb structure so characteristic of the properly made crumpet.

The hotplate should be placed in such a position that it is away from draughts, otherwise the products may well be spoiled. Unless a thermometer is fitted, great care must be taken when commencing to bake, for a plate too hot will not only spoil the goods but lead to extra work in re-cleaning the plate.

Here is a recipe for muffins:

lb.	*oz.*		*lb.*	*oz.*	
3	8	Strong flour		½	Sugar
	1	Salt		½	Fat
	1½	Yeast	2	8	Water (100° F.)

Knock back at 1 hr. Scale at 1½ hr.
Weigh at 3 oz. Yield thirty.

Make up the dough (which is very slack) and toughen it well When ready and scaled, mould the muffins up round. This will not be easy for the inexperienced, because of the slackness of the dough. The rounded muffins are proved in boxes thickly dusted with cones (rice flour) or on boards dusted in the same way.

When ready for baking, they are lifted carefully, and placed into muffins rings on the plate. The rings are lightly greased and placed on the plate immediately before baking is commenced. Turn each muffin over when the bottom is sufficiently coloured. When baked, remove from the rings and brush off the cones that may still be attached to the muffins. Plate XIV (*left*).

Here is a recipe for crumpets:

lb.	*oz.*		*lb.*	*oz.*	
2	8	Flour		5	Water
2	8	Water (100° F.)		¾	Salt
	1½	Yeast		⅛	Bicarbonate of soda.

Stand for 45 min. and add: water, salt and bicarb. soda.
Let stand a further 15 min.

Lightly grease the crumpet rings; this should be done with a greasy cloth so that there is not an excess of grease which would run down on to the burnished plate. Place the rings on the plate. Ladle a sufficient quantity of batter into each ring. It is advisable to hold a small bread pan under the ladle to catch any drips. When the crumpets have holed nicely, they are turned so that they may brown very lightly on the other side, just enough to take away the appearance of rawness. Plate XIV (*right*).

Remove on to a cloth, and proceed to fill the second lot of rings. The first baking can be removed from the rings and packed; the rings can be slightly greased if necessary, and are then ready for further use. The water content given is approximate; the consistency of the batter can be adjusted when adding the final quantity of water.

The essential difference between muffins and crumpets is in the water content. The muffin is in effect made from a very slack dough while crumpets are made from a batter.

CHEMICALLY AERATED BREAD

The quickest way to make bread is to mix flour, salt, baking powder and water or milk together, place the resultant dough in a tin and put it straight into the oven. While fairly good bread can be made by this method, it will be entirely different from yeast fermented bread, for baking-powder will aerate only and has little or no effect on the gluten structure. The student will know that yeast has a dual function in fermentation, the production of gas and the conditioning of gluten during the fermentation period. The resultant bread, if fermentation is correctly controlled, will have good volume and shape, a healthy looking crust and a bright, soft, stable crumb.

With this understanding and with the requisite technical knowledge, good bread, however, can be made by means of chemical aeration. A medium strong flour of good colour is advisable and for this Australian flour is ideal for the purpose, for the gluten of a flour of this type offers less resistance in the oven to the expansion of gas from the baking powder and so a loaf of fairly good volume can be expected.

If, however, an initial lactic ferment is used, even better bread can be produced, for lactic acid has a maturing effect on gluten, rendering it more extensible and certainly conferring softness on the crumb. The addition of lard will confer flavour which is not developed as a result of chemical aeration.

A slack dough is required to effect maximum gas production and a lower baking temperature is necessary so that even expansion is assured before crust development.

If the loaves are washed and floured and given a deep cut to assist expansion before placing into the tins, quite attractive bread will result.

Irish soda bread is chemically aerated and this is effected by the use of bicarbonate of soda, the acid component coming from the buttermilk with which the bread was traditionally mixed. Buttermilk is rich in lactic acid, thus the maximum gas production is assured and the gluten matured by the excess acid present.

Scottish farls are another type of chemically aerated bread; these are greatly improved by the use of an initial lactic ferment. Both Irish soda bread and Scottish farls are included in the syllabuses of bakery schools and the student must expect questions on them or be expected to make them in City and Guilds examinations.

Here are recipes for chemically aerated white tin bread, soda bread and farls:

(1) *Tin bread*

Lactic ferment

lb.	*oz.*	
1	4	Cold fresh milk
	10	Soft flour

Let stand 30 min. in a temperature at 70° F.

Dough

lb.	*oz.*	
1	0	Australian flour
	½	Salt
	½	Syrup
	1½	Lard
	1	Baking-powder

Make up into a soft dough, weigh and mould. Wash with diluted egg, dust with flour and after giving a deep cut, place into tins. Bake at 420° F. Yield three at 1 lb.

(2) *Irish soda bread*

lb.	*oz.*	
1	12	Soda bread flour
	¼	Salt
	½	Bicarbonate of soda
	1½	Lard
1	4	Buttermilk (approx.)

Make up into a soft dough, weigh and mould round. They may be baked in this shape or slightly flattened. Bake at 420° F. Yield three at 1 lb.

(3) *Wheatmeal farl*

Lactic ferment

lb.	*oz.*	
1	10	Cold fresh milk
	6	White flour
	12	Wheatmeal

Let stand 60 min. in a temperature at 80° F.

Dough

lb.	*oz.*	
	14	Wheatmeal
	½	Salt
	¾	Syrup
	2	Lard
	2	Egg
	1½	Baking-powder

Make up into a soft dough and mould up round. Pin out to about 12 in. Place on a baking sheet and cut into four similar to a round of scones. Wash, dust with flour and dock. Let stand for 20 min. and bake at 410° F. Yield one round at 4 lb.

MILK BREAD

As the student will have learned (page 112), the standard for milk bread has been laid down by regulation. It is probable that questions on this subject will appear on a written examination paper and its manufacture must be expected as a possible item in a practical examination.

Here is a formula and the instructions for making and finishing milk bread. The ferment and dough process is used.

Ferment

lb	*oz.*	
1	3	Water (90°F.)
	1	Yeast
	¼	Sugar
	8	Flour
	2¾	Full cream milk powder

Dough

lb.	*oz.*	
2	0	Flour
	2	Fat
	½	Salt
	5	Water (approx.)

The ferment is allowed to stand until it drops. To make up the dough, rub the fat into the flour, dissolve the salt in the water and add the solution to the ferment. Add the flour and make into a fairly

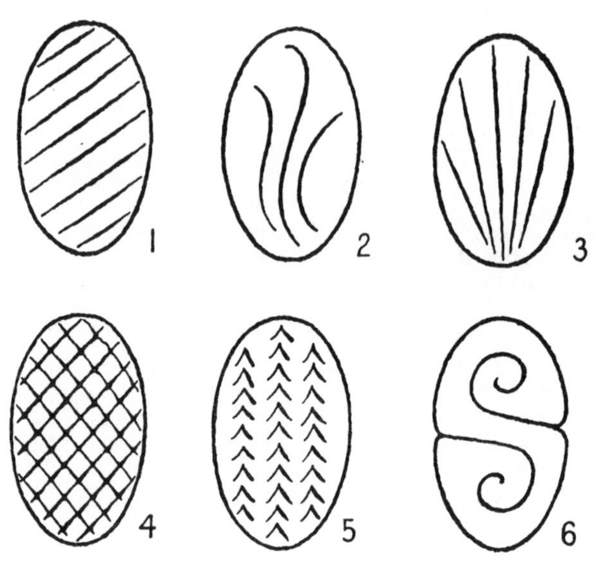

FIG. 41.—Milk bread. Decorative cutting.

soft dough. Knock back after an hour and scale after another 30 min. There will be a yield of four loaves scaled at 1 lb. each.

After scaling, the dough pieces are handed up, covered with a cloth and allowed to recover from the manipulation. When fully expanded they are moulded and placed on to a clean baking-sheet, washed with diluted egg, cut, and covered with oval or oblong tins. One piece is placed upside down in a tin so that the final proving can be watched. When ready this one is turned over like the rest.

Because lactose (milk sugar) is sparingly fermentable by yeast, and is in consequence left in the dough, increasing the crust colour, milk bread must not be baked in a temperature normal to ordinary bread. The temperature should be lower and the baking time increased.

The drawings (Fig. 41) illustrate some cutting designs for milk bread. The student must remember that this is a form of decoration to enhance the appearance of the loaf, therefore it must be done carefully.

(1) Parallel lines.
(2) Three shallow cuts in the form of curves.
(3) Five fan-shaped cuts.
(4) Trellis design.
(5) Herring-bone finish. This is done by nicking the dough with a corner of the blade.
(6) The dough piece is pinned out to a long ribbon about 8 in. wide, and folded over into three, lengthways, so that there is a ribbon of dough about 2½ in. to 3 in. wide. This is then folded up into an 'S' shape. It is then washed, and placed into a tin which is not turned over.

Plate XV illustrates a very fine milk loaf.

FRUIT BREADS

In his practical work, the student will be introduced to a variety of fruit breads and he will almost certainly be expected to make one or more of the varieties in his practical examinations, or to answer questions pertaining to them on a written paper.

Fruit breads can be considered doubly enriched, for not only do they contain added fat, milk and sugar, but fruit also. The fruit can be of one kind, a mixture of fruits, or the addition can be a mixture of fruit and nuts. Wheatmeal instead of white flour can be used to make further variety.

Bun Loaves.—Strictly speaking, bun loaves are not fruited bread; they are as the name implies, made from a fruited bun dough. Any good bun dough containing currants and finely chopped peel will do (page 22).

The pieces are generally weighed about 12 oz. each, moulded up, egg-washed and placed into square or oval tins. When baked (at about 430° F.) they are given a further glazing with bun wash. Plate XVI illustrates bun loaves.

Currant Bread.—There is less sugar and fat in currant bread compared with bun loaves. Here is a formula and the method of making:

lb.	*oz.*		*lb.*	*oz.*	
2	2	Flour		1½	Sugar
	1	Milk powder		4	Oil or shortening
	1½	Yeast	1	4	Water
	½	Salt		10	Currants

The dough is made up at a temperature of 80° F., and allowed to ferment for 30 min. The warmed currants are then carefully folded in. Excessive pressure must not be used or the currants will 'bleed' and stain the dough. After a further 30 min. the dough is scaled at 14 oz.; there will be a yield of five. They are moulded, washed with egg and placed into square or oval tins or in coburg pans. The student may be asked to bake them on the oven sole, in that case the dough will be made a little tighter and the final proof will be a little less. The baking temperature is approximately 450° F.

Sultana or Raisin Bread.—The same dough can be used as for currant bread, sultanas or raisins being used instead of currants.

Walnut and Raisin Bread.—The combination of fruit and nuts in bread is a delight, not only because they both add to the food value of the loaf, but because the combination of flavours is so attractive to the palate. Almonds can be used instead of walnuts to make a further variety. Here is a formula and the method of making:

lb.	*oz.*		*lb.*	*oz.*	
2	0	Flour		1½	Yeast
	2	Shortening	1	4	Water
	2	Sugar	1	0	Raisins
	1	Milk powder		6	Walnuts or almonds
	½	Salt			

The temperature of the finished dough is 78° F., and it is allowed to ferment for 30 min. before the fruit and nuts are carefully folded in. After a further 30 min. the dough is scaled at 15 oz. and there will be a yield of five. The pieces can be moulded up into a variety of shapes or may be plaited. They are carefully egg-washed and after final proof are baked at 420–440° F. Plate XVII shows walnut and raisin bread.

Stollen.—With the growing introduction and popularity of some types of continental breads and confectionery, the student may be expected to make something similar in his final examinations.

XIV Muffins and crumpets

XV A very fine milk loaf

XVI Bun loaves

XVII Walnut and raisin bread

XVIII Stollen

Stollen is a rich tea bread, and even if not mentioned by name, an examination paper may have as an item a rich tea bread of this type. In this way the ingenuity of the student will be tested together with his knowledge of fermentation and the use of raw materials in the fermentation process.

Stollen is a great favourite in many European countries. It is of Saxon origin, although it is now made in countries all over middle Europe—in Holland, Germany, Russia, Austria and Scandinavia. The bread has a religious background going back through the centuries. History suggests that the characteristic stollen shape is that of the Holy crib.

Dresden and Leipzig are the historical centres, and from these cities stollen is exported to Germanic peoples all over the world. There are two shapes, the oval and the baton, each with the characteristic crease down the centre, and finished either with vanilla icing sugar or with a fondant or water icing glaze. They may have different fillings, such as mixed fruit, cherries, marzipan, praline nougat, almonds and walnuts etc., Stollen can be weighed and made in various sizes from 8 oz. to about 4 lb.

Here is a formula for the famous Weihnachtstollen (Christmas stollen).

Ferment

lb.	*oz.*	
1	4	Milk
	5	Yeast
	1	Sugar
	10	Flour

The ferment is allowed to stand until it drops.

Dough

lb.	*oz.*	
2	0	Flour
		Salt
	12	Butter
	3	Brown sugar
	8	Currants
	4	Chopped mixed peel
1	8	Sultanas
	4	Chopped cherries
	1	Rum
		Zest of one lemon

When the ferment has dropped, make up the rest of the materials, except the fruit, into a fairly tight dough. Let it ferment until ripe (about 1–1½ hrs). The fruit is then carefully pulled in and the dough is weighed into pieces of 10 oz. The pieces are then moulded into oval or baton shapes and allowed to recover, covering with a damp cloth to prevent skinning.

The stollen are prepared by taking each in turn and pressing down the centre with a rolling-pin, rolling to and fro a little, several times. The two thick unpinned edges are folded over, one on top of the other. If they are of baton shape they are placed directly on to baking sheets. The oval shapes are given a crescent shape as they are placed on to the baking sheets by bringing the ends slightly forwards towards the thick lips. They may be washed with egg before being carefully proved. Bake very carefully indeed at 410° F. Brush with melted butter as they are drawn from the oven.

When cool, dredge with vanilla icing sugar, or brush over with thin, vanilla flavoured fondant into which a little cornflour has been stirred. The stollen illustrated (Plate XVIII) has a rope of marzipan placed in the centre before folding over.

17

Moulds; Flour Spoliage: Infestation; Retardation of Fermented Goods; Deep Freezing Bakery Products

MOULDS

Moulds are members of the fungi group of plants. They develop from air-borne spores that are so small that they can only be seen with the help of the microscope. When the spores alight on a substance where there are suitable conditions for growth, they germinate and grow and we see them as patches of mould.

Just as there are different seeds for different plants so also are there different and characteristic spores for each type of mould. Investigation has shown that there are not less than fifteen different moulds that can cause spoliage of bread.

Moulds develop first on the crust of an uncut loaf, but for this to happen there must be moisture present. Once on the crust, and given time, the growth will continue into the crumb by penetration, generally at the oven break or through cracks in the crust. If the student will carefully cut a loaf into which internal moulds have developed, he will often see quite distinctly, the channel by which the moulds have entered.

It will be readily seen that conditions of humidity where bread is stored, is of the utmost importance when considering mould formation. The crust of well baked bread is comparatively dry and mould therefore will not develop. If, however, conditions favour moisture condensation on the crust of the bread either as a result of insufficient cooling or bad storage conditions, then the formation of moulds is inevitable, unless the air in the storage room has been filtered to remove fungal spores.

With an understanding of the conditions leading to mould formation, the student will have a greater understanding of the problem in connection with wrapped bread. A moment's reflection will pinpoint the importance of correct cooling conditions both in regard to the temperature and the humidity figures.

If the bread is sliced before wrapping, two other factors arise, firstly that a greater surface area of the loaf is exposed, and secondly, by its nature, the crumb exposed is a better media for mould growth than the drier crust. This brings into focus another important point and that is the necessity for cleanliness, for the spores will lodge upon conveyors, racks, cutting blades and wrapping paper and may cause spoliage rapidly when conveyed to the bread, more especially as the bread wrapper will act as an ideal incubator if the spores and conditions for growth are present.

Proprionic acid at the maximum levels of 13.4 oz. per sack, or, sodium proprionate 17.4 oz per sack, or calcium proprionate 16.9 oz. per sack, can now be used in bread as mould inhibitors. This, however, does not absolve the baker from the responsibility of ensuring hygienic conditions in the bakery.

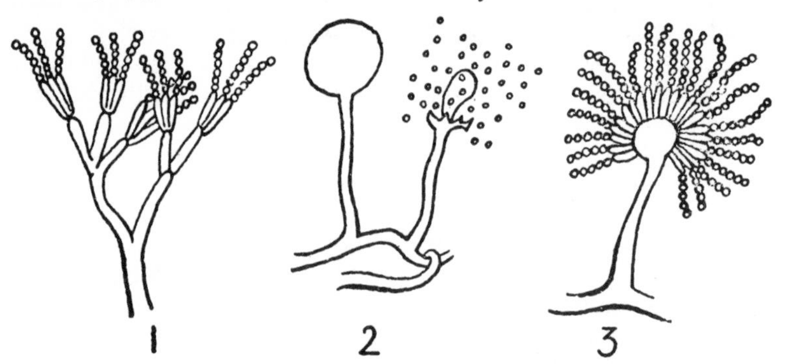

FIG. 42.—Moulds. Three examples.

Air filtration plants have been installed in large bakeries and special attention is paid to wall surfaces, where it is found that a smooth surface created by the use of a hard, glossy, mould-resistant paint will keep the mould spore population at a minimum, even although this type of surface is conducive to condensation.

Cakes, because of their different composition, are less liable to spoliage than bread, small cakes being even less liable than the larger units like slab cakes.

Not all mould development on bakery products is the result of neglect or carelessness in the bakery, for many complaints can be traced to storage conditions in the purchaser's home. This, however, can only be established tactfully by an experienced person. The finest preventative, undoubtedly, is a quick sale of oven fresh goods and it is here that the small craftsman baker, with technical knowledge, will have less worry than his larger competitor.

Here are illustrations (Fig. 42) of the three most common moulds found on bakery products.

(1) The common blue-green mould, Penicillium glaucum. The name Penicillium comes from the generic word, penicil, meaning a brush-like arrangement. The illustration shows the round spores in this formation.

(2) The white mould, like fine gossamer. On the *left* is seen the spore case before it bursts (*right*) scattering the spores into the air. This is the mould, Mucor mucedo.

(3) The Aspergillus niger. This is the black pin-head mould.

FLOUR SPOLIAGE AND INFESTATION

Flour should be sound and sweet, free of any foreign odour or flavour, free of insect pests and contain no deleterious extraneous matter whatsoever. Apart from extraneous matter, flour goes out of condition by becoming musty, or absorbing off-flavours through faulty storage, insect infestation, or by the gluten losing its cohesive quality.

Extraneous Matter.—Foreign seeds. Drs. Kent-Jones and Amos in *Modern Cereal Chemistry*, have recorded more than 150 types of foreign seed taken from samples of wheat submitted to their laboratory. Every care is taken at the mill to remove all unwanted seeds before milling takes place, but cases have been known of small seed tailing over the wheat when the sieve has been blocked. The seed enters the mill-stream and the flour can become tainted.

Kent-Jones and Amos list ten as being the more common or important and six of these are important to the student, for the purpose of answering a possible question on this subject.

Melilot.—A very small oval-shaped seed found mainly in wheats from the Argentine and the U.S.S.R., giving flour and bread a pronounced flavour and aroma of new-mown hay or cherry wood.

Charlock.—A seed contaminant common to most wheats. If a large proportion reaches the mill-stream, a strong aroma of mustard may be imparted to the flour.

Wild Radish.—Another seed contaminant found in most wheats and liable to impart an acrid flavour if milled with the wheat into flour.

Darnel.—Considered to be the 'tares' of the Scriptures. They are considered harmless unless a fungus is present, when a toxin temulin, can kill certain animals and cause serious illness to human beings.

Corncocle.—This seed contains a slightly toxic substance, a saponin, which is not destroyed by the baking process. It is a seed common to most wheats.

Bur Parsley.—This seed has been separated from European wheat in which it is fairly common. It has toxic properties that can cause the death of animals.

Garlic.—Alternatively known as wild onion. This seed is common to European wheats and confers a distinct smell and taste of onion to flour.

Vetches.—These are found in most European wheats and if milled with the wheat, produces black spots in the flour.

Indelible Pencil.—Complaints of violet-blue spots in bread have been made to millers in the past, although it has by no means been common. Investigation has shown that the spots are caused by tiny particles of indelible lead from pencils that have been sharpened near wheat or flour. The use of indelible pencils is now prohibited in flour mills. The student should bear in mind that this type of pencil should not be used in the bakery.

Bacterial Infection: Rope.—The bacillus Subtilis mesentericus is responsible for the condition in bread known as 'rope'. It is a soil-borne organism that is not destroyed during baking. It develops in the baked loaf under favourable conditions of temperature and humidity, starting as a brown spot, finally turning the crumb into a nauseating sticky mess. It is inhibited by increasing the acidity of the dough. The bacillus can be identified by the use of a high powered microscope.

Bleeding Bread.—It is known by this name because of the development of a red pigment in the crumb of the loaf. The bacteria responsible are individuals of Erythro prodigiosus, seen as small rods under the microscope. The disease is extremely rare in this country.

Fungoid Infestation: Rust.—In its several forms rust attacks the growing wheat. The grain produced is small and shrivelled with a low yield per bushel.

Smut or Bunt.—The fungus enters the grain causing some malformation. Black spores with a fishy smell take the place of the endosperm. When broken, the spores blacken uninfected grain and impart the smell.

Ergot.—This fungoid covers the grain with a dark purple mass. It contains the alkaloid toxins, ergotoxine and ergotanimine. To the human or animal body, it is gangrenous and produces uncontrolled nervous spasms. In sufficient amount it is lethal. Ergot can be detected microscopically in flour and bread, and by colorimetric test.

Insect Pests: Wheat Bug.—This pest punctures the wheat grain, introducing an enzyme which breaks up the cohesive property of the gluten. A small dough made from the infected flour will disintegrate within 3–4 hr. when immersed in cold water. A sound gluten under similar conditions will retain its stability for 24 hr.

Weevils.—The damage to stored grain by this pest each year costs many millions of pounds. The female bores into the grain and lays its eggs, and the grubs feed on the endosperm. The adults themselves bore into fresh grain to feed themselves. Weevils can be detected by careful scrutiny after the flour has been sieved on to a smooth slab.

Flour Moth.—This is one of the most troublesome of pests. The larva spins a silken thread which in time covers the whole surface of the flour. The larva is readily seen by the naked eye, having a pinkish body with a few small black dots. The moth has grey wings with black wavy lines.

Mites.—These can be detected by smoothing some flour on a slab. If the smooth surface after a time is found to be roughened by small round heaps, then mites are present. This can be verified by sieving through a fine sieve and examining the tails by the use of a magnifying glass. Flour infested with mites has a pungent odour.

Meal Worms.—These are found mainly in wholemeal and wheatmeal flours stored in dark and damp conditions.

There are other insect pests that may infest the bakery, of which cockroaches, crickets, silver fish and flies may be mentioned. Modern methods of hygiene, however, together with modern insecticides and sprays have largely eliminated them from the well managed bakery.

The use of a machine known as an entoleter in flour mills and bakeries has reduced the spoliage ot flour from insect infestation. The flour is passed into the machine where it is subjected to centrifugal force which destroys both eggs and insects.

Filth.—Microscopic examination may show rodent hairs, droppings and insect fragments. Bad storage conditions may be responsible. This must be treated as a matter of urgency.

Proximity Contamination.—Flour will quickly absorb strong odours and care must be taken in transit and in storage. The author remembers bread, straight from the oven, with a pronounced odour of peardrops. Investigation proved that the flour had been transported in railway trucks heavily contaminated with amyl acetate.

RETARDATION OF FERMENTED DOUGHS

The conservation of food by the use of low temperatures is not new. History records the use of snow and ice by the ancient Chinese and by the Romans. Wherever and whenever snow and ice were available, then this method has been used. In our own country for centuries past, ice pits have been made, into which winter ice has been packed, using straw and earth as insulation materials. In this way perishable foods could be preserved during the summer months.

Modern refrigeration is a scientific development of these earlier practices and is now playing an increasing part in the conservation of food. Refrigeration is merely the removal of a certain quantity of heat, so that control can be effected of temperatures low enough to arrest the natural processes that lead to spoliage and decay.

The student should be quite clear on what is meant by dough retardation and quick freezing when these terms are applied to bakery products. Retardation simply means the arresting of fermentation activity by holding dough in bulk or in smaller made-up units at a temperature between 34–38° F. At these temperatures yeast activity practically ceases. Retardation of fermented dough is not new, for the principle has been used in continental countries for many years, chiefly in the production of sweet yeast goods like Danish Pastries. These can be made up, placed on to baking-sheets and held at a low temperature until required for baking, finishing and despatch to the sales counter.

Rich doughs are more successfully retarded than those of lower quality because, as the student will know, fermentation is slower, due to the effect of enriching agents. Experience has shown that the richer doughs can be held successfully for up to 72 hours against a time limit of about 48 hours for doughs less rich.

There are two methods that can be used for retarding dough:

(1) After the dough has been given 50–75% of bulk fermentation, it is weighed into 8–10 lb. pieces, rolled into sheets and refrigerated to about 34–38° F. If the refrigerator is maintained at 85% relative humidity or over, there will be no crusting; otherwise, the dough pieces should be put into polythene bags. The dough pieces should not be stacked one upon another in the refrigerator, but placed singly on trays or on a shelf. When required, the dough is removed and brought to bakery temperature, made up, proved and baked, in the usual way.

(2) With the second method, the dough is given the same bulk fermentation as before (50–75%). It is made up in the usual way and placed in unit pieces in baking tins or on baking sheets as the case may be, and placed immediately into the refrigerator. When required they are removed and brought to bakery temperature, proved and baked. Final proof should never be forced.

In either of the above methods, the dough should be cool initially or there will be an increased load on the refrigator unit. High dough temperatures will, in addition, extend the fermentation before retarding is effective.

Both methods are commercially sound; the first giving the baker the opportunity of producing a variety of goods fairly quickly with less refrigerating space. The second method allows for rapid production of freshly baked goods, but of course, more refrigeration space is needed. Oven freshness is assured by the use of either or both methods.

To summarize:

(1) Retardation is the arresting of fermentation by the use of low temperatures between 34–38° F.

(2) The process can be carried out in two ways—
 (*a*) the retarding of dough in 8–10 lb. pieces, sheeted to ensure the rapid extraction of heat.
 (*b*) the retarding of unit pieces ready for baking.

(3) It gives the baker the opportunity of banking surplus production towards week-end and holiday demands.

(4) The lengthening of the period between making and baking gives the opportunity of intermittent fresh bakings.

(5) Retardation ensures oven freshness.

DEEP FREEZING BAKERY PRODUCTS

Deep freezing is different from retardation in that the products are quickly and deeply frozen: retardation in relation to bakery practice is the suspension of fermentation activity by holding dough either in bulk or in made up units, at temperatures between 34 and 38° F.

Deep freezing is the practice of holding in a completely frozen condition:

(1) Products baked and ready for sale.

(2) Baked products that are to be decorated or finished after defrosting.

(3) Unbaked goods.

Regarding bread, the student will know that staling can be considered in two parts—firstly crust staling, when some of the moisture from the crumb is retained by the crust in its passage to the atmosphere. This retention under certain conditions, renders the crust tough and 'leathery'. Secondly, within the crumb, there is a shift of moisture from the starch to the protein. In new bread the starch cells are soft and elastic, holding the maximum of water. The starch at this stage is termed alpha starch; as the temperature lowers it becomes unstable, changing to a mixture of alpha and beta starch. This change in starch is a chemical change. Beta starch holds less water and some of it is exuded and taken up by the protein, this being a physical change known as syneresis.

The temperature range of staling is approximately between 75–23° F. At 23° F. the water content of bread begins to freeze the salt in bread being responsible for a lower freezing figure as compared to water. Staling is more rapid between 30–40° F. It now becomes clear why rapid freezing is important in arresting the staling process in bread and rolls, for if the baked products can be rapidly reduced in temperature below the staling zone to a point where the moisture freezes, then syneresis and the physical changes consequent on it cannot occur.

The rate of freezing has another important aspect, for it is known that the size of the ice crystal is related to the rate at which the temperature is lowered; the higher the rate the smaller will be the crystal size. If refrigeration is carried out slowly, not only will there be relatively larger local deposits of moisture present on defrosting, but the large crystals will also cause injury to the structure of the products.

The humidity of the freezing chamber is important, for a low temperature may cause dehydration during the period before the freezing point is reached. It is established that a relative humidity figure of approximately 80% is necessary.

To reduce the load on the refrigerator unit it is essential to bring the temperature of baked goods to that of the room as quickly as possible. This can be carried out normally on racks. The time necessary for cooling, will of course, depend on several things such as room temperature, the size and density of the product. The freezing rate will also depend on the size and character of the produce to be frozen and also upon the loading in relation to the capacity of the refrigerator, and on the circulation of air within it. Here are some comparative figures for the student's notebook:

Small items: 30/90 min. from room temperature to 0° F.

1 *lb. loaves:* about 4 hr. from room temperature to 0° F.

1¾ *lb. loaves:* about 6 hr. from room temperature to 0° F.

Cakes stale more rapidly at increasing temperatures, therefore the necessity for such rapid cooling to room temperature as for bread does not arise, neither is it necessary to equip with the powerful freezing equipment so necessary when bread is to be frozen.

Loading and Storage

Loading and storage should be done systematically if the maximum efficiency is to be expected from the freezing unit. Firstly, the freezer should not be overloaded, and it should be of a size to fit the amount of produce to be frozen and/or production so controlled to suit the freezing capacity of the unit.

To minimize strain on the freezing unit by the continuous opening of the doors, goods to be frozen should be assembled first, then placed directly in the cold air currents to freeze rapidly. When completely frozen they can be stacked in another part of the freezer at a holding temperature. A method of keeping the products dated and under rotation control then obviously becomes desirable.

Every cubic inch of space in the unit costs money, therefore it must be used to the best advantage and consideration must be given to the means of carrying the goods to be frozen. There are three methods:

(1) *Racks.*—The bakery trays will prevent the free circulation of air resulting in slower freezing. In addition the ratio of rack space to goods frozen must be considered. With plenty of baking trays available it has the advantage of minimum handling from oven to freezer.

(2) *Fitted Shelves or Racks.*—Again there is the disadvantage of space used against the amount of goods frozen. The packing trays also prevent the free circulation of cold air. It has the advantage however that the packed trays can be removed for defrosting and the goods transported to the sales point without further handling.

(3) *Wire Baskets.*—Wire baskets which can be nested and put on small trolleys are ideal for using space efficiently and at the same time ensuring the unimpeded circulation of air. This is a considerable advantage outweighed only by the fact that the products require extra handling.

Defrosting

When required for sale or for further processing, the products must be efficiently defrosted. Where bread is concerned the same precautions must be observed when freezing, for it must be rapidly taken through the staling temperature range to 70–75° F. This can be done in a warm part of the bakery, or in a recovery room fitted with defrosting units circulating warm forced air at 100° F. at a relative humidity of 50%. A 1¾ lb. loaf will be completely defrosted under these conditions in about 90 min.

The student will be interested to learn that for each 1 lb. of bread defrosted, approximately 100 B.Th.U's are required. It can be seen that with bulk defrosting a considerable source of heat is required. Here again humidity is important or there will be excessive condensation.

The 'flash-off' method of defrosting certain goods such as Vienna bread and rolls has adherents. This is effected by returning the goods straight from the freezer to the oven for a few minutes. The efficacy of this method however can be decided by trial and error experiment.

Freezing Cake Batters

The question of hygiene becomes of paramount importance when considering the deep freezing of unbaked cake batters either for sale in foil containers unbaked or for baking before sale.

The student will know that refrigeration within limits will suspend the activity of bacteria. It will not destroy them, there being a resumption of activity when the temperature conditions again reach the optimum. While of course, thorough baking will destroy harmful bacteria, there is always a possibility of danger from batters that have not been quickly frozen to —35° F. and subsequently underbaked.

Batters should be baked directly after removal from the freezer; certainly within four hours after leaving the unit.

What can be Frozen?

The student must understand that possession of a deep freeze does not mean that anything and everything can be frozen successfully. Some products can be frozen satisfactorily while others are not so tolerant. Here is a list of products tolerant to deep freezing:

Tolerant

1. Bread and Rolls	(B)
2. Morning Goods—especially fermented scones	(B & U)
3. Short and Puff Pastry	(B & U)
4. Biscuits and Shortbreads	(B & U)
5. Almond Goods	(B)
6. Batters	(U) Provided metal containers and baking tins are properly maintained.
7. Buns and Soft tea breads	(B)
8. Bath Buns	(B & U)
9. Doughnuts—fried	
10. Fillings	(B & U)
11. Fruit Pies	(U)

(B—Baked; U—Unbaked)

Those less tolerant

1. Vienna bread (B & U).

Investigation and experimentation is necessary for satisfactory results. For baked goods a 'flash' defrosting in an oven at 370–400° F. for about 6–8 min. is suggested. For unbaked goods there should be no proof after shaping. A limited time in a steam prover before proving will prevent blistering.

2. Buns and Soft tea breads (U).

   The same procedure as above is suggested.

3. Icings, Chocolate Pastes and fillings.

   Baked cakes covered with almond and sugar pastes are not successfully frozen because of the effects of condensation. Fondant and parfait icings and decorated cakes are not successfully frozen for the same reason although in some cases this can be prevented by wrapping. Custards tend to separate and jellies to crack.

Deep Freeze Installations

These can be built to any size and competent advice is freely available from refrigeration engineers.

There are two types:

(i) *Reach-in cabinets.*—These will hold anything from 20–100 baking sheets and are useful in small bakeries.

(ii) *Wheel-in units.*—These are designed for wheeling in racks or trolleys and are built with or without air-locks. The purpose of an air-lock which is the space between the outer and inner door to the freezer is to reduce the flow of warm humid air into the chamber when the inner door is opened for loading. If the flow is not prevented there will be a temperature rise which will add to the running costs. In addition there will be a rapid frost formation both on the evaporator and on frozen goods. This causes loss of efficiency in the freezer and the possibility of condensation on goods when removed for defrosting. Again, there will be a tendency to fogginess within the chamber after an intake of moist warm air. With an air-lock the goods can be wheeled in and the outer door closed before the freezer door is opened. The air-lock space is useful for the short period storage of eggs and creams.

There are several disadvantages such as the necessity for extra space with an increased initial cost. It is also difficult to operate properly. For these reasons, freezers are now being fitted without them, by installing automatic defrosters within the freezing chamber, and fitting the door with an air curtain which prevents cold air escaping and warm air from entering. Provided that bakery and freezer have the same floor levels, racks and trolleys can be wheeled in and out with ease.

For the student interested in figures, here are some approximations:

A 1,000 cu. ft. freezer 10′ × 15′ × 7′ high will hold 1,500–2,000 lb. of products, 1,500 cu. ft.—2,600 lb., 3,750 cu. ft.—8000 lb., 95 cu. ft. cabinet—250 lb.

Costs vary and the following are only given as a rough guide (1958):

95 cu. ft. cabinet	£500
1,000 cu. ft. room	£2,000
3,750 cu. ft. room	£5,000

The electrical operation cost of a cabinet would be approximately 20–24 units per day, 1,500 cu. ft. room, 120 units, and 2,200 cu. ft. room, 150 units.

In conclusion, the student must remember that the practice of deep freeze for bakery products is comparatively new. Changes will take place in equipment and procedure as more is learned by continued research and experience.

Deep freeze is an addition to bakery equipment and should be fully understood if it is to be part of planned production.

Lastly, it must be understood there is no magic about it for while efficiently used it will retard the onset and process of staling, it cannot be expected to rejuvenate goods that have already gone stale.

18

Physical Methods of Dough Testing: History; Dynamic and Static Tests; Hagberg Number

PHYSICAL METHODS OF DOUGH TESTING

FLOUR quality can be assessed by chemical analysis and by actual baking tests. Baking tests, however, depend largely on the assessments of the test baker concerned. It is obvious that if it were possible to make accurate measurements of the physical qualities of flour when it is made into dough, and the changes that dough undergoes during fermentation, in order to assist or to supplement the important work of the test baker, it would be extremely useful.

Apparatus designed to evaluate gluten have been in use for many years and at the present time have reached a high degree of efficiency.

Historical.—Tibor (1933) made an historical survey of dough-testing apparatus, and mentioned that the earliest types were used for the purpose of testing the water-absorbing property of flour.

Bolland (1888) recommended, as did Jago, an instrument known as an Aleurometer, in which gluten was tested for expansion at a temperature of 150° F., which was recorded. The errors possible were, however, considerable.

James Hogarth (1889), a Scottish miller, patented an instrument which registered the resistance to the mechanical arms during mixing of the dough under test. He also registered the degree of gluten degradation after prolonged mixing and the W.A.P. of the flour under test. His methods were very similar to those employed today. It is interesting to note that Hogarth's method went into abeyance for a long time, and then formed the essential basis for Brabender's well-known Farinograph.

Hankoczy (1905) devised an apparatus which measured the force necessary to expand gluten, the principle being adopted later by Chopin in an instrument which measures the expansion of the gluten in a dough bubble.

Amongst other workers in this field were Rejto (1907), Barbade (1932), Krtinsky (1932), Matejovsky (1937) and Auerman (1939).

A stretchometer was devised by Hlynka and Anderson (1946) in which a ring of gluten was cut, frozen to facilitate cutting, thawed for 30 min. at 25° C., folded into four strands, then suspended from a balance and stretched downwards at 40 cm. per second, until the breaking point was reached.

In 1921 Chopin introduced his well-known Extensimeter, which was subsequently marketed a few years later. The design was improved and the name changed to the Alveographe. This apparatus has considerable merit.

Hankoczy still continued his investigations into the plasticity and elasticity of dough and later in collaboration with Brabender, the Farinograph was perfected and marketed. Improvements have since been made and it still remains a popular dough-recording apparatus of its type.

Later Brabender designed the Extensograph, in which a cylinder of dough is stretched mechanically, and the stretching force and the degree of extension is continuously recorded automatically. He also invented the Amylograph which records the viscosity of a starch suspension as it is gelatinized.

Workers at the Research Association of British Flour-Millers made a fundamental study of the physical properties of dough, and utilized their findings to design an instrument, the Extensometer, for the evaluation of dough quality. This instrument was subsequently marketed.

Continual work is still going on in the whole field of mechanical dough testing; well tried instruments are improved from time to time and new instruments are introduced, resulting not only in a greater knowledge of the subject itself, but in a greater application of the knowledge so gained to commercial practice.

Dough-testing apparatus can be placed under two headings, (*a*) dynamic and (*b*) static. Those which automatically record the properties of a dough over a period of up to 20 min. of continuous mixing may be termed dynamic. The static type are those that record the stress/strain relationships during the short time taken to stretch a piece of dough until it breaks.

Farinograph.—This well-known example of the dynamic type of dough-testing instrument (Plate XIX) consists of a twin-bladed water-jacketed mixer, operated by an electric motor which is free to rotate about its axis when a torque is applied by the resistance of a dough to the action of the mixing blades. The motor housing is connected through a damping device to a pen which operates over a moving band of paper. During the mixing of a wheat flour dough in this instrument, the pen traces a curve on the paper, the shape and general configuration of the curve depending on the physical properties of the dough. A typical farinogram, as a curve given by this instrument is known, is shown (Fig. 43). The paper is printed with a scale along its length indicating the time in minutes, and across its width, an arbitrary scale of 0–1,000, which measures the consistency of the dough.

The apparatus can be considered in two parts, (*a*) a thermostatically controlled water tank and (*b*) the Farinograph unit.

The water tank is connected to the mixer by a rubber hose. Its purpose is to maintain the mixer at a constant temperature of 30° C. and to effect this, the water is pumped to, and circulated round the mixer walls at a constant temperature.

A burette is fixed over the mixer and this is filled with water at 30° C.

All farinograms are made with doughs of fixed initial consistency, so that before flour is tested it is necessary to ascertain its W.A.P. This is done by placing 300 grams of the flour into the mixer and bringing it to a temperature of 30° F. Then with the mixer switched on, water from the burette is carefully run in until the curve on the chart is maintained along the 600 line. The amount of water used is read off and recorded.

After the mixer has been carefully cleaned, another 300 grams of flour is placed in and brought to 30° C., and with the mixer in operation the correct amount of water previously determined is run in. A curve is now recorded which shows the total formation of the dough and its behaviour under continuous mixing. This graph is known as a 'normal' curve.

It is not easy to obtain from a farinogram, measurements of individual physical properties. Rather does the farinogram present a composite picture of dough behaviour. The information that may be obtained from the experiment is as follows (Fig. 44):

A. The W.A.P. calculated either as c.c.s. per 100 grams of flour, or as a percentage.

B. The dough development time in minutes which indicates the mixing time required, from the moment doughing up starts to the optimum development of the dough, and to give at the same time maximum width of band.

C. The dough stability measured in minutes on the curve from its highest peak to the point where it begins to drop.

D. Dough resistance, which is the sum of B and C.

E. Dough weakening is measured by the extent to which the curve falls below the 600 line during a definite mixing time.

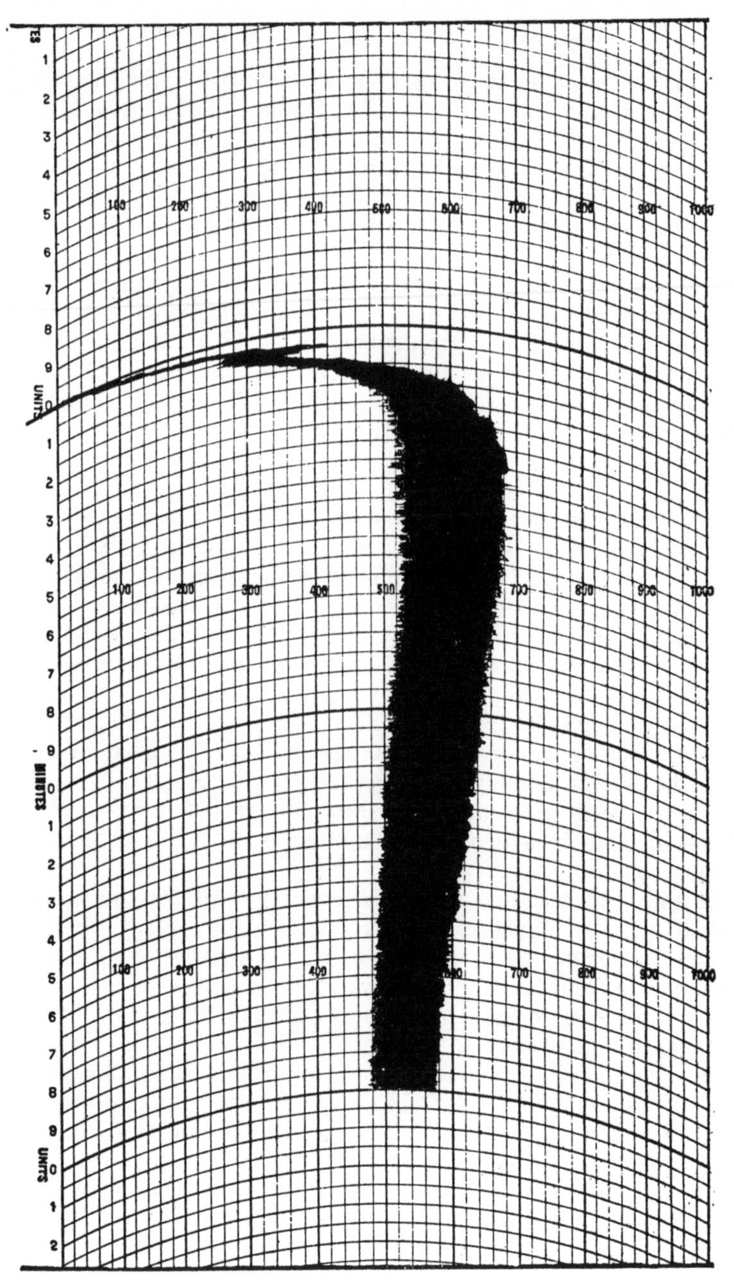

FIG. 43.—A typical farinogram.

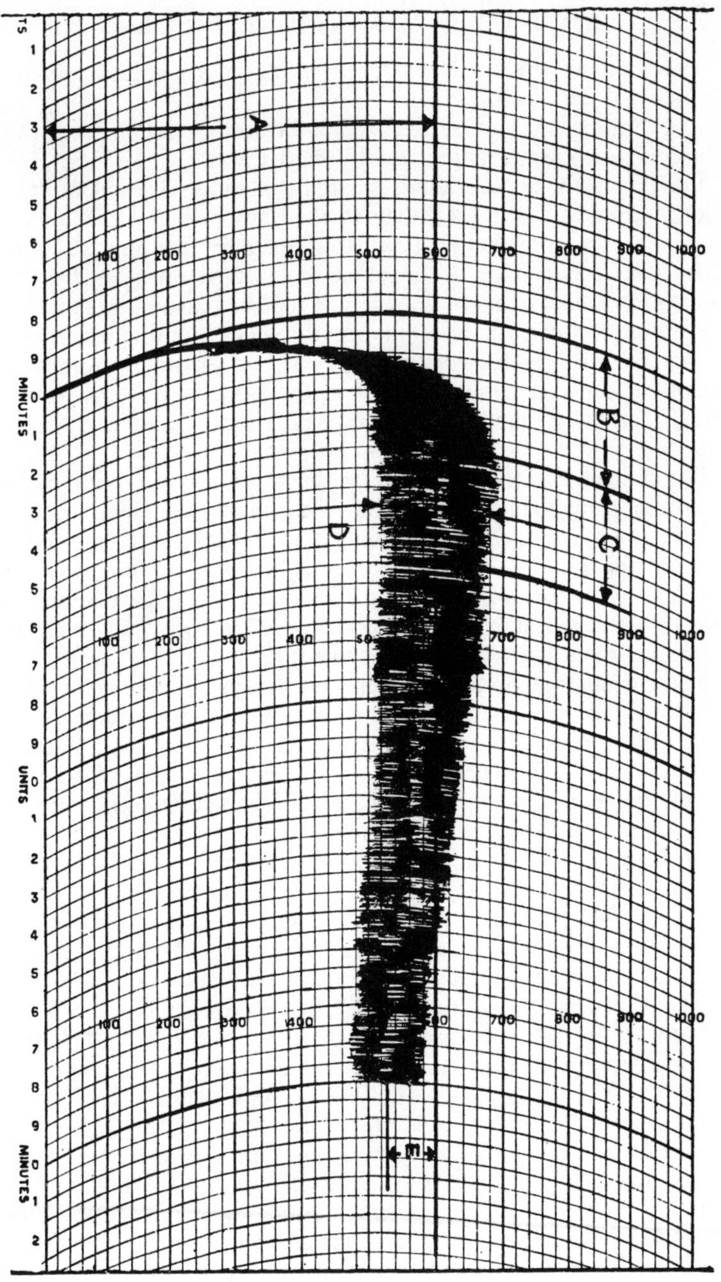

FIG. 44.—Farinogram. Interpretation.

The width of the band is sometimes taken as a measure of the elasticity of the dough.

The Farinograph can be used with a fermenting dough producing a farinogram known as the 'Rest Period Curve'.

For this test a similar dough is made containing 6 grams of yeast and 3 grams of salt; the mixer is then stopped and the dough, covered to prevent skinning, is left to ferment for one hour at 30° C. After this resting time, the machine is switched on again for two minutes and a curve made. This can be repeated many times and the curve obtained consists of a number of 'blocks' each representing a two-minute mixing time with an interval of an hour's fermentation time between them. This shows the behaviour of the relaxed dough against mechnical abuse. A 'Rest Period Curve' is shown in Fig. 45.

It is claimed that the 'block' which remains horizontal is indicative of correct dough ripeness, and that if a two-minute 'block' inclines upward or downward, then the dough at that stage is either under-ripe or over-ripe. The comparative levels between two 'blocks' is the measure of the 'drop in consistency' as it is termed. This is the difference between dough compactness recorded by two minutes mixing after the dough has fermented for one hour.

The Farinograph is ideal for preparing doughs of uniform or varying consistencies for use on other dough-testing instruments. In addition, farinograms can be made which will show the influences exercised on dough structure and consistency as a result of different dough temperatures, fermentation periods, enriching agents, chemical additives and balance of materials.

Mixograph.—This is a dough-testing instrument which is in use in America and similar in principle to the Farinograph and which produces somewhat similar curves. The mixing head of this instrument carries four vertical pins on its underside, and, when the head rotates, these move among four fixed vertical pins in the mixing bowl with a planetary motion. The tendency for the bowl to rotate because of the pressure exerted on its fixed pins is recorded on a moving paper band.

Brabender Extensograph.—In 1938 a supplement to the Farinograph was introduced and is known as the Extensograph (Plate XX).

When the Farinograph was first introduced it was thought that the standard curves recorded would reveal everything relating to the quality and baking properties of the flours under test. It was soon found, however, that a measure of the elasticity and extensibility of the dough would have to be determined in order to get a complete picture of the flour and its performance in panary fermentation.

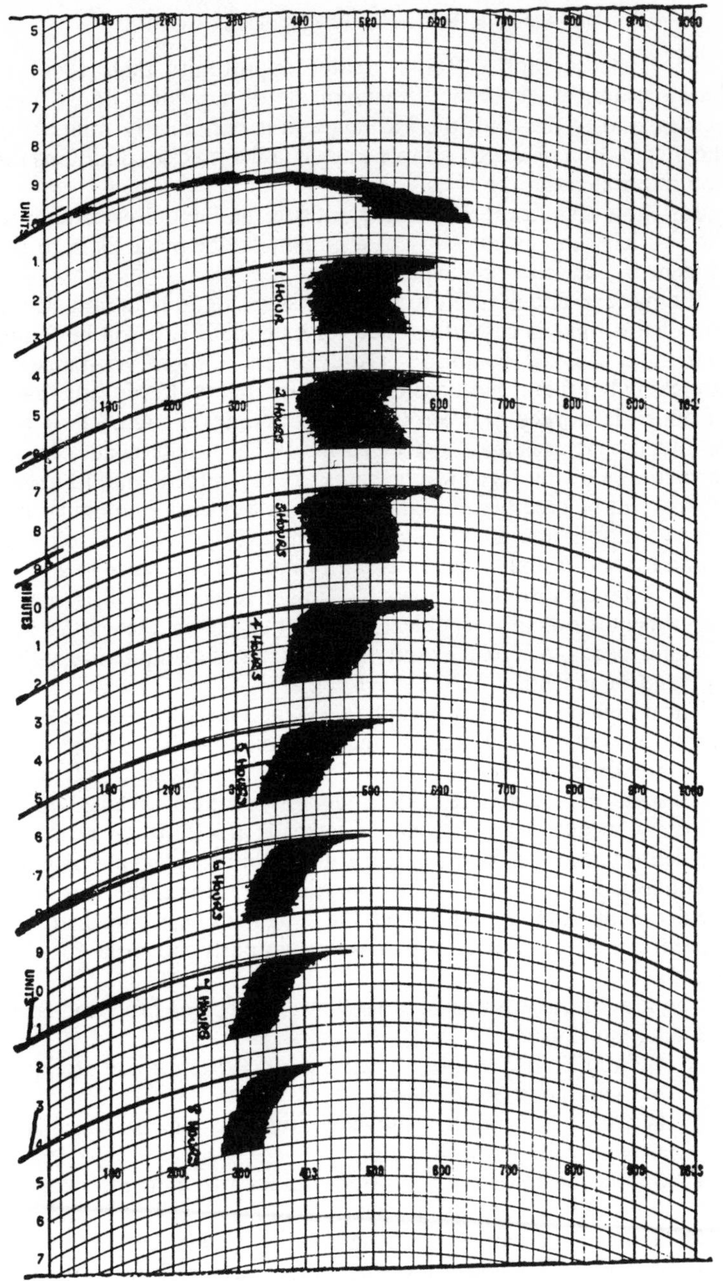

FIG. 45.—The 'rest period curve'.

The Extensograph offers a greater opportunity than does the Farinograph for obtaining measurements of individual dough properties, and to this end, the Farinograph is particularly valuable in the preparation of dough samples, made under precise conditions for accurate Extensograph tests.

Just how significant and important are the factors pertaining to the elasticity and extensibility of a dough, can be made plain to the student by the following experiment:

If a piece of dough is left to stand for say, half an hour and, at the end of this time, is carefully tested for extensibility, it will be found that in its relaxed condition it only offers a slight resistance to stretching but that it has considerable extensibility. If this same piece of dough is worked between the fingers and again stretched, it will be found that resistance and extensibility have undergone a transformation. Greater force will be necessary to stretch it, and its extensibility will be greatly reduced. The dough by 'work-hardening' has become shorter and more tough. If the dough is allowed to rest, it is found that extensibility increases with time, and resistance to stretch is less. This condition is known as 'dough relaxation'. This simple experiment shows in a very clear manner that the characteristics of a dough depends to a great extent on the effects of manipulation either by hand or machine.

The dough under Extensograph test is mechanically moulded into baton shapes of fixed weight and allowed to relax for 45 min. At the end of this period, the roll is clamped at each end in the Extensograph. The middle of the dough piece is then stretched downwards by means of an arm which descends at a constant rate, and the deformation continues until the dough breaks. The moving arm is connected with a pen which continuously records the tension in the dough and the extent to which the dough has been stretched. The type of curves produced by the Extensograph is shown in Figs. 46 and 47.

The first of these Extensograms shows the curves produced from five different flours.

A. Is from English wheat showing poor resistance and strength, but with good extensibility.
B. Is from Plate wheat showing much better resistance and strength with good extensibility.
C. Shows the test on an Australian flour that is comparable to flour milled from Plate wheat.
D. Shows the typical curve from a strong Canadian flour.
E. Is from Indian wheat showing a measure of resistance but with poor extensibility.

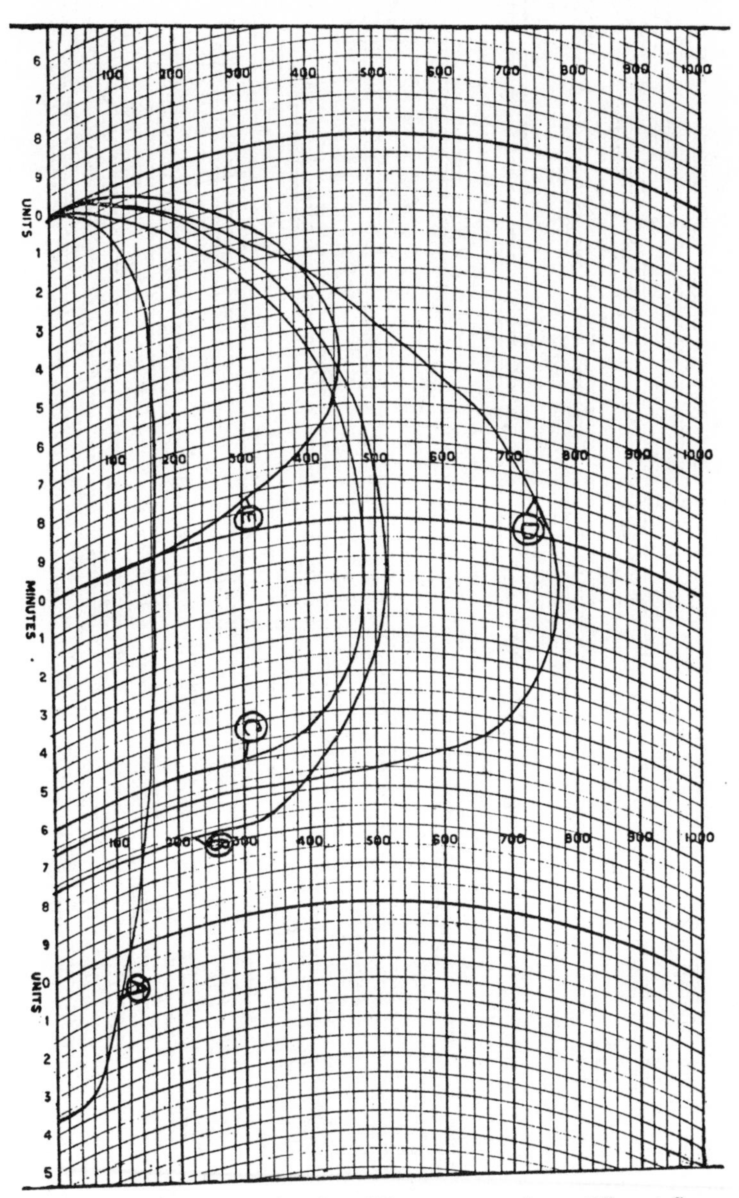

FIG. 46.—Extensograms showing different curves from different flours.

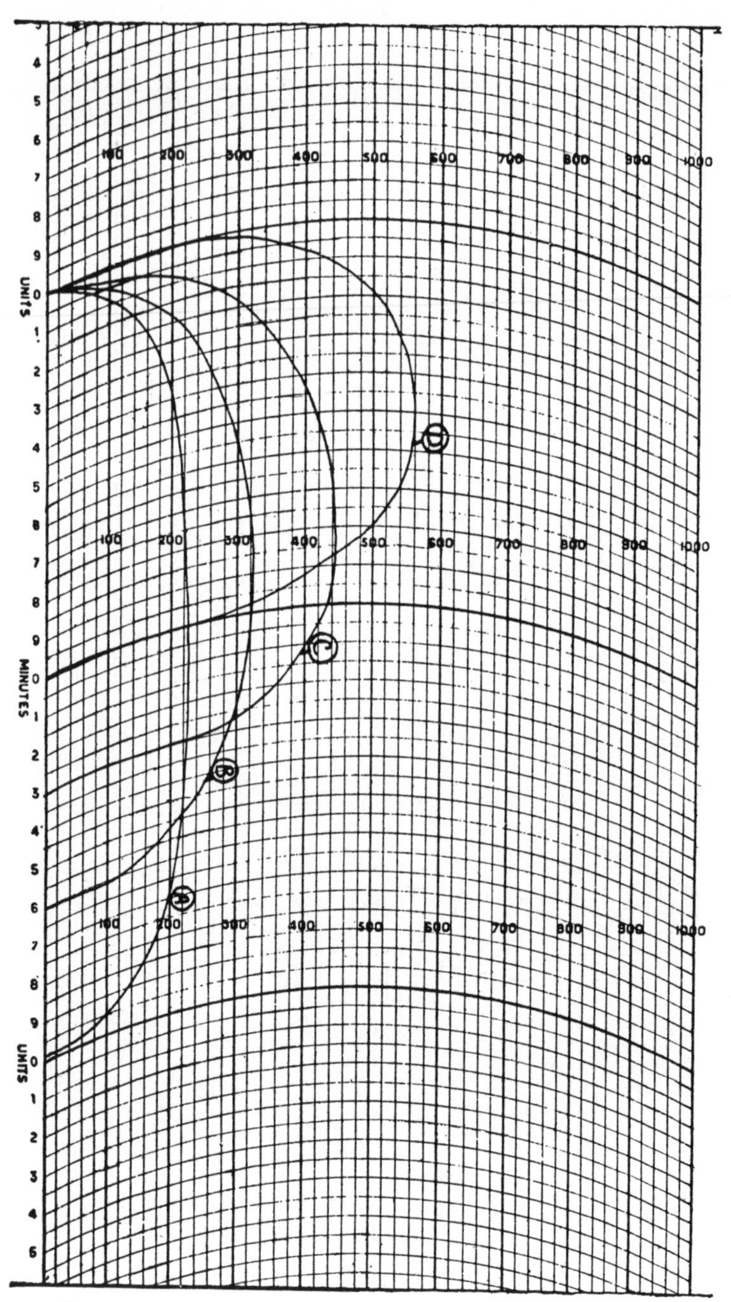

FIG. 47.—Extensograms showing the effects of gas treatment.

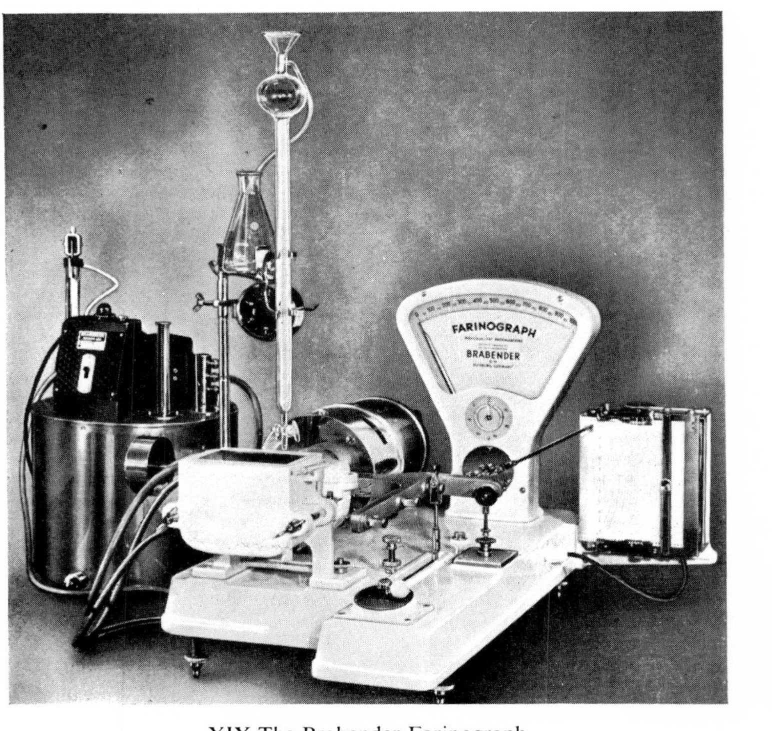

XIX The Brabender Farinograph

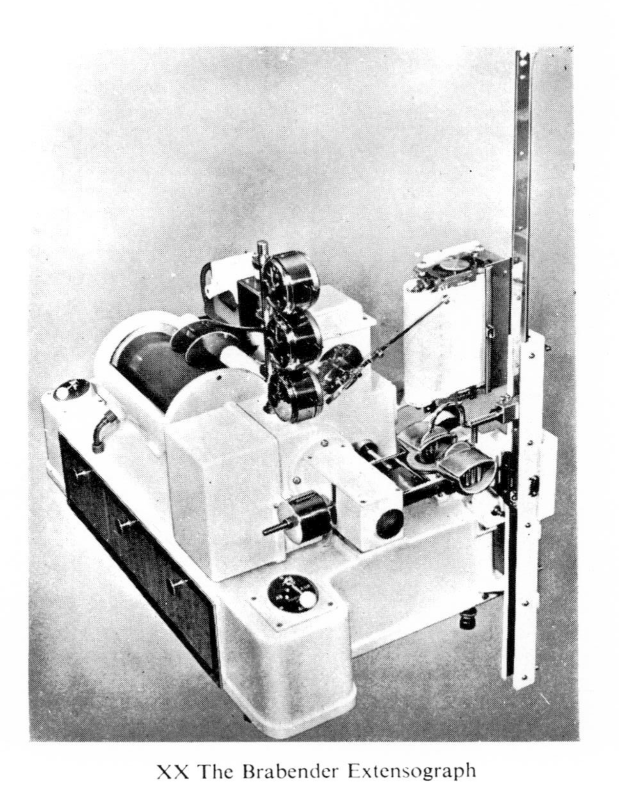

XX The Brabender Extensograph

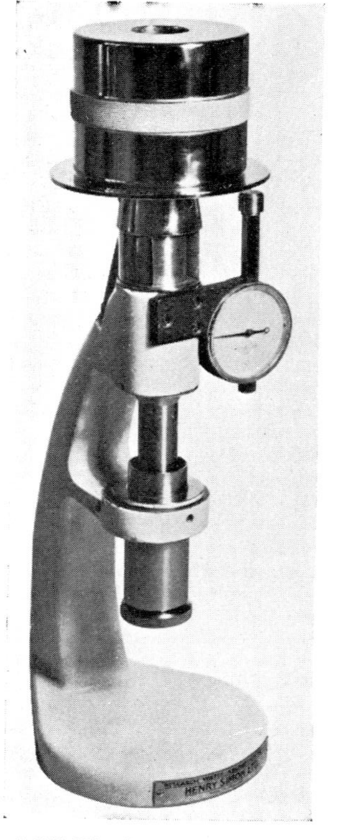

XXI The 'Research' water absorption meter

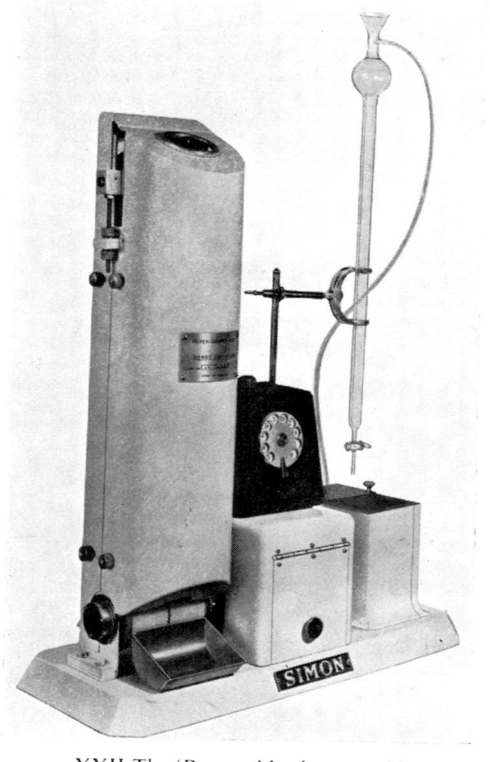

XXII The 'Research' mixer-moulder

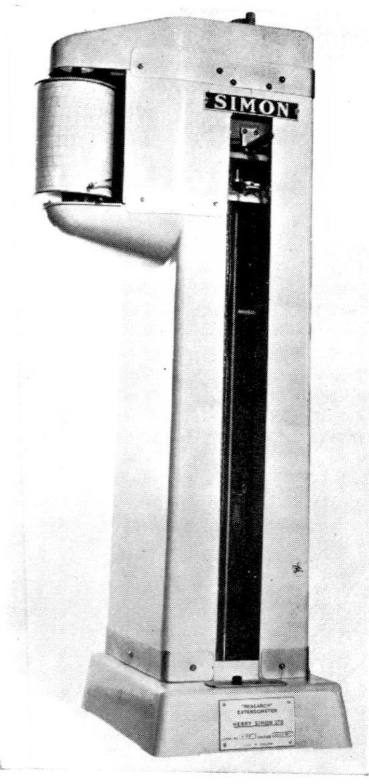

XXIII The 'Research' Extensometer

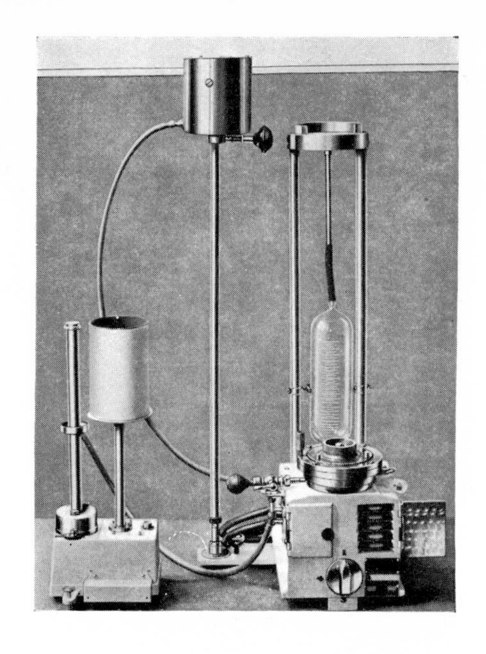

XXIV The Alveographe

XXV The Zymotachygraphe

XXVI A two-storied bakery showing breadmaking plant

XXVII A section of a single-floor bread bakery

The second Extensogram gives a visual picture of the effects of gas treatment on a single flour.

A. Is untreated.

B. Shows the effect of 2 grams of gas per sack.

C and D show the effects of 4 and 6 grams respectively.

The student will note that the effect of gas treatment on this particular flour was to increase the stability and decrease the extensibility as treatment became progressively heavier.

When the dough piece has been stretched, it is reformed into a baton shape, and again rested for 45 min. and again stretched; this is repeated yet again until a series of three Extensograms are obtained, i.e. after 45, 90 and 135 min.; this series demonstrates in the form of curves the influence of the mechanical working, combined with the effects of fermentation on dough elasticity and extensibility. When accurately carried out, this test is completely independent of the operator and the conditions in the room where the test is being carried out.

To interpret the curves (Fig. 48), the maximum height is taken as the measure of dough resistance, while the extent to which the curve has progressed horizontally is the measure of its extensibility. The area under the curve is an indication of the strength of the dough.

Extensometer.—This instrument gives a curve which is similar in shape to that produced by the Extensograph. It was designed at the British Flour Millers' Research Station at St. Albans.

The Extensometer is one of a series of instruments which together form a testing unit which consists of the following:

(1) Water absorption meter (Plate XXI) in which a standard volume of dough of known water content, mixed and fermented for a specific time, is extruded under pressure through a nozzle. Calculation of the correct W.A.P., is then measured by the time taken for the dough to extrude.

(2) Mixer-moulder. This instrument (Plate XXII) consists of a mixer and a shaper unit. The mixer can be adjusted to take amounts of flour from 280–450 grams, the latter amount allowing for a test bake to supplement the physical tests.

(3) The Extensometer is shown in Plate XXIII.

For the Extensometer test the dough is shaped into a ball and placed upon two spikes, and when the instrument is set in operation the lower of these spikes moves downward while the top one remains stationary. The tension in the loop of dough that is formed, and the extent to which the dough is stretched is recorded on a moving sheet of paper until the dough breaks.

A study of Extensometer curves has thrown an interesting light

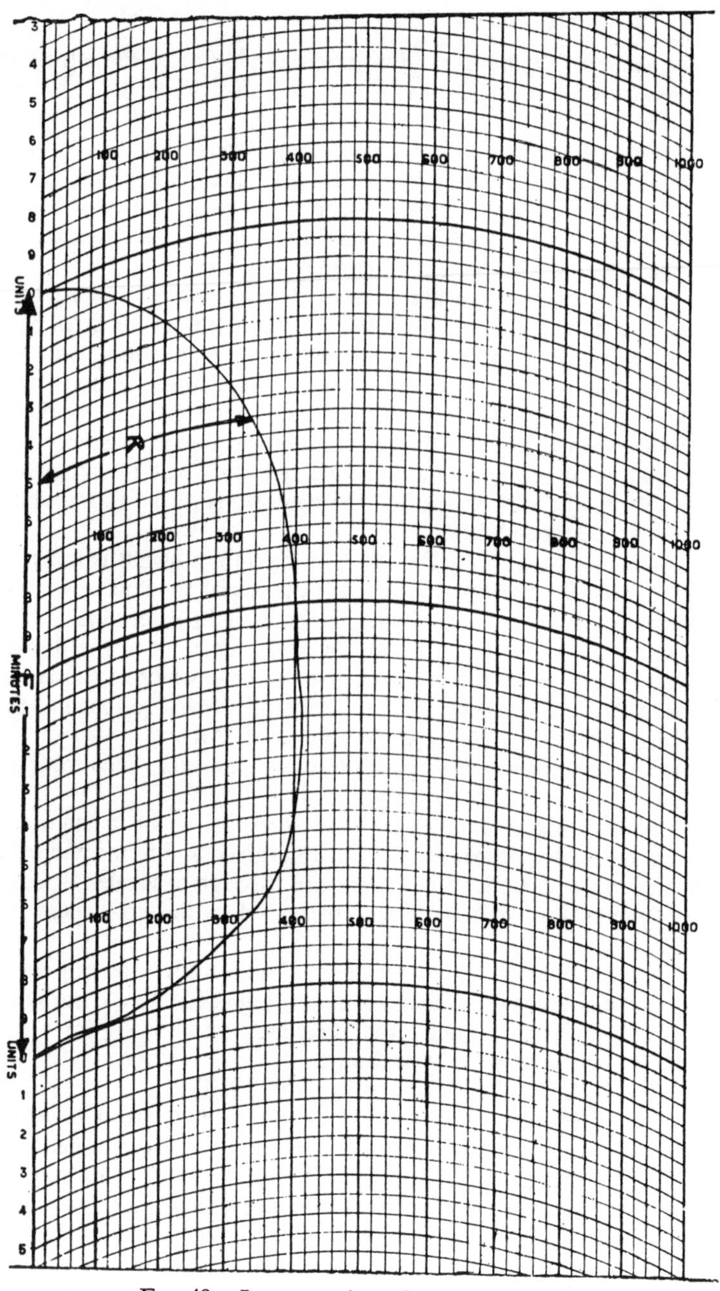

FIG. 48.—Interpretation of an extensogram.

on the chemical treatment of flour. If an untreated flour is tested on the Extensometer and the test repeated after the flour has been treated at different levels with a chemical improver, it will be found that as treatment is increased the height of the curve increases while its length decreases. This is to be expected because it is well known that as a flour is progressively treated the dough it yields becomes progressively less extensible but more stable. An interesting discovery, however, was that although the curves in such a test show a progressive change in height and width, the area remains essentially constant. This finding has led to the suggestion that the area under an Extensometer curve is a measure of the potential strength of a flour, and, according to this idea, the addition of an improver to a flour does not make the flour stronger but alters its physical characteristics in such a way that its potential strength may be more fully realized.

Alveographe.—Another of the static type dough-testing instruments, much older than the previous two, is the Chopin Alveo-

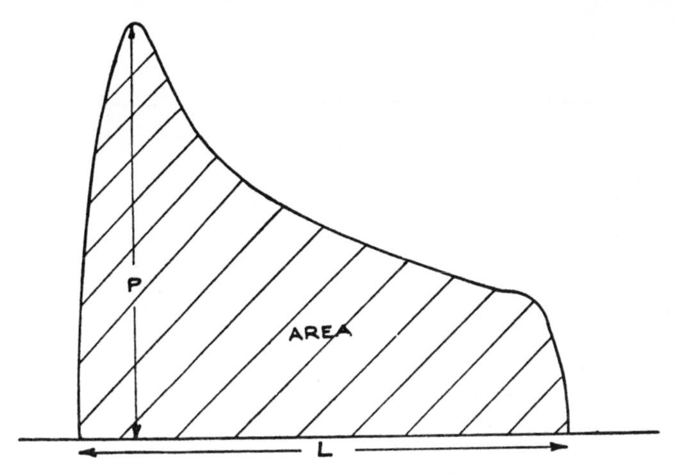

FIG. 49.—A typical Alveographe curve.

graphe, previously known as the Extensimeter. This is shown in Plate XXIV.

Like the Extensograph and the Extensometer, this instrument furnishes a record of the changes in the stress/strain relationships in a dough while the dough is stretched until it breaks, but it employs a different method for deforming the dough. A disc of dough is blown into a bubble by means of air pressure, and the pressure within the bubble is recorded continuously from the time the bubble starts to form until it finally bursts. All doughs tested contain the same proportion of total water. A typical Alveographe curve is shown in Fig. 49.

It will be noticed that the Alveographe curve is distinctly different from the shapes of Extensograph and Extensometer curves. The Alveographe curve shows a sharp point of inflection. This point, i.e., the 'peak' of the curve, occurs at the yield point of the dough.

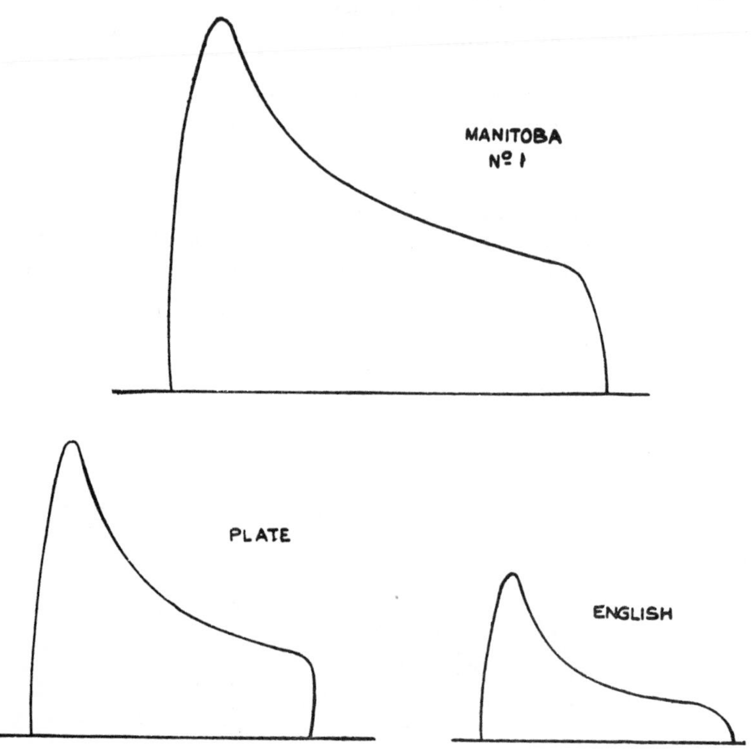

FIG. 50.—Alveographe showing different curves.

All the deformation represented by the curve at the left of the peak is recoverable, that is, it is elastic deformation. Once the peak has been passed, some non-recoverable deformation occurs which means that the bubble has started to flow. This explains why, although the bubble is increasing in size throughout the test, the pressure continuously falls once the peak of the curve has been passed.

The interpretation of the curve (Fig. 49) is as follows:

P. The height of the peak, which is a measure of dough stability.

L. The length of the base line represents dough extensibility. The area enclosed by the curve, is the measure of the strength of the dough.

A study of Alveographe curves reveal how important it is when studying dough behaviour to supplement an assessment of strength by measurements of other physical properties.

From a study of Fig. 50, showing three Alveographe curves, the student will see quite clearly the differences in dough stability, extensibility and strength of the three flours under test.

Zymotachygraphe.—This is an instrument designed to record automatically and simultaneously both gas production and gas retention (Plate XXX).

A fermenting dough is placed in the thermostatically controlled fermentation chamber, and once every 2½ min. this chamber is automatically put into connection with the water manometer, which carries a pen operating on a moving sheet of paper. The first four connections are made direct, so that the pressure recorded is that of the total gas produced by the yeast, whether it is retained within the dough or has escaped from the surface into the fermentation chamber. The next four 2½-min. readings are automatically made by way of an absorption vessel, which removes any CO_2 which has escaped from the dough, and they measure, therefore, only the gas retained within the dough. When the stage is reached at which the dough allows the gas to escape, the consecutive blocks of four readings vary in height, the higher blocks measuring total gas produced and the lower blocks gas retained.

Brabender Amylograph.—The gelatinization of starch within the loaf during baking has an influence on the condition of the crumb of the baked loaf, i.e. whether it is dry, sticky or normal.

The Amylograph simulates the effect of baking on starch step by step, by raising the temperature of a flour/water suspension at a constant rate, during which the starch gelatinizes.

A graph is recorded, the height of which is related to the viscosity of the paste. A high curve reveals a starch with a good water binding capacity resulting in bread with a dry eating crumb. A low graph line shows a starch with a low water binding capacity and is usually indicative of high alpha-amylase activity which will result in a damp sticky crumb. The mean between the two, shows the most suitable flour for breadmaking.

Hagberg Number.—A relatively new and extremely simple test which has the virtue of being accurate and quickly made is now in use in research establishments to measure the diastatic activity in flour. The test is known as the Hagberg test and the result is given as a number.

A flour/water suspension in specific amounts is placed in a stainless steel beaker in a water bath under controlled conditions. When the mixture has gelatinized, the consistency is determined by a penetrometer; the depth of penetration into the gel in millimetres, in a given time (10 sec.) is taken as the Hagberg figure.

A good flour with a normal diastatic balance gives a jelly in which the penetrometer does not sink quickly and therefore the Hagberg figure is comparatively low, between 20–30. If the figure is 11 or under, malt or fungal amylase is necessary if breadmaking is to be satisfactory. Between 11–20 such additions, at a lower level may be desirable. A figure over 40 gives a warning of excessive diastatic activity and over 50 the certainty of it.

There are other types of dough-testing equipment in use all over the world with the certainty of others to come. Excellent as they may be, the student must never forget that the critically conducted baking test in the hands of a competent person is perhaps the finest test for commercial baking flours. Instrumental methods may be valuable in supplying supplementary information and enable more permanent records to be kept. They should, however, never be substituted for a baking test.

19

Bakery Layout; Bakery Organization; Management of Personnel; Automatic Bread Production; Definition of Terms

BAKERY LAYOUT

QUESTIONS on the layout of a bakery are possible on the final examination papers and the student should have some knowledge of bakery planning in order that he can answer such questions. Later in industrial life the time may come when he will, in consultation with the architect and builder, take his part in the planning of a fine new bakery.

With the financial details settled and with knowledge of the initial production expected from the proposed new bakery, the first consideration must be the site and at this stage many important points must be borne in mind.

(1) *Room for Expansion*

This is essential for it would show a complete lack of ambition and foresight, if all the space is used and it is found later that there is no room for necessary extensions, consequent on increased business.

(2) *Publicity Value*

The site should be so chosen that the finished bakery becomes a landmark. A fine building dwarfed and hidden by giant factories can never be such, so potential publicity is lost.

(3) *Utility Services*

The proximity and ease of access for utility services must be considered for they are absolutely essential. The services are drainage, water, power, light, gas, etc.

(4) *Access for Raw Materials, etc.*

Local road and rail services must be studied and the bakery so sited that incoming raw materials and equipment can be delivered easily and without undue delay. Ease of access and exit for road transport must be part of planned bakery also, for in these days it is a tremendous asset if vehicles can drive in to load and unload and drive out without hindrance. A wide one-way drive is good business.

(5) *Area Population*

Proximity to a well populated area is a first-class consideration, for not only must the bakery be assured of a constant supply of raw materials and be well equipped, it must have personnel to man the machines, for processing, finishing, packing and dispatch. It is easier to recruit a labour force from a well populated area. Another important consideration is that in a well populated area, the sale of finished products can be better effected without heavy transport costs.

The site selected and acquired, then thought becomes necessary on building layout. Here, many points must be carefully studied:

(1) *Number of Floors*

A single ground-floor is less expensive to build than a multi-floored building, but requires more room, which in turn costs money. The conveyance of both raw materials and finished products is more difficult in a single floored factory for there is not the opportunity for a gravity flow so easily obtained in a multi-floored building. On the other hand the multi-storied building must be constructed more strongly and is more costly. It is less easy to deploy labour in a multi-storied factory and this in turn makes supervision more difficult. Each production level tends to become detached from the whole, assuming semi-independent production.

(2) *Flow Line*

Modern equipment is streamlined both in design and layout, therefore the production line, whether it be through several floors or straight through on a single floor, should be unhindered through its entire length. Pillars should be avoided.

A clear flow line will allow for the shortest distance to be travelled by workers between each operation, and allow for the maximum working space. This in turn will ensure that a uniform speed of operation is maintained by the operative.

(3) *Regulations*

In planning the bakery, careful thought must be given to the requirements of the Factory Acts and the Hygiene regulations. In this connection, advice will be readily given by the British Baking Industries Research Association, the Home Office and local Health Authorities. Specialist advice may also be necessary on other matters pertaining to construction, equipment and welfare. This will be obtainable without difficulty from firms and organizations concerned. Here are some points—some necessary by law, others in the interest of good planning.

Floors.—These should be so constructed that they are easily and effectively cleaned. They should be durable and non-slippery. Tiles are excellent. Metal plates are necessary where there is heavy wear, as in dough rooms.

Walls.—Walls and ceilings should be so constructed that they can be cleaned. Rough absorbent surfaces are conducive to mould growth. Close-fitted tiles and/or a smooth surface treated with high gloss mould resistant paint is recommended. Corners and floor skirtings should be rounded.

Changing Rooms.—Adequate and suitable accommodation for clothing not worn during working hours, with such arrangements as are reasonably practicable for drying such clothing, must be provided.

Space.—There must be in each bakery at least 400 cubic ft. of space for every person employed, not counting space more than 14 ft. from the floor.

Temperature, Humidity and Ventilation—are of great importance when planning a bakery, for nothing will impair efficiency more than unsatisfactory working conditions.

Lighting.—There must be sufficient and suitable lighting in every part of the bakery where persons are working or passing. The maximum use of daylight will save electricity costs. Artificial lighting in industrial plants is a highly specialized science and the Electric Light Manufacturers Association will gladly advise and assist.

Welfare.—First aid accommodation, washing and sanitary facilities are all necessary. The provision of accommodation and facilities for the preparation of meals under well planned conditions is desirable. An adequate supply of drinking water must be provided.

Fire.—A certificate must be held from the local authority that the means of escape in case of fire are adequate.

BAKERY ORGANIZATION

The alternative to organization and planning is chaos. No business can function efficiently without control, whether it is control by one person in the case of a small business, or by a directorate in a large business, where responsibility is sub-divided right through the concern until it reaches those in charge of the worker at the bench and the assistant at the counter.

It is barely possible in these islands that there is a truly one-man bakery business, where one person does buying, costing, manufacturing, selling and book-keeping entirely himself. There are some, controlled by one person and assisted by a family, each person responsible for some part of bakery activity. Such a business is, in fact, an example of simple sub-division of responsibility.

From such an example it is easy to envisage concerns that are a little larger where outside help is necessary. At this level the help generally is in production, such as in breadmaking or confectionery, and assistants for shop sales.

At a higher level, the smaller bakery unit will have one person in control, generally the owner. He will be responsible for buying, production and sales. According to the size of the business and the volume of production, he will have clerical assistance for invoicing, costing and general office work; a bakery staff for production and assistants for sales.

The three sub-divisions of responsibility—office, production and sales—are more sharply defined as the business increases in size and scope. Each will have a responsible head, each controlling a specialized staff.

As the business still further increases, especially if it is a limited liability company, then it becomes necessary for control to be in the hands of a chief executive, a treasurer and a secretary, to whom a general manager is directly responsible. He, in turn, is in control of the three main activities, which by now will probably have grown into five distinct departments, each having a manager; there will be a personnel, business, production, and sales managers, together with a manager for research and development.

The personnel manager will control a staff concerned with industrial relations, staff welfare and educational training.

The business manager will sub-divide his control under buying, maintenance and accountancy. Maintenance will include buildings, plant and equipment, vehicles, general cleansing and hygiene.

Vehicle maintenance will, in turn, need a chief mechanic and an appropriate staff of motor mechanics. Accountancy will include costing, wages and statistics.

The production manager will control the test bakery, laboratory, and the bakery itself. In immediate charge of each will be the test baker, the chief chemist and the bakery manager. It is the bakery manager who will accept the responsibility for all foremen in charge of engineering, machines, mixing, bench work, ovens, decorating and finishing, packing and storekeeping.

These charge hands, in turn, are in control of mechanics and firemen, table hands, dispatch and weighing assistants. In many large firms shop stewards, elected by the rank and file workers, will have direct access, through their convenor, to the management where matters concerning trade union, welfare and working conditions can be discussed.

The sales manager will have an assistant who will manage route supervision, drivers and roundsmen; branch manageresses and sales assistants are also part of his responsibility. Parallel with him is the sales promotion manager who will deal with market research, advertising and display.

The development and market research manager will be responsible for pioneering new products, investigation into processes and in the study of time and motion.

The student will understand that the necessary sub-division of responsibility should not mean rigidly contained departments, each with only their specialized tasks. Good management will encourage collaboration, if and when necessary, so that the whole will function as a team. For instance, it may be necessary to discuss the quality of raw materials. It is then that the production manager will be in consultation with the buyer, the chemist, the test baker and possibly the store clerk.

On a question of quality in the finished products, the production manager will probably meet the test baker, the bakery manager and a representative from process research.

From time to time experiments will be tried, emanating from outside suggestions or from any of the departments within. Their successful outcome may mean new responsibilities. In this way a business will make a contribution to both business and production practice and also to the community.

There can never be perfection in businesses either large or small. Always there are incompatibilities, with friction in consequence. It is the measure of managerial ability that these are quickly resolved, so that efficiency with smoothness is maintained.

Without any doubt, the greatest contribution to efficiency is competence, and the finest lubricant is common sense.

MANAGEMENT OF PERSONNEL

The art of managing personnel is to weld individuals together by systematic organization into a productive group. This is only possible by confident leadership born of competence, respect and goodwill.

It can be argued that the manager need only concern himself with the procedure of management and not with the means and results of production, the control of which can be in the hands of specialists and technicians, who are themselves subject to the manager. Nevertheless, a background of technical and practical knowledge is of great importance, for this added competence increases the respect in which the manager is held. In a bakery, a manager may well be craftsman, technologist, mathematician and engineer. With this background he will be better able to instruct and advise if and when it becomes necessary.

Respect will also come of self-control and an honest sense of responsibility, both of which lead to good judgement and the ability to make prompt decisions. To win goodwill, it is well, at the outset, to remember that all members of the staff are human beings; some no doubt, easy going, while others may have more complex characters. This calls for the humanist approach. It follows then, that the successful manager will not use excessive authority; his requests will be carried out and there will be no need to issue orders, except perhaps in an emergency, when the crisp order will be expected. He will never threaten unless he can carry it out. He will be strictly fair in his dealings with others and will have no favourites.

To take an interest in a worker's welfare, generally brings a ready response and engenders an atmosphere of approachability. A sense of humour is a wonderful lubricant—people cannot laugh and grouse at the same time! Foul language will never solve a problem, only complicate it. Gossip will sabotage good relations and cloud a happy atmosphere.

A word of praise when it is earned pays good dividends. On the other hand, when criticism is necessary it should not be used as an opportunity for self-aggrandizement before an audience; keep the matter between yourself and the person concerned. To belittle a person is a serious psychological blunder, for the good manager will make the best use of the worker's ability.

With the finest organization and the best will in the world, there are bound to be problems that will arise from time to time. The competent manager will deal with them promptly before simple problems become complicated or serious problems become catastrophic. The ancient Greeks considered that if a problem is adequately discussed, then eventually an approximation of the truth will be found. The same still applies today, for adequate discussion will soon reveal the facts together with various opinions; the assessment can then be studied with due regard to any regulation, rule or custom.

Action can now be considered after careful thought on the probable effect on any individual or group, and ultimately on production. Before action is taken, the manager will have satisfied himself on whether the problem can be successfully handled either by himself or by co-operation with others, or should be passed to the directorate.

Problems have many origins, some simple others more complex. Action is taken in an endeavour to resolve the difficulties. Results are the only means of checking the diagnosis and the cure. If the operation is successful without serious repercussions, then diagnosis must have been correct.

A bakery wherein the management and the production staff have a pride both in the products and in their workmanship, adds to the dignity of all concerned, and to the dignity and status of the baking industry. It is here that the technically trained manager is valuable, for not only will he be in a position to inform and instruct, but he will also be able to co-operate to the full with the technical schools for staff training. In this way, each member of the bakery team will have a sense of purpose.

Good management can be summed up as competence, co-operation and common sense.

AUTOMATIC BREAD PRODUCTION

Many students are familiar with automatic bread production because of working in such plants. Others are less familiar, but no doubt have had the opportunity of seeing large-scale production as a result of visits arranged by their teachers as a part of bakery education.

Let us travel through a modern plant, say with a capacity of six sacks of flour into bread per hour. The production flow line starts at the point of flour intake at one end of the building, and proceeds progressively through the bakery to the slicing, wrapping, packing and dispatch at the other end.

Flour Store.—In a well planned bakery, this room is situated over or close to the dough room. It should be so constructed that there are no crevices, beams or rafters that will hold flour or dust to encourage the growth of moulds. For this reason the roof will be continuous, the floors of close fitting hard wood and the walls either finished with close fitting tiles or with a hard-gloss, mould-resistant paint.

As far as possible, the room should be pest and vermin proof.

The store should be well ventilated with a temperature maintained at 60–70° F., and with a relative humidity approximating to 60%; it should be so planned that systematic cleaning can be maintained.

Intake is generally by elevator and a travelling band, to the point where the flour is to be stacked. Bulk delivery from tanker lorries has now passed the experimental stage and is practised commercially in many large plants, the flour being conveyed from the lorry to the storage tanks in the bakery by compression.

Flour delivered in bags should be stacked on end no more than two or three high. Overstacking will result in compressed, lumpy flour in the bottom bags. The flour should be stacked on wooden slats or palettes to allow for the free circulation of air.

The flour room should be large enough to store three weeks' supply of flour and have room enough for movement.

In such a store may be found a sack-cleaning plant by means of which flour can be recovered from emptied sacks by the use of a strong air current which turns the bag inside out so removing all adhering flour.

Before dough-making, the flour is sieved and blended. This is important, for not only is any extraneous matter removed and the flour aerated and rendered free of any aggregation, but also a thorough mixing is given to different flours that may be blended together. This may be done automatically so that the correct proportion of each flour to the whole is effected.

Another machine that may be present is an entoleter in which the flour is spun centrifugally at high speed to kill by impact any living organisms.

Dough Room.—The blended and sieved flour at correct weight is delivered to the dough mixer where the water at correct temperature and weight, together with yeast, salt (if used at this stage) and other materials are added. If the mixers are high speed machines, the dough after mixing is ejected into wheeled machine bowls. If they are open pan mixers the bowls are simply wheeled out. These are clearly seen in Plates XXVI and XXVII.

The temperature of the dough room should be maintained at about 80° F., and if humidity is not controlled, the dough in the bowls should be covered to prevent skinning. If the salt-delayed method is being used, the bowls are wheeled back to the mixer for the salt addition at about three-quarters of bulk fermentation time.

Dividers.—When the doughs are sufficiently ripe they are conveyed in strict rotation to the dividers where they are cut into pieces of a pre-determined weight. A scale nearby is for frequent weight checking.

Handing-up.—The dough pieces are conveyed to a machine which hands them up into a ball shape. The machines in general use are the conical type known as the 'umbrella'.

Intermediate Proof.—From the handing up machine the dough pieces are dropped into fabric pockets on an endless chain which convey them through a temperature and humidity controlled intermediate prover. The time necessary for the dough pieces to recover in this prover from the mechanical manipulation received in the divider and on the moulder is approximately 10–15 min.

Moulder.—From the prover the dough pieces are conveyed to the moulding machine for shaping.

There are two types of moulder each employing different moulding principles. In the spindle moulder the dough piece is received by two rapidly revolving spindles which form it into a tight roll after which the dough piece is elongated between two canvas bands. The second type first sheets the dough pieces and then rolls them Swiss roll fashion. There are moulders which employ modifications of these principles.

Final Prover.—The moulded pieces are placed into greased tins which are in swinging trays on an endless belt.

The temperature of the prover is maintained at a figure between 95–98° F., and with a relative humidity about 80–85%. The dough pieces are conveyed in an up-and-down motion through the prover taking between 40–50 min.

Travelling Oven. Final proof being effected, the bread is transferred to the oven.

Bread Coolers.—The bread after being removed from the baking tins is then transferred to the wooden trays of the cooler which is a travelling conveyor on which the bread travels for about 4 hr.

Initially the bread is conveyed at once to the top of the cooler and is maintained there for a sufficient time to make certain of steam release so that it cannot condense on the cooler bread on the conveyor.

Slicers and Wrappers. When sufficiently cool, the bread is fed into slicing and wrapping machines and then placed on to racks ready for dispatch.

DEFINITION OF TERMS

It is essential that the student should be familiar with, and understand, the technical terms used by the baker, the bakery engineer, cereal chemist and the miller in the field of baking. It is necessary to be able to define them so that they may be used correctly and intelligently, either in the classroom, the laboratory or in commercial practice.

Absorption

The maximum amount of liquid that may be used to form a particular fermented batter or dough.

Aroma

The complex mixture of volatile flavours emanating from the crust and crumb.

Bag (of flour)

140 lb. Sometimes referred to as half a sack.

Base

Bottom portion of the loaf.

Bloom

The healthy sparkle found in the crust colour of a well fermented loaf.

Body

Firmness and response of the crumb to pressure.

Break

That part of the crust formed during oven spring. It may be predetermined by cutting the dough piece before baking.

Bucky

A tough dough that exhibits an excessive elasticity when stretched.

Bulk fermentation

Fermentation time calculated from dough-making to scaling or dividing.

Clarity

A crumb free from cores, seams and streaks.

Clearing

The thorough dispersal of all ingredients during dough-making.

Condensation marks

Patches of dark colour in the crumb structure caused by the condensation of steam whilst cooling.

Consistency

The 'feel' of a dough, it is the measure of proper absorption.

Cores

Hard spots in the crumb structure. They may be discerned by the light pressure of the thumbs on the crumb surface.

Crumb

All the loaf except the crust.

Crust

That part of the outside of the loaf that is dehydrated and caramelized during baking.

Delayed salt method

A method of breadmaking where the salt is omitted at dough-making and added at the 'knock-back' stage.

Development

The optimum condition of the dough during the whole of the fermentation process which will result in bread of maximum volume, without any impairment of the crumb.

Extensibility

The degree to which dough may be stretched or deformed without break or rupture.

Face

The side crust of a tin loaf.

Ferment and dough

A dough made with a preliminary ferment.

Fermentation tolerance

The period before and after the optimum dough ripening is reached when good bread can be produced.

Final proof

The period of fermentation after final shaping and before the bread is placed into the oven.

Flavour

The total sensation of taste and odour when bread is taken into the mouth.

Flying ferment

A ferment that is allowed to stand for such time as it takes to assemble the materials for the dough.

Flying sponge

A sponge allowed to ferment for two hours or less.

Foxy colour

The red-brown colour of the crust indicative of an under-fermented dough.

Grain

The size, shape and arrangement of the cells which make up the crumb surface.

Green dough

An under-fermented dough.

Handing up

The shaping of the dough piece immediately after scaling or dividing. It is invariably a round shape.

Harshness

A term used to describe a tough tenacious gluten.

Intermediate proof

The time allowed for the dough piece to recover after handing up and before final moulding.

Knock back

The further mechanical manipulation given the dough in bulk at about two-thirds of the bulk fermentation time. When doughs were made by hand this operation was known as cutting back.

No-dough-time dough

A straight dough that has little or no bulk fermentation, it being sent to the divider almost immediately after dough-making.

Oven spring

The difference in the size of the loaf when it enters the oven and when it is baked.

Over-developed

A dough which, because of excessive fermentation yields bread of large volume, uneven crust, pale in colour and without bloom, and with an irregular unstable crumb.

Pan crust

That part of the crust in contact with the baking-tin.

Pile

The 'build-up' of the crumb structure.

Porosity

The closeness or openness of the grain.

Response

The reaction of a dough to a known and specific stimulus, substance or set of conditions, usually observed by baking it in comparison with a control.

Rope

A condition in bread brought about under certain conditions by soil borne bacteria. The crumb of the loaf discolours, becomes sticky and emits a bad odour.

Sack (of flour)

280 lb. in two bags of 140 lb. each.

Seams

Continuous hard layers in the crumb that can be seen and felt.

Sheen

Reflection from the cells in the cut surface of the crumb.

Shell or flying top

A top crust separated from the rest of the loaf by a long, deep crack. The crust comes away easily in the form of a cap.

Shred

Character of the surface at the break. It may be smooth, ragged or broken.

Sour

A dough in which excessive acidity has been allowed to develop yielding bread small in volume with little crust colour and a dark crumb. There will be a pronounced acid flavour and aroma. 'Sour' is also a term used to describe the added 'old' dough used as a leaven in rye breads.

Sponge and dough method

A dough made with a preliminary sponge.

Stability

The quality in the gluten of a dough that enables it to withstand the effects of fermentation and manipulation.

Straight dough

A method of breadmaking in which all the ingredients are mixed together at the dough-making stage.

Streaks

Continuous patches seen in the crumb structure.

Symmetry

The degree in which a loaf is harmoniously proportioned.

Texture

The tactile sensation experienced when the thumb or fingers are lightly passed across the cut crumb surface. It may be harsh or 'drummy', silky, over-soft or 'woolly'.

Top crust

That part of the crust above the break or above the pan.

Total fermentation time

The time from when yeast activity commences in the brew, ferment, sponge or dough to the time when the yeast is inactivated in the loaf during baking.

Total production time

The time taken from the commencement of the assembly of the raw materials to the time when the finished loaf is ready for dispatch.

Vesiculation

The cell structure of the crumb of the loaf.

Viscosity

The property of a dough that is measured by rate of flow.

PART TWO

Flour Confectionery

20

Powder Aerated Goods: Basic Formulae and Production; Baking Confectionery Products: Reasons for Different Temperatures

POWDER AERATED GOODS

As the name implies, these are bakery products that are aerated solely by means of baking-powder, that is, they are aerated chemically. It will be noticed from the recipes given, that they contain little or no egg and the fat content is low, therefore they will stale fairly quickly. To be at their best they must be sold and eaten in as fresh a condition as possible. It follows, therefore, that they should be made and be on sale early in the day, hence the name by which they are better known—morning goods.

Scones are probably the best known of this group, and it is a pity that these and other morning goods are less popular than they were many years ago, when greater care was taken in the choice of raw materials and in the manufacture. Probably the greatest single factor in this loss of popularity is the 'bite' or after taste, due to faulty balance of the constituents of baking-powder. This point will be explained in greater detail when the chapter on 'Chemical Aeration' is reached.

Here is a formula for baking-powder:

lb.	*oz.*	
2	0	cream of tartar or cream powder
1	0	bicarbonate of soda

The two chemicals are thoroughly sieved together and stored in a tin with a close fitting lid. It is essential that the powder be kept dry or premature reaction will take place and the powder will be spoiled.

Scones properly made are delightful, and there are many varieties that can be made and studied by the student. Overleaf are basic mixings for white and wheatmeal scones.

There are two methods of making scones. With the first method the fat is rubbed finely into the flour and baking-powder which are sieved together. A bay is made into which the sugar, egg, milk, salt and nutmeg is placed. The sultanas are placed round the flour on the outside of the bay. After the sugar has been dissolved in the milk a little of the flour from the inside of the bay is drawn in. Using the fingers, the rest of the flour is brought in and the whole of the ingredients are thoroughly dispersed. The mix is then cleared by applying reasonable pressure.

Scones	*White*		*Wheatmeal*	
	lb.	*oz.*	*lb.*	*oz.*
Flour	1	0		—
Wheatmeal		—	1	0
Baking-powder		1		1
Butter or shortening		2		3
Sugar		2		2
Milk		8		8
Egg		2		2
Nutmeg		q.s.		q.s.
Colour		none		none
Sultanas		2		2
Salt		$\frac{1}{8}$		$\frac{1}{8}$

q.s. Quantum suff.—in sufficient quantity.

The second method consists of a preliminary creaming of the fat and sugar. The creamed mixture is placed with the other ingredients in the bay made in the sieved flour and baking-powder. The dough is then made as described for the first method.

The student must practise making small mixings by hand, so that he can make dough free from scraps and not unduly toughened. It will not be easy at first, but with the guidance of an older craftsman and with continued practice the task will become easier.

Scone Rounds (White or Wheatmeal)

After making up, the dough is scaled and moulded into round shapes. The basic mixing given will make three rounds at 10½ oz. or four rounds at 8 oz. After about 10 min., the pieces are re-moulded and then pinned out and placed on to clean baking-sheets, cut into four with a scraper and carefully washed with egg. After resting to recover from the manipulation they are baked at 450–460° F.

When baked, the scone round should have a soft silky crust, golden in colour; the division should be clear and well defined; the crumb should be soft, and, if white flour is used, a natural creamy white in colour.

Turnover Scones (White or Wheatmeal)

Proceed as for scone rounds weighing at 8 oz., but after the second moulding pin out a little thinner. Cut into four and arrange them singly on a clean baking sheet and egg-wash them. After the usual time for recovery, place into the oven. As soon as they can be handled without mutilation they are carefully turned over and replaced in the oven to finish baking.

These scones should be soft to the touch, with an upper surface on which should be seen a distinct triangle of golden brown.

Victoria Tea Scones (White or Wheatmeal)

Again proceed as for scone rounds, but in this case, the whole of the dough is pinned out to about ½ inch in thickness. Pieces are then cut out with a 2½ in. plain cutter and arranged on a clean baking sheet and carefully washed with egg. After the usual recovery period, they are baked at 450° F.

Plate No. XXVIII shows a scone round, turnover scones and Victoria tea scones.

Victoria scones should be uniform in thickness and shape. The top crust should be a circle of golden brown, in direct and pleasing contrast to the lighter colour of the sides. The crumb should be soft and mellow. If required to be fruited, use 2 oz. of currants to each pound of flour.

Among the many varieties of powder goods—knowledge of which can be obtained from the many bakery recipe books—are four that appear from time to time in the examinations of the City and Guilds; these will be described in some detail. The formulae are overleaf.

If these goods are to be 2 oz. in weight after baking, they should be weighed at 2 oz. each. The addition to weight of the egg-wash and sugar, etc., will be counterbalanced by the normal baking losses. These goods can be made by either of the two methods given for scones.

It sometimes happens that a small quantity of baking-powder is required which would be impossible to weigh accurately on the bakery scales. For this reason, what is termed 'scone flour' is made up and kept ready to hand. It is made by thoroughly sieving together 4 lb. of flour and 3 oz. of baking-powder; thus, 2½ oz. of scone flour contains approximately ⅛ oz. of baking-powder. Scone flour is known as 'soda flour' in Scotland.

Rock Cakes

This mixing will produce rock cakes of good quality, assuming that the ingredients are the best that can be procured (this applies, of course, to all goods). After making, they should be placed out in rough, rocky pieces on a cleaned and greased baking sheet; they are then egg-washed and sprinkled with castor sugar. Baking temperature is 450° F.

	Rock cakes		*Rice buns*		*Raspberry buns*		*Coconut buns*	
	lb.	*oz.*	*lb.*	*oz.*	*lb.*	*oz.*	*lb.*	*oz.*
Flour	1	0	1	0	1	0	1	0
Rice flour		—		2		—		—
Baking-powder		1		1		1		1
Butter		3		2		2		2
Shortening		2		2		2		2
Sugar		5		4		4		4
Milk		7		8		7		8
Egg		2		2		2		2
Sultanas		2		—		—		—
Currants		2		—		—		—
Peel		1		—		—		—
Fine coconut		—		—		—		2
Essence	lemon		vanilla		vanilla		almond	
Colour		q.s.		q.s.		q.s.		q.s.

Rice Buns

There is no inconsistency in expecting rice in rice buns, and the granularity of the ground rice should be apparent by its crunchiness when the bun is being eaten. It is a pity that there are so many finishes seen on rice buns. This standard finish is suggested. After the pieces have been moulded round, they should be egg-washed and the tops dipped into fine sugar nibs, no other decoration being added, such as red jam or cherries. They should be carefully baked at 440° F.

Raspberry Buns

The speeding up in modern methods has seen an alteration in the finish of these goods. Formerly they were moulded round and pressed flat. With a spot of raspberry jam placed in the centre the bun was then so folded that the jam was enclosed, after which it was egg-washed and pressed into castor sugar and placed on baking-sheets. It was completed by cutting a cross in the centre so that the red jam would boil out and be seen.

The practice at the present time is to make an indentation with the finger after the buns have been washed and sugared and placed on the baking-sheets; a spot of raspberry jam is then piped in to fill the indentation. Baking temperature 450° F.

Coconut Buns

After moulding round and egg-washing, the buns are pressed into medium coconut and then, after arranging on to baking-sheets, marked with a knife in a trellis pattern. They are very carefully baked at 440° F.

It is well to emphasize at this point that all baking sheets should be clean. There is no sense at all in being careful in manufacture, finish and baking if at the end the goods are soiled underneath from baked sugar, flour, egg or grease left on the sheet from a previous baking.

BAKING CONFECTIONERY PRODUCTS

Confectionery products are baked so that they are rendered suitable for human digestion, and just as the choice of raw materials, formula and manipulation are all important, they are all useless if the cake is spoiled during baking either by an incorrect temperature or timing, or by carelessness. Not only is there a loss of materials, but of time also.

There is a correct temperature and timing for every type of confectionery. Temperatures too low or too high for a particular type will lower the quality or spoil the product.

Temperature figures are governed by:

(1) Size of product.
(2) Quality of formula.
(3) Density.
(4) Thickness.
(5) Oven loading.
(6) Oven humidity.

A cake is baked when heat penetrates to the centre and upwards to the crown, therefore the heat will penetrate to the centre, of a small cake much more quickly than in the case of a larger cake; a thin cake more quickly than one more thick. A cake that is 'light' takes less time to cook than one that has a greater density.

The quality of the formula also must be considered. A cake rich in sugar, which caramelizes easily, will not need a high baking temperature. Buns, therefore, will need a higher baking figure than Madeira cakes, which in turn contain less sugar than macaroons. Meringues having a high sugar content, need the lowest temperature of all; in fact, the figure is such as to coagulate the albumen and dry the meringue only.

Because of the resultant heat loss, an oven full will need a higher temperature than an oven only partially full, and in this connection, humidity is a consideration. The greater the oven loading the greater the amount of steam generated, and the better the baking atmosphere. An oven, baking small quantities in proportion to its size, will need water pots so that the steam generated will increase the baking humidity.

Oven thermometers will vary, and the student is advised to study them. Bakery organization is important; goods should be produced in a sequence that will suit the oven temperature prevailing at any given time—for instance, one would not produce rock cakes and meringues, expecting one to be baked immediately after the other.

It is for this reason that in smaller bakeries certain types of goods are produced at certain times, or on definite days in a week, because they require different baking temperatures.

Lastly, oven-firing control is necessary, together with correct firing practice for the type of oven being used.

Temperature figures that are *too high* will cause cakes to have:

(1) Loss of volume.
(2) High crust colour.
(3) Underbaked centres.
(4) Distorted shape.
(5) Unpalatable flavour.

Temperature figures that are *too low* have the following effects:

(1) Dryness.
(2) Crust lacking colour and brightness.
(3) Loss of weight.
(4) Loss of flavour.

Baking temperatures (approximate figures):

	° F.
Fermented goods	450–460
Bath buns	420
Chelsea buns	420
Powder goods	450
Richer powder goods	420
Queen cakes	400
Short paste	420
Custards	400
Meat patties	420
Choux paste	450
Éclairs	420
Gingerbread	320
Ginger cakes	350
Bride and birthday cakes	330
Sponges	400
Savoy fingers and drops	440
Swiss Rolls	420
Light genoese	380
Macaroons	360
Meringues	250
Shortbreads	420
Thick	380
1st quality—1 lb.	380
1st quality—over 1 lb.	350
Cheaper—1 lb.	420
Cheaper—over 1 lb.	380
Slabs	
Heavily fruited	330
Medium fruited	350
Madeira	380
Cheaper madeira	400
Sweet paste	360
Puff paste	420
Heavy genoese	360
Madeira and Genoa cakes	
1st quality—1 lb.	380
2nd quality—1 lb.	400

A careful study of these baking figures will emphasize the necessity for care in baking confectionery products. They illustrate quite clearly the factors that govern temperature figures.

It will be seen, for instance, that the baking temperature for ordinary buns is between 450–460° F. Bath and Chelsea buns, both of which are enriched and contain more sugar, therefore, are baked at a lower temperature. The same considerations apply to powder goods; as the quality is increased so the baking temperature is lower.

Custards are baked at a lower temperature than ordinary short paste goods. This is because of the necessity of ensuring the baking of the short crust without overbaking the custard. Overbaking causes 'wateriness' due to the release of some of the water from the milk and egg proteins which become completely coagulated. Meat patties contain no sugar, so that a higher temperature for baking can be used, although not so high that sufficient baking time cannot be given to cook the meat properly.

A high baking temperature is one of the necessary factors for the maximum expansion of choux paste for cream buns. Less expansion is needed for éclairs and the shape must be not distorted. Cream buns are baked in special covered tins, or under inverted bread tins; éclairs are baked uncovered; this also explains a difference of about 30 degrees of heat.

The same difference in baking temperature is seen in ginger goods; gingerbread has a greater density and is baked in larger units and so is baked at a lower temperature than ginger cakes. The overall baking temperatures for ginger goods is low because of the high percentage of syrup they contain, syrup having a lower caramelization figure than ordinary sugar.

Puff pastry depends partly on a high baking temperature for expansion. Puff pastry pieces that are not sugared can be baked at a higher temperature than the 420° F. figure given.

The extra sugar contained in sweet paste explains the difference between the baking figures of short and sweet pastes.

Savoy fingers and drops are small and require to be baked very quickly to preserve the shape. Swiss rolls are thin and contain no fat: the heat penetrates quickly, baking temperature, therefore, is lower. Light genoese goods contain fat, have a greater density and are made in larger units, and this explains the lower temperature.

Macaroons and meringues have a high sugar content so that the baking temperatures are low, the meringues lowest of all, the temperature being such that they are dried without any caramelization of the sugar.

Size and thickness determines the baking figures of shortbreads.

Richly fruited cakes and slabs, particularly bride and birthday cakes, need a lower baking temperature because of the richness and the density of the mix.

21

Cake Decoration: Principles; Decorative Media; Icing and Piping; Tools and Equipment; Exercises; Colour: Theory and Classification

CAKE DECORATION

WHENEVER the subject of cake decoration is introduced the vast majority of people, even those within the baking industry, immediately think in terms of royal icing and its use in the decoration of bride, birthday and Christmas cakes.

This is quite wrong, for cake decoration covers far more than that. Anything that is added to any type of cake to render it more pleasing to the eye and the palate, or any form of manipulation that has that end in view, is a form of decoration.

The student, who can take pains in correctly cutting and egg-washing a round of scones, is a better decorator than someone, who finishes a birthday or similar cake in such a way that only a hungry person with a hardy stomach, or a person completely devoid of good taste, will enjoy it. One appeals to the palate through the eye; the other repels.

The cream cookie or Viennese tart that gets a perfunctory flick of the icing sugar dredger cannot be so appealing as those that are properly dusted. More important still, the cake becomes an index to the confectioner's attitude to the job, or to his lack of training, just as careful finish will show the good craftsman. The flour on the top of a farmhouse scone, the icing on a Swiss bun, the almonds on a Dundee cake, all these are examples of simple decoration that enhance the appearance of a cake.

With the exception of window showpieces, which are also a form of creative confectionery art, all cakes have to be sold and eventually eaten, therefore nothing added must detract from sales value or palate appeal.

Cake decoration is the form of creative art, and just as surely as the artist uses the pencil and brush, the musician sound, the sculptor wood and stone, so the confectioner uses the many bakery raw materials to express himself.

When careful work becomes a habit and the possibilities of raw materials are fully understood, additional skills are required—manipulative skill with a bag and pipe; skill in the use of colour; knowledge of form and design—but all these things must be subordinate to good taste. It is only then that the student can aspire to the standards of the great British craftsmen who are without equal in the world in the decoration of bride, birthday and Christmas cakes, and of the Continental craftsmen who are such masters in the art of freehand decorative work and the imaginative use of decorative materials.

Plate XXX is an illustration of superb work in chocolate and marzipan, by Spanish craftsmen.

Cakes can be covered or decorated with such media as

Water icing	Gum paste
Fondant icing	Chocolate
Almond paste	Royal icing
Sugar paste	Creams

Water Icing.—This is an icing that is easy to make. It is prepared by mixing sufficient boiling water with icing sugar and mixing until it is of spreading consistency.

Another method is to mix stock syrup with icing sugar and heat it over the gas, stirring all the time with a wooden spatula until it is just right for spreading. Water icings can be coloured and flavoured as desired. Stock syrup is made by boiling 3 lb. of lump or granulated sugar with 1 quart of water for a few minutes; remove the scum and add 8 oz. of glucose. When cool the syrup is bottled and used as desired.

Fondant.—Another material used by the baker for decorative work, differing a great deal from both royal and water icing, is fondant. Excellent fondant can be bought from manufacturers, so that it is not now an economic proposition for the baker to make his own, although at one time it was all part of the work of the confectioner.

The student, however, will be advised to make a small batch so that he will know more clearly what fondant is, and how it is made. Here is the formula:

lb.	*oz.*	
4	0	Lump or granulated sugar
1	4	(1 pint) water
	12	Glucose, or $\frac{1}{6}$ oz. cream of tartar or substitute, dispersed in a little water

The student will need a saucepan for boiling, a sugar boiling ther-

XXVIII Scones

XXIX Othellos, Iagos and Desdemonas

XXX A most excellent example of Spanish craftmanship

XXXI An excellent Chocolate roll

XXXII Good Madeira and Genoa cakes

XXXIII and XXXIV Examples of marbling

mometer, wash brush and a pot of clean water and four steel bars about 16 in. long.

The sugar and water are placed in the pan, put on the gas and stirred with a wooden spatula; it is not allowed to boil until the sugar is properly dissolved. At 225° F. the spatula is taken out and the warmed glucose poured in, or if used instead of glucose, the cream of tartar dispersed in a little water, either being allowed to mix into the sugar solution by the convection currents set up by heating. On no account should either be stirred in.

During the whole boiling period the sides of the pan must be carefully washed down. The scum should also be taken off. When the sugar solution has reached 240° F. it is removed at once from the gas, and the bottom of the pan immersed in cold water so that the heat retained in the metal of the bowl shall not still further raise the temperature of the solution.

While the sugar is boiling, the four metal bars are arranged in the form of a square on a clean marble slab and then splashed with water. The boiled sugar is poured into the square and allowed to cool to 100° F. Any sugar left in the bowl must not be scraped into the mass or it will grain.

When sufficiently cool the metal bars are removed, and with a metal scraper the sugar syrup is spread and turned. It will first change in colour to a milky white and finally into a stiff, white, creamy mass; it is covered with a damp cloth and left for about 30 min., after which it is rubbed down and moulded into a smooth plastic condition. It is placed in a tin with a close fitting lid and stored in a cool place until required.

The important points to remember are:

(1) The sugar must be carefully dissolved before boiling.
(2) When adding the warmed glucose or the cream of tartar at 225° F. do not stir.
(3) The pan must be washed down at intervals, so that no sugar thrown up on the sides of the pan during boiling will crystallize, thus graining the mass. The scum must be removed.
(4) Watch the thermometer carefully.
(5) Cool the solution to 100° F. before agitating.

When wanted for use, fondant is placed in a saucepan and carefully heated in a bain marie (water bath) to a temperature of about 100–105° F., the consistency being adjusted by the addition of stock syrup which is much better than water for adjusting fondant consistency. Stock syrup is a near saturated solution and will dissolve very little crystal, whereas water will do so before becoming saturated and thereby lower the gloss.

The fine gloss so characteristic of well prepared fondant is the reflection of light from myriads of tiny sugar crystals; overheating will dissolve these crystals, which on cooling will recrystallize into larger crystals, and in consequence there will be less reflection and so less gloss. Under-heating will cause the fondant to be runny and sticky. Plate XXIX shows the beautiful gloss on fondant covered Othellos, Iagos and Desdemonas.

Fondant can be coloured with any confectioner's colour, and in the case of chocolate fondant the good craftsman will add melted couverture or chocolate compound using chocolate colour only to adjust the depth of colour.

A good craftsman will also remove the spatula from the pan when he has finished, and after scraping down the sides of the pan will run in a little cold water to cover the surface of the fondant; it will then be in good condition when next it is wanted for use.

Dry Fondant.—A new type of fondant is now available to the baker. It is produced by a process which mixes microscopic sucrose crystals and particles with a highly super-saturated solution of sucrose, dextrose and levulose. When all the minute sugar crystals are enveloped in the sugar syrup, the whole mass is crystallized to form a dry product.

An examination will show that the resultant product resembles granulated sugar in particle size; the particles are, however, aggregates of crystals. When water or stock syrup is added, the insulating envelopes dissolve and the sucrose crystals are floated into suspension the whole becoming a creamy fondant.

The makers claim that dry fondant can be reconstituted with fruit juices, milk or cream, in fact anything that has in it sufficient moisture to produce fondant of a spreading or dipping consistency.

Royal Icing

There are few things that give greater pleasure to the young confectioner than a bowl of royal icing, some icing pipes and icing bags. Before him is the vista of the whole range of classic cakes, from the early masters of the art, through Borella and Schur to the acknowledged genius, the late Ronald Rock. With this medium, the young craftsman-to-be can aspire to a well decorated commercial cake, to the exhibition show bench, and—who knows?—to something new in cake decoration. So a new name will arise, a new style will be copied and something different will be admired.

There are other popular decorative materials, such as fondant, chocolate, sugar paste and marzipan, but nothing quite like royal icing. With it, work of the most incredible fineness can be executed;

it can be coloured to give the most beautiful pastel tints; it will, in competent hands, give a fine surface on which to pipe, that will be a joy both to the geometrically minded decorator and to the one with a flair for freehand work.

Royal icing is an intimate mixture of egg whites or an egg white substitute and icing sugar, into which air is incorporated by beating. Here is the formula and the method of making it:

lb.	*oz.*	
1	4	(1 pint) egg whites or substitute
7	0	Icing sugar (approx.)

One egg white weighs about an ounce.

Place the whites into a basin, add about a third of the sugar and stir in. Add another third and beat well. Sugar should then be added a little at a time, beating well between each addition, until the correct consistency is reached. This can be tested by lifting the spatula from the icing; if the point of the peak so made remains upright without sagging, the icing is ready.

It is absolutely essential that the ingredients and the utensils are free from grease. The basin and spatula, or machine bowl and beater, should be washed with hot water and soda or some preparation that will ensure that the utensils are grease free.

Fat has a shortening effect on the whites, so that they will not hold the air that is beaten in. For this reason also, if shell eggs are used, care must be taken in separating the whites and yolks. Yolks are rich in fat and any spots that are allowed to get into the whites will spoil the icing.

The icing sugar should be dry and powdery. The question of whether it should be sieved should not arise, for if it does need sieving it is not in an ideal condition for making royal icing. Further, if it is sieved, there is a danger of getting particles of other materials, including fat, from the bakery sieve.

Shell whites are strengthened if allowed to stand for some hours before use. Stability can be conferred on whites if they are weak by the addition of a few drops of lemon juice or acetic acid. It is extremely important to remember that it is not the sugar alone that confers stiffness to royal icing; the minute air bubbles entangled in stable whites, are equally important.

If the icing is to be white, a little blue should be added. If any other colour is to be used, blue must be omitted, otherwise the purity of the colours used will be spoiled. If made in a machine, the beater should be used and not the whisk. High speeds should not be used, neither should the icing be overbeaten, because the honeycomb texture of overbeaten icing will make coating difficult and fine piping impossible.

Royal icing must at all times be covered with a damp cloth to prevent skinning. Nothing is so conducive to bad temper and loss of time than to be constantly unblocking icing pipes that have been choked with hard particles of icing. Palette knives or any metal utensil should never be left in the icing, or bad discoloration will occur, especially if acid has been used.

ICING AND PIPING

There is nothing highly technical about the skill necessary for icing and piping. It is a manual skill in which dexterity is acquired by constant practice. It is simply a matter of pressure control and flexibility of wrist.

During the first lessons in piping the student must learn to relax. There is always a tendency to tense the body, and even to suspend breathing for short intervals while an attempt is made to pipe an accurate line. Unfortunately for the line, but fortunately for the student, the heart continues to beat, and its rhythm is transferred to the line through the tensed body—so the line bears a fair resemblance to an electrical recording from a medical research establishment.

The student, therefore, must relax and breathe naturally while at work, and practise continuously until the thumb and wrist obey the dictates of the brain. The heart and lungs have nothing to do with icing and piping; the thumb, wrist and brain *are* important.

The practice of hygiene and cleanliness is a necessity and must be learned at the beginning. *Never* suck an icing pipe; it is a bad habit that is easy to acquire, but hard to discontinue. A good demonstrator or teacher never does this, because he has more respect for himself and his craftsmanship. A clean damp cloth is a much more hygienic and efficient means of wiping the end of a tube.

Making an Icing Bag.—Craftsmen have different ways of making an icing bag, all of them correct if the result is a compact bag that will hold a pipe and some icing, which after folding can be used to pipe cleanly and efficiently without strain to the operator's thumb, wrist and temper.

A standard sheet of strong greaseproof paper can be folded into four, eight, or sixteen rectangles, which when cut diagonally will produce icing bags of three sizes. The student will meet occasionally a smart person who can get one bag from one sheet by the simple expedient of cutting off a corner, the rest of the sheet invariably being wasted. This type of rugged individualist is, of course, mentally retarded, because if he had the team spirit and cut the whole sheet up into bags, work would be easier for all.

To make the bag, take the triangle of paper in the left hand (Fig. 51), with the right angle to the lower right (*a*); the top is then folded back to a sharp point about halfway along the longest edge (*b*). Keeping the point secure, the folding is completed (*c*). The bag is finished when the flap is tucked in (*d*).

Never use a bag that is too big for the type of work being executed;

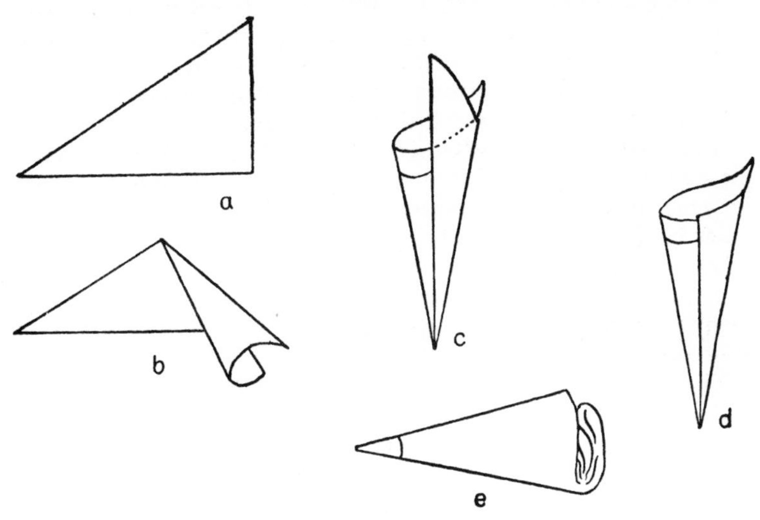

FIG. 51.—Making a piping bag.

it is impossible to do fine work with a big bag of icing clutched in the hand. Furthermore, the thumb and the wrist will rapidly tire. At the same time, it is obviously unwise to start a large border with a tiny bag that will need constant refilling.

A bag should never be filled so full that it cannot be properly folded and closed. Quite apart from the fact that the icing will escape, it is necessary to fold sufficient paper to act as a pressure lever (*e*). As the bag empties, so a further fold is made, and the icing is thus constantly where it should be—between the thumb and the tube aperture.

Equipment.—The student, proficient now in the making of royal icing, and able to make a bag, will be ready for the next step, provided he has acquired the few tools necessary for practice.

Turntable.—This is a piece of equipment that is designed to take the weight of a cake, so that it can be rotated in any direction and at any speed that the decorator desires. In its simplest form it is in two parts, the table which rotates and the pedestal on which the table spins. If the pedestal stands firmly, and the table spins freely and with precision, that is all that is necessary, especially if it is made with rustless metal. Complicated turntables with tilting devices and clips are not really necessary for the beginner.

The turntable must be kept clean, the spindle wiped occasionally and kept well oiled.

Palette Knife.—This is indispensable. The blade should be about 7 in. long and not too flexible. After use it should be cleaned and wiped dry. In this way the knife will be kept bright and serviceable and not stain and discolour the icing. Apart from other uses, the small palette knife is an excellent tool for mixing colour into small amounts of icing on the marble slab, or on a small piece of plate glass.

Icing Pipes.—To start with, six pipes are all that is necessary; later the student will need about ten more. Never be tempted to buy pipes for which there is little or no use, or sets of tubes, many of which may never be used. Remember that a competent decorator can finish a cake without the use of pipes. The mere possession of them does not of itself make a good decorator, any more than the possession of many pairs of tennis shorts will mean playing on the centre court at Wimbledon!

The six pipes suggested are Nos. 1, 2, 3 and 4, known as the writers, and a small and large coarse star.

Having purchased the pipes, the next important thing to do is to decide to look after them, so that they are always in good condition and ready for use. More pipes are spoiled by misuse and lack of care than are discarded after genuine wear.

When work is finished the pipes should be taken from the paper bags, dropped into water and allowed to soak. If it is necessary to clean them at once it will be easier with a camel-hair brush. Never leave icing to harden in the pipes; time will be wasted in soaking before they can be properly cleaned, or they will be damaged if the hard icing is forcibly removed with a sharp instrument.

Plastic Scrapers.—It is a good plan to get a few plastic scrapers and keep them solely for cake decoration purposes, preferably those of larger size, strong and barely flexible. They will be found to be excellent for a smooth finish when coating the side of a cake. They can also be cut in many patterns for side decoration.

Other Requirements.—Apart from basins, wooden spatulas, colours and cloths, it is advisable to get a rigid straight edge of metal, preferably stainless steel. This should be about 18 in. long and is an excellent tool for obtaining a smooth unbroken surface on the top coating of a cake.

Some rectangular pieces of sheet metal or perspex are advisable for piping practice; the icing can easily be scraped off, and if it has not been left to harden, can be used again. Perspex is particularly useful for the student because designs, after being drawn on paper, can be placed under the perspex; the pattern being easily visible makes an excellent piping guide.

A piece of black plastic board is also useful for practising fine work, the white icing showing up strongly against the black background, which is therefore conducive to careful work because any inaccuracy is more clearly evident.

The First Attempt.—It has already been stated that the two basic skills necessary in piping are pressure control and flexibility of the wrist, so that the first attempt should consist of getting used to the feel of the bag.

For the first experiment, place a No. 2 pipe in a small bag, put in some icing and fold it carefully in the way already described; put the thumb on the pressure point, let the forefinger rest along the side of the bag, the other fingers resting in the palm of the hand out of the way.

To steady the bag, use the tip of the forefinger of the other hand, just keeping contact with the side of the bag, then spend a short time pressing and releasing the thumb, moving the bag all the time. It is easy to do, satisfying, and great fun, because before long some measure of control will be apparent, and there will be a conscious effort to control the movement so that some order will come out of the chaos on the board. The student is not anything like a good piper yet, but he is ready for the next lesson.

It had been said that anybody who can pipe a straight line and an accurate rhythmic curve can do the most complicated and exacting piping on a cake. To a certain extent it is perfectly true, for not only does it infer mastery of the piping technique, but emphasizes the fact that most designs are based on the line and the curve.

Pencil a line on a sheet of paper and place it under the sheet of perspex, or pencil a line on a small rectangular sheet of metal, then place the tip of the pipe at the starting point and begin to press, lifting the bag a little so that an inch or so of icing is suspended in the air as it is guided along the line. Stop pressing just before the end is reached, and carefully lower the bag so that the thread of suspended icing can be carefully placed to complete the line.

When the line has been piped satisfactorily, place another on either side, as close as possible without actually touching, and repeat this until a number of parallel lines have been piped. Repeat this exercise with a No. 1 pipe. This apparently simple, but necessary exercise will need constant practice before any degree of efficicncy is attained.

It is important during practice that the body is relaxed and free from any tension. The placid approach makes for better and finer work.

COLOUR IN CONFECTIONERY

The predominant colour in almost all confectionery products is the golden colour imparted by the baking process. This is varied by the use of highly coloured materials such as cherries, angelica, jellies and jam. In display, colour is also added by meringues which can be produced in a variety of pleasing pastel tints. Cakes that show colour in the cut surfaces such as genoese fancies and battenburg all help in the colour display, especially if they are adorned with coloured almond or sugar paste. Further sources of colour come from creams, fondant and chocolate.

The internal appearance of the cake is enhanced by the use of colour; the rich colour of egg, for instance, suggests quality in some types of cake, the equally rich colour of raw sugar, in others. The function of colour in confectionery products, therefore, is to add to the general appearance and to heighten the sales and palate appeal.

Before the student uses the variety of colours that are to be found in the bakery, he should have an elementary knowledge of what colour is and its source.

It was Newton who discovered that colour was derived from light. He found that a beam of light, when passed through a prism, was broken up into a band of colours which emerged from the other side, and could be shown on a screen. This is the spectrum and can be seen in magnitude when looking at a rainbow. Seven distinct colours are visible—violet, indigo, blue, green, yellow, orange and red. Colours are known as hues.

The only true white light is daylight and it is an intimate mixture of all the colour rays. If a substance absorbs all the colour rays except one, that exception is reflected and that is the colour that we can see. Substances that reflect back colour rays are called pigments. Confectionery colours are therefore pigments. Red confectionery colour will absorb all the colour rays except red, which is reflected back. We say then that the colour is red. Blue colour reflects blue, yellow colour reflects yellow and so on. Green colour reflects back yellow and blue; orange colour yellow and red; mauve colour blue and red.

White reflects all the colour rays and black absorbs them all reflecting none. Black and white do not possess colour, they are achromatic. Grey is a reflection of two complementary colours and the greying of icing invariably shows carelessness in the use of colours.

Primary Colours.—There are three primary colours—red, blue and yellow. From these three all other colours can be produced.

Secondary Colours.—These are mixtures of any two primary colours.

Orange—Red and yellow
Mauve—Red and blue
Green—Yellow and blue

Tertiary Colours.—These are mixtures of any two secondary colours.

Complementary Colours.—These are the colours that contrast more strongly with one colour than another. They are the opposites on the colour circle. Complementary colours mixed together in equal proportions produce grey.

Tints.—A tint is a colour mixed with white, that is, it has its luminosity increased. When a colour is used with a white icing base the result is a tint of that colour.

Shades.—A colour that has had its luminosity decreased by the addition of brown or black is a shade of the colour used.

It is essential that the basic colour in cake decoration shall be pale pastel tints (chocolate and possibly coffee excepted). Deeper colours can be used sparingly to give contrast and to ensure harmony.

22

Short Pastry: Principles of Manufacture; Basic Formula; Diagnosis of Faults; Puff Pastry: Principles of Lamination; Types and Methods of Manufacture; Basic Formulae; Reasons for the lift; Diagnosis of Faults

SHORT PASTRY

THE dictionary meaning of the word 'short' in the bakery sense is—friable, easily broken; in fact the direct opposite to tough, resilient or elastic.

The student will know that when insoluble wheat proteins take up water, an elastic substance is formed, known by both miller and baker as gluten. It depends a great deal on the type of wheat milled, whether the resultant flour will have a strong, medium or weak gluten; this in turn depends on where the wheat is grown and the soil and weather conditons in that area. It can be said then that the measure of flour strength is based mainly on the strength and quality of the gluten.

Short pastry is a mixture of flour, fat, sugar, egg, or egg and milk; it follows logically, therefore, that the flour used should be one with a low gluten strength, i.e. one milled from soft wheats such as Australian or English.

All fats are shortening agents, that is, they reduce the extensibility of gluten according to the amount used to a given weight of flour, and according to the article being manufactured, and the method of production.

The usual method of making short pastry is to rub the fat into the sieved flour and to do this so that it is finely dispersed without turning the fat/flour into a continuous paste. A bay is made into which is placed the sugar and the liquids. After the sugar has been dissolved, the whole mass is lightly mixed until the ingredients are properly distributed, when reasonable pressure is applied to turn the mass into a plastic paste. As an alternative method, the fat and sugar can be creamed, the egg/milk added, then dispersed through the flour and finished as described.

If it is remembered that insoluble protein plus water develops gluten, and that fat is a shortening agent; it can be seen that it acts as a barrier between protein and water; by dispersing it thoroughly in the flour it insulates the protein particles against hydration. Carelessness in this dispersion will obviously allow some development of gluten.

Sugar has a solvent property on gluten and to exert this it must be in solution. The water content in the small amount of egg/milk is low, so that it becomes necessary for the sugar to be fine and of soft grain so that it may be more easily dissolved. A coarse hard-grained sugar will not be dissolved in so small a quantity of liquid; the crystals will remain in the pastry and will not exert a softening influence on the gluten; finally, they will caramelize in baking and will be seen on the surface as dark brown spots.

These are the basic principles of short pastry manufacture. There are, however, other precautions that must be observed if the pastry is not to be subsequently toughened. If too much working is given the paste, it is possible that gluten may be developed, due probably to a forcing of the fat barrier. This can happen when scraps and cuttings are being incorporated. The use of too much dusting flour will also cause toughening due to the protein in the added flour becoming hydrated.

If the only flour available for short pastry is too strong, the strength can be decreased by diluting with a flour containing no gluten forming protein, for instance, cornflour; two ounces of each pound of flour being replaced by a similar amount of cornflour.

It must be remembered also that margarine and compound fat contain differing percentages of fat—margarine contains about 84% and compound 100%—and that 13½ oz. of compound is equivalent to 16 oz. of margarine in shortening properties. If compound fat is used alone then it is necessary to add a little salt.

Here is a formula for short pastry:

lb.	*oz.*	
1	0	Flour (soft)
	8	Butter or margarine
	4	Fine castor sugar
	2½	Egg/milk
		Colour

Here is a summary:

(1) Use soft flour.

(2) Rub fat in finely.

(3) Use a soft fine sugar.
(4) Disperse ingredients thoroughly without undue pressure, before applying reasonable pressure to make a plastic paste.
(5) Use very little dusting flour.
(6) Do not overwork scraps.

PUFF PASTRY

There are two types of puff pastry, full and three-quarter. There are three well-known methods of manufacture—English, French and Scotch.

The differences in these types are in the fat contents and in the number of rolls and folds given them. Full puff pastry contains flour and fat in equal ratio, while three-quarter pastry contains three-quarters of fat to each pound of flour. The differences in method are in the way that the fat is incorporated.

The flour for making puff pastry should be strong, with a good quality gluten that is resilient and has elasticity. This is necessary so that it will stand up to the manipulation entailed in building up a laminated structure and because only a strong stable gluten will assist in giving the lift to the pastry piece in the oven.

A weak acid such as lemon juice, tartaric or cream of tartar is sometimes used to confer a greater extensibility on the gluten. The natural lemon juice is best, or tartaric acid which is more readily soluble in cold water than cream of tartar.

Without doubt the best fat to use is butter, provided that it is of good flavour and is tough and stable enough for a structure to be built up. A good substitute is a high quality pastry fat or pastry margarine. They are only completely satisfactory, however, if the melting-point is lower than the temperature of the human body, otherwise there is the possibility of a film of fat remaining on the roof of the mouth after the pastry has been eaten. They will, however, stand up to the rolling and folding during manufacture without squeezing out.

The whole purpose of rolling and folding is to build up a structure of alternating layers of dough and fat. If it were possible to count these layers when the pastry piece is ready for the oven, it would be found that there are many hundreds. This build up is known as aeration by lamination.

Here is a formula for puff pastry which can be made either on the English or French method:

lb.	*oz.*		*lb.*	*oz.*	
1	0	Strong flour		10	(½ pint) cold water (approx.)
	2	Butter or cake margarine		14	Butter or pastry margarine
		Colour			

English Method (Fig. 52).—After the flour has been sieved, the 2 oz. of butter or margarine is rubbed in. Into the bay made in the flour, the water, colour and acid (if used) are placed and the whole made into a well developed dough; it is then moulded into a square shape. After recovery from the manipulation, it is pinned out to a long rectangular shape about 18 in. by 6 in. Two-thirds of the surface

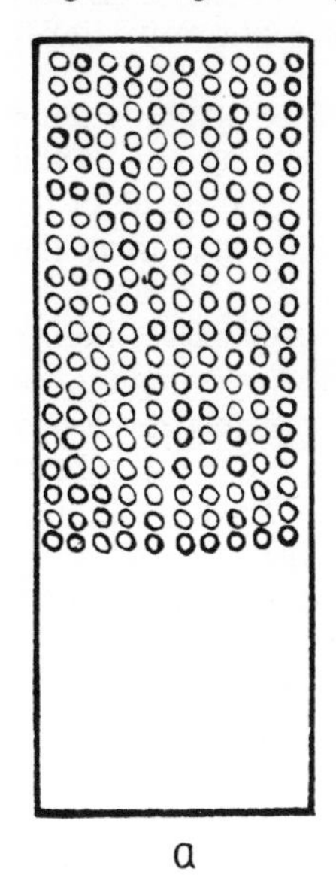

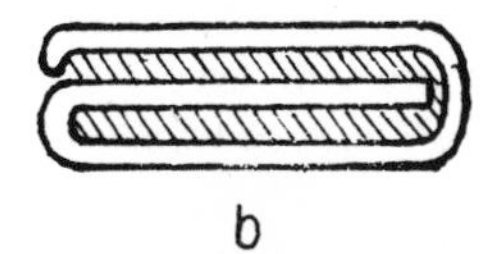

FIG. 52.—Puff pastry.
The English method.

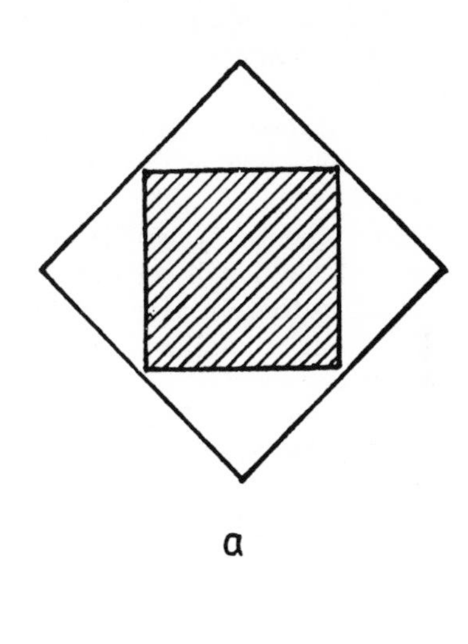

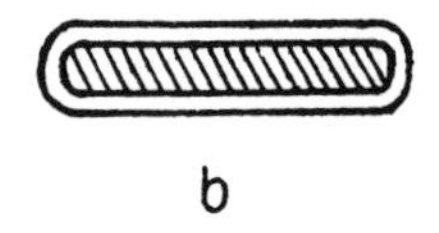

FIG. 53.—Puff pastry.
The French method.

is covered with small pieces of butter, taking care that the pieces are not too near the edge (*a*).

The flap of dough containing no butter is brought up and the top third of the dough containing butter is brought down, so that there are three layers of dough and two of butter (*b*). The pastry is given a half turn so that the open ends are parallel to the rolling-pin and again pinned out to a rectangle and folded into three. This process is repeated, the dual operation being known as a full turn. The pastry is covered with a damp cloth and allowed to recover from the manipulation for about 30 min. Altogether six half turns (or three full turns) are given, with a period for recovery between each full turn.

The term 'half turn' originated from the change of position that is given the pastry after folding; this is to ensure that subsequent rolling is done against the open ends of the pastry, rather than against the closed sides which would make it difficult, if not impossible to get a regular rectangular shape for the next folding.

French Method (Fig. 53).—The dough is made in exactly the same fashion as for the English method. The initial pinning out of the dough, however, is different, for it is rolled out to the shape of an opened envelope, with the four angles slightly thinner than the centre.

The butter or pastry fat is placed in one squared piece on the centre of the dough (*a*) and the envelope is closed by bringing the four angles to the centre. The butter should be completely enveloped within dough of uniform thickness (*b*). The pastry is then pinned out to a rectangle and finished in the same way as for the English method, that is, given six half turns with a recovery period between each two.

Scotch Method.—This is the quickest method of making puff pastry. Very old recipe books describe it as the 'blitz' method. As 'blitz' is derived from the German 'blitzen', meaning lightning, it seems possible that this method originated in central Europe.

To make puff pastry on the Scotch method, the butter or pastry fat is mixed into the sieved flour in pieces about the size of walnuts. The water, colour and acid (if used) are placed into the bay and the whole mixed together, without using too much pressure, to form a dough with the butter pieces more or less intact. The pastry is rolled into rectangular shape and folded into three, exactly the same as for the English and French methods. The six half turns can be given without recovery time, although it is not advised.

The Structure of Puff Pastry.—It is necessary for the bakery student, especially if he is mathematically minded, to have a clear mental picture of the laminated structure of puff pastry.

If he will study the illustration of the English method (Fig. 52) he will note that after the inclusion of the butter, there are two layers of butter and three layers of dough. During each folding, two layers of dough meet in two places in the folded structure. Each two are welded together in the subsequent rolling, so that for the purpose of calculation, two dough layers have to be subtracted.

After each half turn, the butter layers are multiplied by three; the dough layers are multiplied in the same way, but the number, as explained, is always less two. The calculations follow on next page.

English Method

	Butter	*Dough*
At start	2 layers	3 layers
1 turn	6 layers	7 layers
2 turns	18 layers	19 layers
3 turns	54 layers	55 layers
4 turns	162 layers	163 layers
5 turns	486 layers	487 layers
6 turns	1458 layers	1459 layers

There is another method of folding pastry made on the English method and it is known as the book fold. After the butter has been incorporated and the pastry pinned out to a rectangle in the normal way, the two ends are folded to the centre after which the pastry is folded into book form so that there are four thicknesses of pastry. This operation is repeated four times in all, with suitable rests between folds. Finally it is pinned out and folded in two.

This time the butter layers are multiplied by four at each turn. The dough layers are also multiplied by four, but as two layers of dough come in contact three times in each fold, three dough layers are lost. At the final turn one dough layer is lost. The structure is made up as follows:

Book Fold

	Butter	*Dough*
At start	2 layers	3 layers
1 turn	8 layers	9 layers
2 turns	32 layers	33 layers
3 turns	128 layers	129 layers
4 turns	512 layers	513 layers
5 turns	1024 layers	1025 layers

Those very fine craftsmen, Harris and Borella were against this method of folding. In their book *All about Pastries* they have a list of puff pastry 'don'ts', one of which is 'Don't fold the two ends of the pastry to the middle'. For good measure the last of the don'ts is 'don't ignore the don'ts—they are of the utmost importance'.

An examination of the illustrations explaining the French method (Fig. 53) shows that at the start there is one layer of butter and two of dough. Again multiplying the layers by three at each turn, but eliminating at each turn two dough layers that are lost in each subsequent rolling, the structure shown at top of next page is built up.

The number of fat/dough layers there are in finished Scotch puff pastry is a matter for conjecture.

Examining these figures, one fact stands out clearly—the ratio fat/

French Method

	Butter	*Dough*
At start	1 layer	2 layers
1 turn	3 layers	4 layers
2 turns	9 layers	10 layers
3 turns	27 layers	28 layers
4 turns	81 layers	82 layers
5 turns	243 layers	244 layers
6 turns	729 layers	730 layers

dough layers in each method is approximately equal. It is seen that English puff pastry has twice as many layers as the French, with the 'book-fold' midway between. The precise person who would want uniformity would simply pin out the French pastry after the sixth turn and fold it in two. The 'book-fold' layering can be brought up more nearly to these numbers by folding into three at the fifth and last turn, instead of into two.

Uniformity, however, does not arise, because the number of turns must vary according to the flour and butter qualities, the type of goods made, and whether the pastry is 'full,' 'three-quarter', or even 'half'—this last being used for making many kinds of pastry cases that are baked before filling, such as large open fruit tarts. The craftsman will not only decide on the method that he uses but on the handling.

When the nature of the laminated structure is understood, the student will realize more clearly the importance of keeping the sides of the pastry straight, and the corners square, when rolling and folding. It is evident that carelessness will mean the loss of many layers; in the last turns many hundreds of layers can be lost. Care in rolling and folding will conserve the structural form so that the best results are achieved.

Reasons for the Lift.—This has been a subject for conjecture for many years. Explanations such as the expansion of air trapped within the pastry during folding; the action of acid; the boiling of the fat during baking; the expansion and pressure of steam from the water in the butter; all are wide of the mark and some impossible. When the amount of manipulation given puff pastry is considered, either by hand or by mechanical rolling, it is obvious that there is little likelihood of there being sufficient air present to give such expansion during baking. Acid is used to confer a greater resilience on gluten and does not generate gas, in any case puff pastry will rise without the use of acid.

That water in the fat is solely responsible for the lift can be easily discounted when it is remembered that compound pastry fats, properly used, make wonderfully light puff pastry and that they contain little or no water.

If the student will take several pieces of gluten of equal weight and place each in an oven of different temperature, he will note that expansion differs—the higher the oven temperature, the greater the expansion. Gluten is insoluble protein hydrated in the ratio of one part protein to two parts water. It is the generation of steam during baking, and the pressure of water vapour within the gluten that is largely the explanation of the lift.

In the oven the pastry piece, which we know consists of thin layers of dough separated by fine films of fat, comes under the influence of heat and the gluten in the dough layers is caused to expand and blister. The fat melts and the dough layers are insulated and as the fat takes on a higher temperature, the dough layers are cooked, the gluten coagulates and becomes comparatively rigid and the structure does not collapse. In short it is the expansion and blistering of the gluten in the dough layers as a result of steam pressure from the water in the dough that is mainly responsible for the lift in puff pastry.

Here is a summary of 'musts':

(1) The flour must be of suitable strength.
(2) The dough must be properly developed.
(3) The fat must be pliable.
(4) Rolling and folding must be done carefully so that a well defined laminated structure is built up.
(5) Any adhering flour must be brushed off before folding.
(6) Sufficient resting periods between turns must be given.
(7) To prevent skinning, the pastry must be covered with a damp cloth.
(8) Correct baking temperatures must be maintained.

Faults in Puff Pastry.—With an understanding of the build up of puff pastry, will come a natural care in rolling, folding and handling. The fact that in the laminated structure there are films of fat will underline the necessity for keeping the pastry in a cool place. If the pastry is not covered during resting periods, then the surface will skin and there will in consequence, be a cracking of the surface when rolling. Bad skinning could have an adverse effect on volume.

The importance of keeping straight sides and squared corners when rolling and folding the pastry has already been emphasized. Because the object of rolling and folding is to build up a structure the rolling pin and the machine roller should be used carefully; the rolling pin should never be used as a bludgeon or the machine as a mangle.

There is no sense in building a structure and then breaking it down again, for the result will only be pastries of poor volume.

Here in itemized form are the principal causes of lack of volume:

(1) Flour too soft; gluten having poor strength and stability.

(2) Dough not properly made; gluten, therefore, not properly developed.

(3) Pastry treated roughly in rolling, thus breaking down the laminated structure, the fat penetrating the dough layers and causing shortening. The dough should be so rested that it will roll easily without the use of too much force.

(4) Fat too soft making it difficult to build up a structure.

(5) Too many turns for the type of pastries being manufactured.

(6) Oven temperature too low, resulting in poor gluten expansion.

(7) Insufficient turns; the fat films are too large and thick, and on melting cannot be absorbed by the dough layers, the excess fat running out.

(8) Fat too hard. Because the fat lacks plasticity it will not film easily remaining in small particles between the dough layers. The insulation being incomplete, the dough layers in contact with the fat particles cannot absorb the concentration of fat when it melts in the oven and the excess runs out.

Here are some causes of mis-shapen articles:

(1) Insufficient resting between turns, or more especially before baking. The gluten is in such an elastic condition that the pastry pieces will 'pull' and be distorted in the oven during baking.

(2) Sometimes open puff pastry tarts will topple in the oven. This is due to over thickness; in consequence the expansion is too great and the tarts heel over before the pastry is set.

(3) Inaccurate folding. It has already been explained that if care is not taken when rolling and folding then many hundreds of layers may be lost, resulting in bad shapes due to uneven expansion.

Flintiness is caused by using a flour with a gluten that is excessively strong and then baking at too low a temperature. Failure to brush off excessive dusting flour, or the excessive use of flour when using cuttings may also be causes.

23

Confectionery Flours: Grades; Special Cake Flour; Other Cereals: Processing; Uses in Bakery Products; Sugar: Sources and Refining; Sugars used in the Bakery

CONFECTIONERY FLOURS

For flour confectionery purposes, four distinct grades of flour should be available if the confectioner is to use the correct grade for the particular product that he is making. It is extremely important that these flours be studied so that the confectioner knows not only more about this important raw material, but why certain flours are used for particular types of confectionery.

Strong Flours.—We know that the gluten of the flour forms the girder or framework of a loaf or bun, and that the gas generated by the yeast is trapped in this gluten network and expansion takes place. For fermented bun goods it follows, then, that the gluten should be resilient enough to give to this expansion and at the same time to retain the gas. A good quality gluten will do this, and it is found in a medium strong flour or in a blend of strong and medium flours.

Puff pastry needs a strong flour with a gluten that is resilient, for not only must it stand up to the rolling and folding necessary in the manufacture of puff pastry, but it must also be strong enough to offer resistance to the pressure of water vapour within it, and so cause the pastry to lift in the oven. Choux paste also depends to a large extent on the structural quality of a strong gluten for expansion, and here again a strong flour is necessary.

Medium Strength Flours.—The girderwork in cakes can be both gluten and egg albumen; both are proteins which coagulate at a temperature of about 140° F., and if the cake formula is balanced, the framework becomes rigid and does not collapse.

In cakes that are aerated by means of baking-powder the gas is generated by the interaction of the chemicals in solution, during baking. As in yeast fermentation, the gas is entangled in the gluten structure, causing the cake to rise. Again the choice of flour is important. For these goods, flour of medium strength is required, resilient enough to withstand the rather rapid generation of gas during the initial period of baking.

If it is clearly understood that gluten and egg provide the cake strength and structure, then it will be seen that there must be a balance between them; as the quality of the cake increases—if more eggs are used, for example—a weaker flour must be used. The cheaper quality pound and slab cakes, and cheaper sponge goods will need the extra strength provided by the flours containing a gluten of medium strength.

Soft Flours.—All high quality sponge goods, slab and pound cakes contain the maximum quantity of eggs, which in a large measure provide the strength and structure of the cake; it follows therefore that to keep the structural balance, soft flours must be used.

Short pastry, as its name implies, must be short and friable, and the method of manufacture is such that the gluten is not developed. The first precaution is to use a flour of low gluten strength—a soft flour.

Special Cake Flour.—Special cake or high-ratio flour as it is more generally known, is marketed under different trade names, and is used in the manufacture of a special type of cake in which the ratio of sugar and milk to flour is very high.

This type of flour is milled from the centre of high-grade wheats, the extraction rate being between 40–50%. The gluten content is low, about 7–8·5%, but of the highest quality.

After milling, the flour is heavily chlorinated which destroys the coherency of the gluten to such an extent that if the student would wish to wash some out, a 5% salt solution is necessary go give sufficient stability for its recovery. The chlorine treatment also increases the acidity of the flour and renders the starch more soluble, increasing absorption and the retention of moisture.

The flour is milled very finely until the particles are minute compared with ordinary flour. The milling, however, is done with care so that the desired particle size is not attained at the expense of fractured starch granules. This smallness gives the flour a much greater power of adsorption.

Because of the smallness of the granule, there is a greater number to a given weight; in consequence there is a greater aggregate surface area to hold the extra moisture necessary for the type of cake in which this flour is used.

To make this more clear, let the student imagine a ball of lead weighing 8 lb. If this ball is immersed in water and re-weighed, it will be 8 lb. plus the weight of water held by surface tension. If the ball is made into tiny lead shot without loss of weight and the whole of them dipped into water, again the weight would be 8 lb. plus the weight of water held on the many surfaces. This time, however, the weight of water would be greater because of the greater surface aggregate.

The holding of moisture by surface tension is termed adsorption, not to be confused with absorption meaning, to take in; to incorporate with.

OTHER CEREALS USED IN BAKERY PRODUCTS

Wheat in the form of flour is such a common raw material in the bakery that the many other cereals used are apt to be forgotten. Many of them in fact are important in one way or another. While wheat is by far the most important cereal to the baker, rye, barley, rice and maize are all used.

Rye.—Wheat and rye are the only two grains that are milled into flour for breadmaking. The main differences are in the colour and in the gluten-forming proteins. Wheat has a fair quantity of insoluble protein that forms gluten on hydration. Rye flour has very little gluten-forming protein and is therefore unstable, producing a dough that, although of necessity made tight, is sticky and dense, having very little oven spring.

Rye bread is dark in colour, is close in structure and has little volume. Because of its density it requires slow baking. Most of the flavour comes from the sour dough used in its manufacture; the use of sour dough is traditional.

Rye bread is eaten extensively in Poland, U.S.S.R., Austria, Germany and in the cosmopolitan quarters of great cities. A whiter rye flour is available to the baker who wishes to add variety to bread sales. Rye bread, with the inclusion of caraway seeds, has a unique flavour and is becoming increasingly popular.

Barley.—Barley contains no gluten-forming protein and is therefore not milled into flour for breadmaking. The value of barley to the baking industry is in the production of malt.

Rice.—Rice has less food value than any other cereal for it has little protein, mineral matter and fat. It contains more starch than most cereals. It is ground to a coarse flour known to the baker as rice cones; this is used for dusting purposes, preventing dough pieces from sticking together on the table or in proving boxes. It is excellent for this purpose because it is dry and granular and does not readily absorb water. Any excess on the dough piece is therefore easily brushed off and can be used again.

For confectionery work it is used in the making of rice buns, rice cakes, rice slab, macaroons, shortbreads and in the filling for rice tarts. It can be used to dilute the gluten strength of flour, and as an ingredient in baking-powder.

Maize.—This cereal has the highest fat content of all, although there is little left after it has been processed commercially in the preparation of cornflour.

Cornflour is the whitest of all the cereal flours and can be recognized readily by its peculiar crunchy feel when handled. It is produced from the endosperm of the grain, the skins, known as the 'hull', and the germ being removed.

The separation is effected by soaking the corn in warm water in which there is a low concentration of sulphur dioxide. The soaking softens the grain and the sulphur dioxide inhibits fermentation.

The corn is next crushed and passed to water tanks where the germ, because of its fat content, floats and is removed. In a semi-fluid state, the hulls and the endosperm are ground finely and screened through fine silks which remove the hull particles. The endosperm is again subjected to gravity separation and the lighter protein particles contained in it are floated off. After filtration the cornflour is carefully dried.

Cornflour is practically 100% starch and so is easily gelatinized in hot water. It is a thickening agent and is used in custards, blancmanges and Turkish delight and as a glaze on fruit tarts and flans. An excellent glaze for 'bloomer' and rye breads, to be applied immediately on removal from the oven, can be made from gelatinized cornflour.

Cornflour can be used to dilute the gluten strength of flour and because it is a dry inert powder, it is used for the moulding of chocolate centres.

Oats.—This cereal has the highest food value of all. It is rich in mineral matter, fat and protein, although the latter has no gluten-forming property. Oats are available to the baker as oatmeal, which is in three grades—fine, medium and coarse.

Oatmeal is used in the bakery for parkins, oatcakes and ginger goods. It is used for flavouring purposes in, and for a dressing on, special types of wheatmeal bread and rolls.

SUGAR SOURCE AND REFINING

Apart from flour, sugar is probably the most common ingredient used in confectionery. It sweetens, and in cakes, according to the amount used and the type of cake being manufactured, it has a softening effect on the gluten of the flour.

It is used in such a variety of products, and in so many ways, that it is necessary for the baker to have available many types of sugar and many grades. The student will know, for example, that dark sugars such as Barbados and Trinidad are used for wedding, birthday and Christmas cakes. Softer brown sugars are useful for bun goods and some kinds of biscuits. Castor sugar is necessary for creaming purposes in cake-making, and for whipping with eggs and egg whites in sponge goods and for meringues. Fine granulated is used for cakes and sponges, the coarser grades for macaroons and for sugar boiling.

Icing sugar is used for all kinds of decorative work. Syrup and treacle is used for ginger goods. Fondant, which is simply sugar in a finer crystal form, is also used for decorative work.

Scientifically, sugar is a carbohydrate, of which there are three groups. Here are examples of each group:

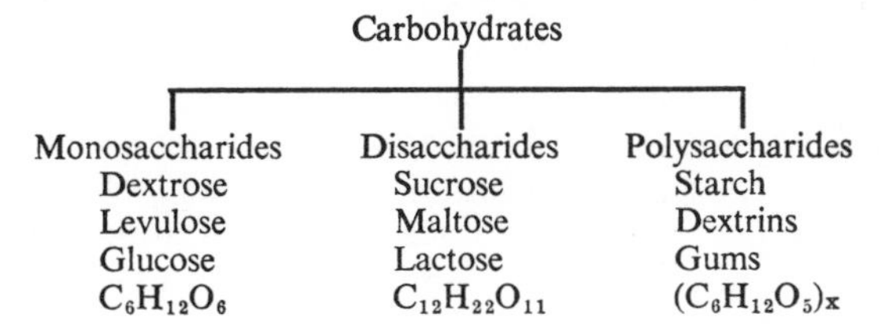

Each member of the group contains carbon, hydrogen and oxygen, and the majority contain hydrogen and oxygen in the same proportion as water (H_2O). Because there are so many sugars they are each given a different name, the one with which we are so familiar both domestically and in the bakery, is known as sucrose, whether it is cane or beet in origin.

Sugar is found in almost all plants, whether in the stems, as in the sugar cane or roots, as in carrots, parsnips and beet, or in the sap of trees such as the maple. When carbon dioxide is taken in by the leaves of the plant, the oxygen is excluded and the carbon combines chemically with the water that is absorbed by the roots.

Sunlight and the green colouring matter in the leaf, which is known as chlorophyll, changes this combination to starch. Further changes take place and sugar is evolved, which being soluble in water is contained in the sap and thus travels to all parts of the plant. The process of the chemical evolution of carbohydrates in a growing plant is known as photosynthesis.

It becomes obvious that for the commercial extraction of sugar, plant life containing a high proportion of sugar must be used, and it is for this reason that the sugar cane and the sugar beet are most successfully exploited, to produce the vast quantities of sugar needed today.

The Sugar Cane.—This grass-like plant is grown extensively in a number of tropical and sub-tropical countries. Some of these, like India, produces large quantities but there is no export. At the other end of the scale is British Guiana in South America which produces a negligible quantity, yet the sugar produced in the Demerara valley is world known. Amongst the more important countries producing sugar for export are Cuba, Puerto Rico and the Dominican Republic. All of these are in the West Indies, where there are also a number of minor producers such as Barbadoes. Sugar is also exported from Mauritius.

When ready, the cane is cut, trimmed and quickly passed through a series of rollers so that the maximum of sap is extracted. The residue or 'bagasse' is used as boiler fuel.

After filtration, the juice is treated with lime to remove organic acids and by heat to coagulate all the unwanted protein matter. The clear liquid is then heated until the moisture content is reduced from 82 to 40%, when it is transferred to vacuum pans for the moisture content to be reduced further until it is about 20%, when crystallization begins to take place. The form of crystallization is controlled by diluting the mass with water, until at last the pan is full of a mixture of crystals and a dark coloured syrup; this mixture is known as 'massecuite'.

The mass is then transferred to centrifugal machines where the crystals are separated from the syrup or molasses. The crystals, covered with a film of syrup, are raw sugar or 'muscovado'. In this condition it is shipped to refineries all over the world; the molasses either being fermented to alcohol, or exported for many commercial purposes, among which is the manufacture of yeast. Molasses is also used in the production of rum.

Refining.—Sugar refining is the separation of the sucrose from the uncrystallized matter, which is either refined to edible syrups or treacles, or sold as molasses to be used as cattle food or for distilling.

On arrival at the refinery the raw sugar is weighed and put into a tank fitted with stirrers, known as a 'mingler', where it is mixed with a liquid which is termed an 'affination' syrup, and which in the course of stirring helps to soften the molasses clinging to the crystals; water being added also to assist in this crystal washing. The mixture, called 'magma', is passed to centrifugal machines to remove as much molasses as possible and from thence to the 'melter' where the crystals are dissolved at 190° F.

After density adjustment and the introduction of lime, carbon dioxide gas is bubbled through, causing chalk to precipitate, taking with it such impurities as waxes and gums. After filtration, the brown liquor is passed through animal charcoal to remove the colour and any dissolved impurities. The charcoal in the filter has to be constantly changed and revived; the solutions that are first through are invariably the best and are known as 'first refined'. These are passed to vacuum pans, where water is removed, after which the 'masse' is cast into slabs, the syrup from which is removed in centrifugal machines. The slabs are dried and cut into cubes.

The rest of the liquor from the filtration plant is treated in exactly the same way as for 'first refined' except that it is not cast into slabs. Instead pure sugar crystals are formed which are washed, spun and dried and as granulated sugar packed into the familiar packets, or into bags.

Beet Sugar.—Stimulated by the extreme shortage of sugar during the first world war, the production and refining of sugar from beet has expanded to such an extent that enormous quantities of sugar are produced in this country every year.

The sugar beet has a large, white, fleshy root and will keep in good condition for a reasonable time after harvesting. It is trimmed and has a preliminary cleaning before it is delivered to the sugar refinery, where further cleaning takes place, after which it is cut up into shreds known to the refiner as cossettes.

The cossettes are put into diffusion tanks with water under pressure and at a controlled temperature. When the rate of diffusion slows down, that is, when the sugar less readily leaves the flesh of the beet and enters into solution with the hot water, the liquid is transferred to a second tank containing fresh cossettes, where it takes up more sugar in solution. Altogether this liquid may go through as many as 16 diffusion tanks, until the density is equal to the juice left in the cossettes, after which it is drawn off.

After the sugar solution is removed from each tank, fresh water is introduced, so that all the diffusion tanks are in continuous operation. When the cossettes are exhausted in the first tank, they are removed and replaced with a fresh supply; number two tank then becomes number one and so on. In this way fresh cossettes are put into each tank in turn. The exhausted beet, after pressing, is mixed with molasses and sold as cattle food.

After leaving the diffusers, the liquid which now contains 12–18 % sugar is sent to clarifiers where it is heated, limed and carbonated; the reaction of lime and carbon dioxide together forms a carbonate of lime which has the property of absorbing impurities as it forms a precipitate. The liquid is filtered under pressure and rendered clear and bright. The precipitate in the form of a press cake is used as a fertilizer. Crystallizing and refining follow the same pattern as for cane sugar.

Cube Sugar and Sugar Nibs.—Cube or lump sugar is made from the first refined syrup which is of the highest grade, and is crystallized in the form of large slabs, the thickness being the same as the familiar piece of lump sugar. The slabs after drying, are placed on to cutting machines and cut into cubes. The debris is graded into fine, medium and coarse sugar nibs. Cube sugar is now cast from small lightly greased moulds and is less suitable for sugar boiling.

Granulated and Castor Sugar.—The sugar crystals necessary for cube sugar are larger than those required for granulated. It is part of the art of refining to induce the sugar to crystallize out, or grow into the required crystal sizes.

For the larger crystals, about two-thirds of the contents of the pan is run out, the remainder being used as seed on which, with a further addition of syrup, the crystals continue to grow in size. For granulated sugars, the pans are seeded with crystals of varying sizes, when, after complete crystallization, the mass is transferred to centrifugals to remove the syrup, leaving the sugar crystals white in colour. They are washed, dried and then graded into crystal size by sieves. The sugar is then packed as fine, medium or coarse granulated.

The medium and coarse granulated is useful to the baker for making macaroon goods, the large crystals assist in producing the desirable fine cracks on the surface that is characteristic of well made macaroon goods. Fine granulated is ideal for sponge and cake batters. Very fine castor is produced by grinding crystals through rollers and sieving through silk cloths. Fine castor is particularly useful for shortbreads, short pastry and biscuits.

On the next page, as a summary, is a diagrammatical lay-out of sugar refining.

Icing Sugar.—Icing sugar is produced by the grinding of high grade crystals. The baker has the choice of three grades, bridal icing, icing, and pulverized. The grading is done by sieving; bridal icing being put through silk bolting cloths having an extremely fine mesh.

Bridal icing is used for the decoration of wedding, birthday and Christmas cakes, or any cake where delicate piping is necessary. The second grade is used for almond and sugar pastes, creams and icings, and for dusting purposes. Pulverized sugar is useful for biscuit making.

Demerara Sugar.—This is prepared in the same way as for raw sugar. Sulphur dioxide is used with the juice, which is treated with sulphuric acid during boiling, when the colour changes to a light yellow. The crystals are then centrifuged, but not afterwards washed. In this way the crystals are covered with a thin film of syrup which imparts the flavour which is so desirable with this type of sugar and makes it ideal in the making of rich fruit cakes.

'Yellow crystals', which are an imitation of Demerara sugar, consist of white crystals mixed with a quantity of golden syrup.

SUGAR REFINING

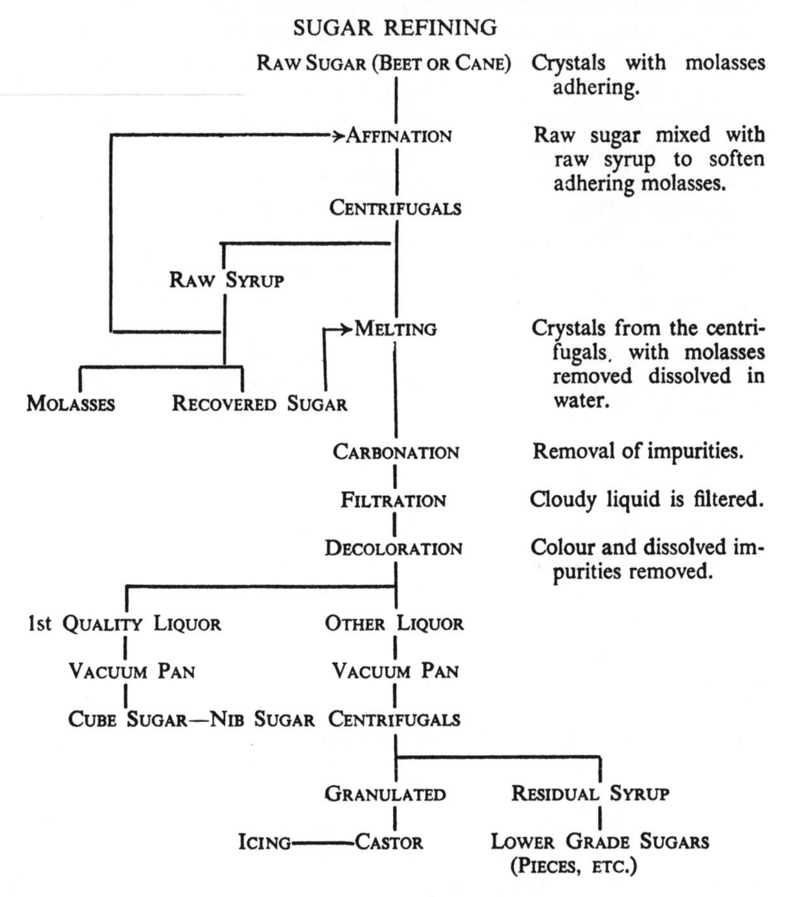

Pieces.—After the syrup has been separated from the sugar crystals in the centrifugal machines, the syrup is collected, re-boiled and again crystallized. The operation is repeated until at last the molasses remaining are almost completely devoid of crystallizable sugar. After each re-boiling the colour of the resultant crystals gets progressively poorer. These inferior sugars are termed 'pieces' and are excellent for bun goods and for certain types of biscuits.

Golden Syrup.—This can be termed a by-product of sugar refining, for when the syrups after many boilings, no longer yield crystals, the syrup is filtered and concentrated. The best quality is amber coloured and contains about 15–18% water, the remainder being a mixture of sucrose, dextrose and levulose, together with some natural undetermined matter that is partly responsible for flavour.

Golden syrup can also be manufactured by boiling sugar and water with a weak acid which changes the sucrose to simple sugars known as invert sugars; the acid is afterwards neutralized. The syrup is then coloured and concentrated. Golden syrup is used in the bakery for ginger goods and biscuits.

Treacle.—This is a syrup much darker in colour and with a more pronounced flavour. It is made by filtering diluted molasses, after which it is concentrated. Good quality treacle is used in the making of ginger cakes. The darker variety is known as black treacle and is used to give colour to bride and birthday cakes and Christmas cakes and puddings, the treacle replacing a small proportion of the sugar.

Honey.—Honey was almost certainly the first sugar used by man. It is a natural product and is obtained by bees from the nectar of flowers. Nectar contains about 80% water and about 20% sugar, most of which is sucrose. It also contains essential oils and aromatic substances responsible for the 'bouquet' of honey.

The sucrose is converted by the bees into an invert sugar and is then stored in the combs, where some of the water is evaporated off by the heat of the hive. The average composition of honey is: 38% levulose, 35% dextrose, the remainder being water, gums and ash.

Honey is frequently adulterated with manufactured invert sugar, or is actually manufactured by inverting sucrose with formic acid and adding colour and flavour, the result being a very poor substitute. English honey which is considered to be the best, is sold mainly for table use. Other countries produce much larger quantities, but the flavour is not so good. Honey is used in honey cakes, sweets, nougats and in chocolate centres.

Care must be taken when baking cakes containing large amounts of syrup, treacle or honey, firstly because the total sugar content of this type of cake is usually high, and secondly, because the monosaccharides or invert sugars they contain caramelize at a lower temperature than sucrose. A lower baking temperature is therefore necessary.

Commercial Glucose. This is sometimes called corn syrup and is manufactured by boiling starch in water to bring about gelatinization. Weak acid is then added in order to change the starch to sugar, after which the acid is neutralized; the syrup is then reduced to the desired consistency in vacuum pans. It contains about 15% water, and a mixture of glucose, maltose and dextrose. It is used in cheap cakes and sponges, helping to keep them moist. It is also used in the manufacture of fondant and jam, and sometimes as an adulterant of honey.

Gelatinized starch can be saccharified by the action of enzymes by mixing with a little diastatic malt. The student can try this for himself by gelatinizing a small quantity of starch and adding a little malt when the gel has cooled down to about 80° F. Starch has the property of giving a blue colour to an iodine solution. If the student will add a little iodine to a portion of the gelatinized starch, he will see that this is so.

The malt having been mixed in, the mixture should be left at a temperature of 80° F., for a sufficient time until it no longer gives the blue colour reaction when spotted with iodine. The mixture has now changed to sugar and is no longer starch. A test with Fehling's solution, which the student will learn in his bakery science studies, will prove that it is in fact, sugar.

Enzyme-converted glucose is now available to the baker and is approximately twice as sweet and three times as fluid as acid-converted glucose.

Scade—*Bakers' Review*—gives the following table of comparisons expressed in percentages:

	Acid converted glucose	*Enzyme converted glucose*
Moisture	19·7	18·2
Dextrose	17·6	30·6
Maltose	16·6	27·9
Higher sugars	16·2	13·1
Dextrines	29·6	9·9
Ash	0·3	0·3

The following table shows the relative sweetness of sugars:

Sucrose (Cane or beet sugar)	100
Dextrose	75
Glucose (enzyme converted)	60
Glucose (acid converted)	30
Maltose	30
Lactose	15

E.C. glucose as it is known has been used in the United States since 1939 as a standard ingredient for cakes, biscuits and icings as well as in the production of bread and sweet fermented goods.

Invert Sugar.—Unlike commerical glucose or corn syrup, invert sugar is not manufactured from starch, but from ordinary sugar. The sugar is boiled with water and sufficient dilute hydrochloric acid to change the disaccharide sucrose, to monosaccharides. The acid is neutralized later by sodium bi-carbonate which leaves a residue of sodium chloride (common salt). Like glucose it is a thick colourless syrup and is used in cakes and biscuits, in sugar boiling and as a yeast food.

The study of the essential differences between glucose and invert sugar will repay the student, for it may be included in the list of questions in a written examination.

24

Milk: Constituent Parts; Processing; Storage; Souring; Its uses in Confectionery; Eggs: Constituent Parts; Grading; Preservation Processes; De-frosting; Uses in Confectionery Products

MILK

MILK is a mixture of a number of constituents, the proportions of which vary considerably. The colour may also vary from white to yellow according to its composition and the breed of cows from which it comes. Whilst the appearance of milk, may, therefore, form some guide to its quality, it is by no means a certain test, for the only thoroughly reliable proof is the chemical analysis of any given sample. Because of the variations that occur in it, it is not possible to give one single definition of the composition since analysts throughout the world all give varying figures. For all practical purposes, however, the figures given by Droop Richmond, who has carried out thousands of tests over the years, may be taken as representing a fair average. They are as follows expressed as percentages.

Fat		3·75
Solids-not-fat		
Milk proteins	3·46	
Lactose	4·70	
Mineral matter	0·75	8·91
Water		87·34

Legally, milk has a presumed standard. The requirements are that milk shall not fall below 3% fat and 8·5% solids-not-fat. If it is sold below these standards, it is presumed not to be genuine milk and the seller can be prosecuted under the Food and Drugs Act.

Milk Fat—Commonly referred to as butterfat, is probably the most valuable constituent of milk from the commercial point of view—particularly where the manufacture of cream and butter is concerned, but so far as the nutritional aspect of milk is concerned, the proteins and minerals of milk are even more important. The fat in milk consists of minute globules which are approximately $\frac{1}{10,000}$ of an inch in diameter. These globules vary, however, in size according to the breed of the cow, those of the Jersey and Guernsey cows being larger than in other breeds.

Milk fat is lighter than water, its specific gravity being 0·91 to 0·92. It melts at 29° to 36° C. depending upon the relative proportions of hard and soft fats present, and solidifies at 19° to 24° C. It is derived from the fats and carbohydrates of the cow's food, but mainly from the carbohydrates. It provides about half of the 'Calorie' value of milk in nutrition. Butterfat is responsible for the pleasing taste of cream and butter; milk of good butterfat content is, therefore, a valuable factor in catering and baking. It is the flavour aspect of fresh cream that gives filled goods their superiority over other cream fillings.

From the nutritional point of view, the butterfat in milk is important also because it provides the vitamin A, D and E content of the milk and these three fat soluble vitamins are resistant to heat, either in the heat treatment of milk, or heat applied afterwards in the cooking processes which may be used.

Milk Protein.—Milk protein is of high biological value, that is, it is more complete in its value as a 'body builder' than any other form of protein. The protein in milk does not vary to the same degree as the fat content.

The main protein of milk is casein, but two others, lactalbumin and lactoglobulin are also present. Casein does not occur in plants or animal products other than milk.

Lactose.—This is sometimes referred to as milk sugar and is the carbohydrate of milk. It provides about 30% of the 'Calorie' value and makes a contribution to the pleasant taste of milk although it is only about one-sixth as sweet as cane or beet sugar. When milk sours, the lactose is converted into lactic acid causing a separation of the milk solids and the water. The curds, as they are known, can be strained off and eaten as cream cheese or used as an essential ingredient in the filling of curd tarts. If curds are wanted quickly for this purpose, the milk can be warmed and inoculated with rennet which is an enzyme prepared commercially from the stomach of the calf. After a short time the milk will curdle.

Sour milk can be used in confectionery, especially in scones, provided that the increased acidity is neutralized by bicarbonate of soda in excess of that contained in a correctly balanced baking-powder.

Lactic fermentation is made use of in the 'ripening' of cream for butter-making and also in the manufacture of cheese. The formation of lactic acid is instrumental in checking the development of certain organisms concerned with objectionable taints. If milk is overheated and 'burnt', the charring effect is due to the formation of 'lacto-caramel' from the lactose.

Mineral Matter in Milk.—Milk contains all the mineral elements needed by the body, calcium and phosphorus being particularly important for growth and the maintenance of bone and teeth formation.

Milk Treatment.—There are three main kinds of liquid milk and they are as follows:

(*a*) Pasteurized.
(*b*) Tuberculin tested.
(*c*) Sterilized.

Pasteurizing.—This is a method by which milk is heat treated to destroy pathogenic bacteria. Two methods of pasteurization are now approved. The first of these consists of heating the milk to a temperature of 145° F. and holding it at that temperature for 30 min.—this is known as the batch or holder method.

In the second method, which is known as the high temperature short-time process (HTST), the milk is taken to 162° F. and held for only 15 sec. In both cases the milk is rapidly cooled after pasteurizing. The word pasteurization is taken from the name of Louis Pasteur, the great French scientist who first discovered that heat treatment was a method of controlling yeast micro-organisms in the fermentation of wines.

Tuberculin Testing.—'T.T.' milk as it is known, is from cows which have passed a periodical tuberculin test. It can be sold raw, in which case it is bottled at the farm where it is produced. Those producing it and handling it must have a special licence to do so. A great deal of tuberculin tested milk is now also pasteurized.

Sterilizing.—Milk is sterilized by subjection, in hermetically sealed bottles, to a much higher temperature than that of pasteurization, i.e. to 212° F. It is first homogenized which is a process by which the fat globules are broken up and uniformly distributed throughout the milk. Thus in homogenized milk, no cream line appears on the milk after standing. Sterilized milk has long keeping qualities and has a distinctive flavour and colour.

Concentrated Milks.—The practice of concentrating milk is to reduce the water content, thus reducing the bulk and at the same time prolonging the life of the milk. Milk in this form finds a great use in the manufacture of other foods and provides a useful and economical method of storage for manufacturers whose day-to-day requirements can be better controlled when in this form.

There are two main types of concentrated milks, condensed and evaporated. It is usual when referring to these milks to call the sweetened forms 'condensed' and the unsweetened form 'evaporated'. Both types are produced by evaporation of the water under vacuum. The ratio of concentration of water to milk solids is 1 : 2·5 for full cream products and 1 : 3 for sweetened condensed milk. Added sugar accounts for from 40 to 45% of the weight of sweetened condensed milk, this high sucrose content also acting as a preservative. Evaporated milk is submitted to sterilizing temperatures after canning.

The Public Health (Condensed Milk) Regulations require that condensed milk shall contain not less than—

	Milk Fat	*Milk Solids (including fat)*
	%	%
Full Cream unsweetened	9·0	31·0
Full Cream sweetened	9·0	31·0
Skim unsweetened	—	20·0
Skim sweetened	—	26·0

Below is a table of average figures that will help the student to understand the differences between the condensed full cream and separated milks.

	Condensed Full Cream		*Condensed Separated*	
	Sweetened	*Unsweetened (Evaporated)*	*Sweetened*	*Unsweetened (Evaporated)*
	(1)	(2)	(3)	(4)
	%	%	%	%
Water	25·3	69·24	30·3	49·3
Fat	10·8	9·6	1·8	2·9
Protein	8·03	9·66	11·1	18·0
Lactose	14·1	9·85	16·0	26·1
Added Sugar	39·5	None	38·5	None
Mineral matter	2·27	11·65	2·3	3·7

These figures may vary according to the quality of milk used in manufacture and to the degree of pre-condensing standardization that may be carried out. Actually today, the principal milks available in this group are those shown in the first three columns.

Dried Milks.—Dried milks offer the same advantages in an even more convenient form to the baker and confectioner as do the condensed and evaporated milks. Two main types of dried milks are available, i.e. full cream dried milk and separated or skim milk powder. Regulations governing composition for standards are for fat only and allow for three grades:

	% *of fat*
Dried full cream milk	26·0
Dried partly skimmed milk	Less than 26·0 but not less than 8·0
Dried skimmed milk	Less than 8·0

For most practical purposes, there are only two kinds made, i.e. full cream and separated. Either of these milks are easily reconstituted by adding water and are, therefore, of great use in the bakery; a simple reconstitution table is as under:

1 lb. full cream milk powder + 8 lb. of water
1 lb. half cream milk powder + 9 lb. of water
1 lb. separated milk powder + 10 lb. of water

Two main methods of drying milk are used:

(*a*) Film-drying.
(*b*) Spray-drying.

There are three common methods of film drying, i.e.:

(*a*) Atmospheric roller-drying.
(*b*) Vacuum roller-drying.
(*c*) Band film-drying.

Roller drying is a popular method, the milk being spread in a thin film on to revolving, steam heated rollers. Evaporation takes place and the dried powder is scraped off, crushed and sieved. In atmospheric drying, the rollers are exposed to the air. This is the most economical method from the viewpoint of installation and operation.

Vacuum roller drying is similar except that the rollers are enclosed in a chamber in which a vacuum is maintained.

Various methods are employed for feeding the milk to the rollers. The simplest method of feeding to a single roller is to arrange that the base of the drum is immersed in the milk. Under this method the milk must be pre-condensed or the film will not be viscous enough for the roller to pick it up.

A more usual method of roller drying is the use of two drums set side by side with the milk fed into the trough between the two rollers. The drums rotate in opposite directions and a thin film of milk is spread on each drum.

In band film drying, pre-condensed milk is fed on to bands which pass through a heated vacuum.

There are various methods of spray drying all of which are more costly than roller drying. The principle of this method is to atomize pre-condensed milk and introduce it as a fine spray into a stream of heated air which evaporates and carries off the moisture, the milk solids being deposited and collected as a fine powder.

A satisfactory spray-dried milk powder is almost 100% soluble. Milk powder produced by the open roller process has usually a maximum solubility of 85%, while vacuum film-dried powder falls somewhere between the two.

Good roller-dried powder will keep longer than spray processed, due to the greater degree of heat applied in the film-drying process. Skimmed milk powder keeps longer than full cream powder owing to the possibility of the oxidation of the fat content.

All milk powders are very hygroscopic, that is they tend to absorb moisture very readily. They should, therefore, be kept in dry storage conditions and containers should be kept tightly closed. More recent techniques of packing milk powders in gas-filled containers has prolonged the life of these powders considerably.

The following table gives the average composition of dried milk powders:

	Full cream	*Half cream*	*Separated*
	%	%	%
Moisture	2·0	2·5	2·5
Fat	27·0	16·5	1·0
Protein	27·0	30·3	38·0
Lactose	38.0	43·8	50·5
Mineral matter	6·0	6·9	8·0

Milk in Confectionery.—In the grouping of raw materials used in confectionery, milk comes under the general heading of moistening agents. The student will know that milk contains approximately 87% of water, but he must know also that the remaining 13% of milk solids will make all the difference in quality between a cake made with milk, compared with one in which the milk has been replaced by water.

Milk is regarded as a most perfect food, containing as it does every constituent of food necessary for the maintenance of life. Milk solids therefore increase the nutritional value of cakes, for protein, carbohydrates, fat, minerals and vitamins are all valuable in diet. Milk also improves the flavour, has a softening effect on crumb structure and helps to keep the cake moist and mellow. In addition, milk confers bloom and colour on the crust. In fermented goods, lactose is sparingly fermentable by yeast and because it remains in the dough has the effect of improving the crust colour in conjunction with other substances.

The student may like to test the effect of milk for himself by making up two small mixings of scones, using milk in one and water only in the other, care being taken to remember that less water is used in comparison with milk for the same weight of flour. About 17½ to 18 oz. of water is equivalent in moistening value to 20 oz. (1 pint) of milk.

When the scones are baked it will be noticed that the milk scone is more mellow and moist and will stale less quickly. The differences in crust colour will be marked.

As a summary, it can be said that milk is preferable to water as a moistening agent because:

(1) It is an enriching agent and increases the food value of the cake.
(2) It improves flavour.
(3) It helps to keep the cake moist.
(4) It softens and mellows the crumb structure.
(5) It confers bloom and improves the crust colour. (In bun goods lactose being sparingly fermentable, is retained and thus helps to improve crust colour.)

EGGS

When the word 'egg' is mentioned it is generally assumed to be a hen egg. Hen eggs are produced in vast numbers throughout the world, and are one of the most important raw materials used in the baking industry. Duck eggs are of less importance to the baker, although to a certain extent they can be used to replace hen eggs.

Eggs are moistening, enriching, colouring and aerating agents, and because of their enriching qualities add to the food value of bread, cakes and pastries.

They may be considered to consist of three main parts: (1) the shell, which is mainly phosphate and calcium carbonate, and of very little use to the baker except for the clarification of jellies; (2) the white, or albumen, and (3) the yolk. The last two are of great importance.

The average proportions of the three parts are: shell 12%, white 58%, yolk 30%.

The average weight of an egg is 2 oz., although this average may vary between 1½–2½ oz. according to the grading. It can be estimated that 12 average size eggs will measure a pint. In the interest of accuracy, however, it is much better to weigh eggs instead of measuring them, and to record them in weight in a formula instead of liquid measurement or as units. Twenty egg whites or between 32 and 36 yolks will measure a pint, but again it is much better to weigh 20 oz., which is an approximate equivalent.

Here is a table showing the percentages of the constituent parts of egg whites, yolks and whole egg (less shell).

	White	*Yolk*	*Whole egg*
	%	%	%
Water	86–87	50–50·5	73–75
Protein	12–12·7	16–16·5	12–14
Fat	0·25	31–32	10–12
Mineral matter	0·5–0·59	0·8–1·5	1–1·2

The component parts of the egg are clearly shown in the diagram (Fig. 54).

The student will note that the egg is very similar to the yeast cell; the shell and inner membrane corresponding to the dual membrane in

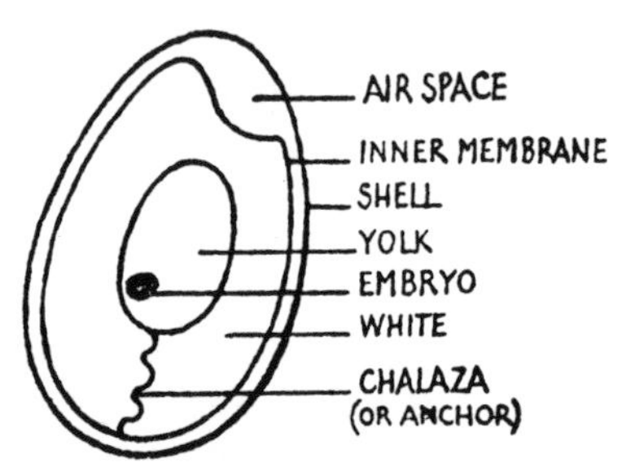

FIG. 54.—The egg.

yeast; the yolk and embryo similar to the vacuole and nucleus; the albumen corresponding to the protoplasm.

In the egg the chalaza is responsible for maintaining the suspension of the yolk within the albumen, although this anchoring breaks down as the egg ages, allowing the yolk to sink and adhere to the shell. The embryo, which is the future chick, is only present in fertile eggs.

Like the yeast cell membrane, the egg shell is semi-permeable. In consequence some of the egg moisture escapes and is replaced by air, the passage of which is responsible for the introduction of bacteria which eventually causes decay and putrefaction.

Shell Eggs.—Without doubt, fresh shell eggs are the best form of eggs for use in the bakery, whole egg being readily available by the simple expedient of cracking a shell, and yolks and whites are to hand after the simple operation of separating them.

There are not now so many objections to the use of shell eggs in the bakery as there were many years ago. Modern methods of packing have eliminated the straw that used to make such a mess. Hygiene has reduced the fly population that used to be attracted to the musty straw, and the clean eggs of today offer no inducement to the smell-tracing proclivities of the fewer flies that are left.

The time taken for the cracking and smelling of each individual egg, however, is an objection against the use of shell eggs where large quantities are used.

Eggs today are cleaned, 'candled', that is examined under a strong light, and packed in boxes between protective layers of papier mâché which are so moulded that each egg travels snugly in its own compartment. Each box contains three 'long hundreds'—360 eggs. Breakages are thus kept to an absolute minimum, and because of improved methods of storage and transport, the percentage of bad eggs is remarkably low.

English eggs are sold under an Egg Marketing Board grading, which is a grading of eggs by weight. The gradings, which are 'large', 'standard', 'medium', and 'small', are done automatically in egg-packing stations. Eggs from other countries are graded according to the weight of eggs per long hundred, the grades being clearly marked on the box. The grades are 18 lb., 16½ lb., 15¼ lb., 14 lb., and 12½ lb. The name of the country of origin has to be stamped on the egg.

Shell eggs do not remain good indefinitely. Due to the putrefying bacteria that enters through the porous shell the eggs will decompose in time. This can be prevented by 'pickling', which seals the pores of the shell. The pickling is done generally by either lime preserving or the use of water glass, which is a 10% solution of silicate of soda in boiling water. This is used when cold.

Lime preserving consists of slaking quick-lime in a wooden tub, leaving it until it is cold; by this time all reaction will have taken place and lime water will settle out on top. This lime water is carefully run off, and most of the slaked lime taken out of the tub, leaving about 2 inches in the bottom. On this layer, new-laid eggs are arranged in orderly rows. The eggs must be carefully examined and all with cracked shells rejected.

They are then covered with more slaked lime, and another layer of eggs is placed in position. Alternate layers of lime and egg are put in until the tub is nearly full, then the lime water is poured in to cover the eggs completely. The tub may need topping up with more lime-water after a few days, due to the small amount that may be absorbed by each shell and possibly by the wood of the tub.

With the waterglass method the eggs are put in a large tub and completely covered with the silicate of soda solution; again the water level should be checked after a few days because of possible absorption. As with the lime method, the eggs must be new-laid and free from crack or blemish.

Eggs preserved by these methods will remain good for up to 12 months, although the whites will be found to have become 'watery'. They will, however, still whip up to a satisfactory foam.

Eggs may be preserved by chilling in the shell at temperatures slightly above freezing-point, usually about 36–40° F.

Frozen Eggs.—The method of freezing an egg to preserve it is used most extensively in all parts of the world. Frozen eggs are imported from Australia, Canada, China, Poland, South Africa and the United States; English frozen eggs are now also available. In different parts of the world, vast numbers of eggs are collected and sent to centres where they are scientifically tested, then cracked out, put into tins, sealed and frozen. They are transported in refrigerated ships and railway wagons to large cold storages, from which places they are delivered to the baker.

The low temperature completely inhibits bacterial activity; in addition, frozen eggs are extremely popular with the baker, because the labour costs of cracking and shelling are eliminated, and compared with shell eggs, storage space is saved. Provided that they have been properly defrosted, they are an excellent replacement for shell eggs, although once defrosted they must be used fairly rapidly. Putrefaction can take place in as short a time as 12 hr. under certain conditions, although they can be kept for about a week in a refrigerator at not more than 40° F.

Frozen egg whites are also available to the baker, and when properly defrosted there is very little difference between them and freshly separated shell egg whites. When defrosted they will keep in good condition for about a week at a temperature of approximately 40° F.

Egg yolks are less successfully frozen, and great care is necessary in defrosting; even then the yolks do not seem to return to the original smoothness, with the result that tiny yellow spots of yolk are visible in the crumb of the cake. It is possible, however, that research and experiment may have got over this difficulty, and supplies in the future may be satisfactory.

Defrosting.—It is a staggering thought that despite the scientific skill and care given to the processing of raw materials, there are people so careless, thoughtless or untrained, that they needlessly spoil or damage the product at the last stage.

Eggs are frozen by the simple expedient of lowering the temperature to below freezing-point; while this temperature is maintained, the eggs remain as a solid block. A moment's thought, and it must be realized that the eggs, before use, must be brought to a temperature at which they will give the maximum aeration efficiency. We know that this temperature is about 70–75° F.; we know also that as the temperature of the egg increases, so the storage life is shortened, until at 140° F. the egg protein coagulates, and the aerating qualities destroyed.

It is obvious, therefore, that it is very bad practice to attempt defrosting by forcing in heat. The correct method is to 'tease' the cold out by immersing the tin in cold running water for about 12 hr. After defrosting, the eggs should be emptied out into bowls and thoroughly mixed, because when an egg is frozen some separation of whites and yolks takes place.

Eggs should be so ordered that delivery is synchronized with usage, and defrosting done accordingly. With system and knowledge, eggs will always be ready at the correct temperature at the time of using and the opportunity will never be given to those unintelligent people who drop lumps of frozen egg into the mixing in a machine, relying on frictional heat for defrosting; or as an alternative, put the egg into a boiling water bath, or on the oven stock in close contact with the oven door.

In small bakeries where there is no refrigerator for the storage of eggs after defrosting, they can be preserved for a short time by adding an equal amount of sugar, allowance being made for it when weighing up a mixing.

Dried Eggs.—The water content of an egg is approximately 75%, and it can readily be understood that in packing and transportation, the question of eliminating the water content has been a subject of much research. It is obvious that if the egg could be dehydrated, four times the amount of egg solids, by weight, could be carried in the same space.

At first, eggs were dried at low temperatures in shallow trays, or on rollers in a similar manner to the roller drying of milk, the resultant product being in the form of small flakes. These, when reconstituted in the bakery, were fairly satisfactory.

The exigencies of war, and the consequent shortage of shipping space, necessitated more urgent research into the dehydration of eggs. Eventually two types of dried egg were made available to the baker—spray-dried and sugar-dried.

Spray-dried Eggs.—The method of drying is similar to that used in spray-drying milk, and the result of the process is a fine, dry, soft powder. After the separation of the egg from the shell, the whites and yolks are mixed and strained, then forced under pressure into a hot chamber, through which runs a current of heated air. The temperature is carefully controlled at 125° F., this figure being beneath the coagulation point of egg protein.

The air current which is filtered and cleaned to avoid bacterial infection, takes away the evaporated moisture, and the egg solids drop in fine powder form. If properly stored at normal temperatures, dried egg will keep for years in good condition.

While egg in this form is extremely useful in the bakery, it is unfortunately, not as good as shell or frozen eggs for some types of bakery products that are aerated mechanically, because the processing results in the egg losing most of its aerating property. Because of this, a great deal of research and experiment resulted in new methods of use being developed, which produced very good sponges and Swiss roll.

One very successful and popular method is to whip the reconstituted egg with the sugar and about 25% of the flour on fast speed for about 20–30 min., the rest of the flour, into which the baking-powder has been sieved, being added in the normal way. In this method the protein of the proportion of flour whipped with the egg became hydrated to gluten, and this held the air whipped in by the machine.

Spray-dried egg powder is reconstituted at the rate of one part by weight of powder, and three parts by weight of water. The powder is sieved, and sufficient of the water is added to make a smooth paste, the rest of the water being added until a smooth mixture, free from lumps, is obtained.

Reconstituted eggs should be used as quickly as possible, because of the possibility of bacterial infection. This applies equally to reconstituted eggs stored in a refrigerator.

Sugar-dried Eggs.—This type of dried egg was an important and welcome addition to bakery raw materials in the long period of shortage during and after the war. It was found that the addition of a proportion of sugar to the egg, before drying, resulted in a product that, after reconstitution, could be whipped quite as well as shell or frozen eggs. The eggs were dried on the spray system, the powder containing approximately 33% sugar.

It was reconstituted at the rate of one part powder by weight to two parts water, producing an egg/sugar solution. If one pint (20 oz.) of egg was required for a mixing, then 7½ oz. of sugar-dried egg powder was mixed with 15 oz. of water, resulting in 22½ oz. of sugar/egg; of this, 20 oz. was egg and 2½ oz. sugar, the latter amount being subtracted from the sugar quantity in the formula.

The egg solution whipped very well; in fact it was necessary not to over-whip, if the best results were to be achieved. The dry powder kept extremely well, although, because of the sugar content, the powder was hygroscopic—that is, it attracted moisture. Care was therefore necessary in keeping the powder stored in a dry place. Sugar-dried eggs were processed and exported from Canada and were a first-class example of the application of science and technology to foodstuffs in a time of national emergency. The student may expect to find sugar-dried eggs again on the market.

Dried Egg Whites.—These are prepared by careful drying at low temperatures, the product being hard, yellow-coloured, semi-opaque flakes. Dried egg whites will keep perfectly for many years if stored under ideal conditions.

The whites, before drying, are allowed to ferment for three or four days, when certain chemical changes occur, which include a change from the normal alkalinity to a slight acidity. This has the effect of strengthening the whites.

They are reconstituted by taking seven parts, by weight, of water and one of dried whites; general bakery practice is 3 oz. of whites to 1 pint of water. They should be left for at least 3–4 hr., stirring occasionally, or preferably overnight.

Here are approximate figures of the composition of dried egg products:

	Dried whole egg	*Dried egg yolk*	*Dried egg whites*
	%	%	%
Water	7·4	3·8	9·4
Protein	43·6	34·6	86·2
Fat	42·7	57·8	1·8
Mineral matter	6·3	3·8	2·6

Reconstituted dried whites will successfully replace shell whites in all types of meringues, macaroons and icings. Some dried whites may be adulterated with such substances as dextrin, sugar and gelatine.

There are many excellent processed egg whites on the market sold under trade names. These are hen albumen reduced to a fine powder to facilitate reconstitution which is effected in a much shorter time.

They must not be confused with icing and meringue powders and liquids, which are, in effect substitutes or alternatives to egg whites; some are defatted milk proteins, others are alginates, while some are finely powdered mixtures of albumen, gums, gelatine, etc. They should be used carefully according to the manufacturers' instructions.

Spray-dried Yolks.—They are reconstituted by mixing one part by weight of water and one part by weight of powder. Leave for 15 minutes before use.

Spray-dried Whites.—Combine one part of water and one part of powder by weight and stand for 15 minutes. Then add nine parts by weight of water and stir frequently.

25

Cake-making Processes: Sugar Batter; Flour Batter; Modified Methods; Aeration in Flour Confectionery: Panary; Chemical; Mechanical; Combination of Methods

CAKE-MAKING PROCESSES (1)

THERE are several methods of making cake batters each of them having their champions and their critics. Indeed nothing is more calculated to provoke discussion among a company of bakers than the relative merits of different cake-making methods. Viewing them objectively, it seems that each of them is good or bad in the degree that it produces cakes of good quality, always assuming that the quality of the ingredients and the balance of them is satisfactory.

It is fairly certain that the first method of making cakes was the simple one of rubbing the fat into the flour, after which the milk, sugar, eggs and other ingredients were added. It seems equally certain that the next method evolved was that in which the fat and sugar were creamed before the addition of eggs, after which the flour and other materials were added. This is known as the sugar-batter method, and is the one most widely used because it is simple and direct. There are, however, certain rules that have to be adhered to if the best results are to be obtained.

Sugar-Batter Method.—All the fats and the sugar are beaten to a light cream. This can be done by hand or by machine beating: the principle is the same in either case. In the creaming process, the rapidly moving hand or beater disrupts the surface and enters the mix, drawing air in with it which is retained, provided that the mixture is stable enough to retain it.

When the fat/sugar is light and fluffy, the eggs are added in portions, beating well after each addition until the mixture is a smooth, complex emulsion of fat, sugar, eggs and air. To do this successfully, certain precautions must be taken, the most important being to ensure the right temperature of the raw materials during mixing, which is between 65–70° F.

It can be understood that if the fat is hard, it is virtually impossible to incorporate air into it, certainly not by hand, and only by machine if the beating is so prolonged that the friction heat softens it. There is little sense in this, however, for not only are time and power wasted, but a great deal of unnecessary strain is put on the machine. It can be understood also that if on the other hand the fat is reduced to an oil, then there can be no aeration by beating, because as fast as air is introduced it will escape.

If the eggs are too cold when they are added it is possible that the batter will curdle; this is caused by the fat hardening and so being incapable of taking up the water in the egg. A separation occurs, and some of the air escapes, the loss possibly affecting the volume of the cakes. Adding the eggs before the fat/sugar is sufficiently creamed, or adding the eggs too quickly, may also induce the mixture to curdle. Warming a curdled mixture and rebeating may restore it to a smooth velvety emulsion.

When the last of the eggs are beaten in, the flavouring is added and the colour adjustment made by the addition of egg yellow. The sieved flour and powder (if any) is carefully dispersed through the mix. If milk is used, it is added after the flour has been mixed in and before the fruit, so that there is no direct contact with the flour, which would result in the formation of gluten and so toughen the cake.

If the cake mix is of a cheaper quality with a high flour and milk content, half of the milk is mixed into the batter before the flour is incorporated; the flour is next mixed in, after which the balance of the milk is added. It is important that at all stages of mixing the side of the bowl is scraped down.

When making very cheap cakes by this method it is usual to develop the gluten of the flour a little by a short period of extra machining after the flour is added. This added strength offers extra resistance to the combined pressure of expanding air, CO_2 and water vapour; in this way an increased volume is effected.

An adaptation of the sugar-batter method is used by some manufacturers who add a proportion of flour during the fat/sugar creaming stage; this prevents the risk of curdling and the possibility of toughening. Up to 50% flour, based on the weight of fat, has given satisfactory results.

Flour-Batter Method.—The flour-batter method of cake-making is in use mainly in large-scale bakeries, although it has its adherents in smaller units. The method is widely used in exhibition cake-making. Its use, however, entails more work and the use of more machinery.

The procedure is entirely different from the sugar-batter method, and it is necessary first of all to rewrite the formula to conform to the method, which is completed in four main operations.

First of all an equal weight of flour is beaten with fat, until they are light and well aerated. The sugar and eggs are whipped together in approximately equal proportions, the whisking not being so prolonged as for sponge cakes. The sugar/egg ratio should never exceed 1 : 1¼, or in bakery parlance, a pound to a pint. As with the sugar batter method, the materials used should be at a temperature of between 65–70° F.

After the addition of egg colour and flavouring to either of the mixtures, the whisked egg/sugar is added to the fat/flour in portions, and carefully blended in; any balance of flour is then added and, finally, milk and fruit (if any) is mixed in.

It is considered that care is necessary in the blending of the two mixtures because of the necessity of conserving the air whisked into the sponge. Investigation has proved, however, that it is the air beaten into the fat/flour that is responsible for most of the aeration, because it is certain that a great deal of air is lost from the sponge, however much care is taken during the blending. In fact, cakes just as good can be made by dissolving the sugar into the eggs and adding the solution to the well-beaten fat/flour, in portions in much the same way as the egg is added in the sugar-batter method.

In cheaper cake mixings, the formula is rebalanced so that the sugar, milk and flour are increased in relation to the fat and eggs; baking-powder is added or increased. In using the flour batter method the principle is the same even if the balance of materials is altered. In this case, again the fat is beaten with an equal weight of flour, and an equal amount of egg and sugar is whisked, the balance of the sugar being dissolved in the milk and added to the blended mixtures after the rest of the flour, containing the powder, has been mixed in.

In a very cheap cake mixture, half of the sugar/milk solution is added to the blended batters, the remainder after the flour balance is mixed in.

Some bakers consider it an advantage to add the acid constituent of the baking-powder to the fat/flour mix, and the bicarbonate of soda to the sugar/milk solution. In this way it is considered that little or no reaction will take place between the chemicals until the cake is in the oven.

For further clarity, here are some formulae for lightly fruited cakes in three qualities, both for the sugar and flour-batter methods.

Lightly fruited cakes—Sugar-batter method

	First quality		*Second quality*		*Third quality*	
	lb.	*oz.*	*lb.*	*oz.*	*lb.*	*oz.*
Butter (Salted)		12		8	—	
Shortening		4		8	1	0
Sugar	1	0	1	4	1	8
Eggs	1	4	1	0	1	0
Colour	q.s.		q.s.		q.s.	
Essence	q.s.		q.s.		q.s.	
Salt	—			¼		½
Flour	1	8	2	0	2	8
Powder		⅛		½		¾
Milk		3½		13	1	4
Fruit	1	8	1	12	2	4

Lightly fruited cakes—Flour-batter method

	First quality		*Second quality*		*Third quality*	
	lb.	*oz.*	*lb.*	*oz.*	*lb.*	*oz.*
Group 1:						
Butter (Salted)		12		8	—	
Shortening		4		8	1	0
Salt	—			¼		½
Colour	q.s.		q.s.		q.s.	
Essence	q.s.		q.s.		q.s	
Flour	1	0	1	0	1	0
Group 2:						
Sugar	1	0	1	0	1	0
Eggs	1	4	1	0	1	0
Group 3:						
Flour		8	1	0	1	8
Powder		⅛		½		¾
Group 4:						
Milk		3½		13	1	4
Sugar	—			4		8
Group 5:						
Fruit	1	8	1	12	2	4

The group numbers given with the flour-batter mixings indicate the order in which the groups are added.

Here is a summary of the flour-batter method of cake-making:

(1) The fat with an equal amount of flour is creamed. Colour and flavour are added.

(2) Approximately an equal weight of sugar is whisked with the egg to a half sponge. Maximum egg to sugar, 1¼ to 1.

(3) The sponged egg/sugar is added in portions to the fat/flour mixture and carefully blended in.
(4) The balance of the flour, with the powder, is mixed in.
(5) Any milk, with balance of sugar, is added. The exception is in very cheap mixings, when half the solution is added to the batter before the flour balance, and the rest after the flour addition.
(6) Any fruit is added last, and carefully distributed through the mix.
(7) As with the sugar-batter method, the temperature of the raw materials should be between 65–70° F.

CAKE-MAKING PROCESSES (2)

Just before the last war, new types of raw materials were introduced to the baking industry. Because of the exigencies of war some materials were unobtainable, and others were available in new forms and in differing qualities, so that modifications of the sugar-batter and flour-batter methods of cake-making were developed, and a great deal more was learned during the experimental use of these materials concerning the whole science of cake-making.

It has always been thought, and countless people have been taught in the past, that in a first quality mixing containing no baking-powder, the eggs are solely responsible for aeration. That this is not so has been proved with the introduction of dried egg. This product, after reconstitution, cannot be whisked to a sponge with sugar in the same way as shell or frozen eggs. Yet it was found that cakes comparable with those made from normal egg could be made, provided that there was a slight addition of baking-powder to the mix.

It was then found that fat is of great importance in aeration because it holds the air in the creaming process, and that air-holding capacity is increased and strengthened by the addition of eggs. The student can prove this conclusively for himself by making up four small mixings of madeira cakes, using the same weight of materials, and making each under the same conditions.

The first is made with compound fat and frozen eggs; the second with the same fat and reconstituted egg, plus a slight addition of baking-powder; the third with lard and frozen eggs, and the last with lard and reconstituted eggs, again with a slight addition of baking-powder.

Lard is a fat that has little or no creaming properties. The result of the experiment will show that the fat/frozen egg and the fat/dried egg cakes are approximately equal in volume and appearance, and the other two are lacking in volume, proving most convincingly that fat is most important in the aerating process.

It was the introduction of dried eggs that led to most of the modifications of the two main methods of making cakes.

Modified Sugar-batter Method.—With this method the fat, sugar and dried egg powder creamed together, and the amount of water necessary for the reconstitution of the eggs is added in portions. The dried egg, of course, can be reconstituted and added in the normal way, but by this modification the operation is avoided. In addition, the water can be the means of adjusting the batter temperature; warmer water can be used in cold weather and cold water under warmer conditions.

Modified Flour-batter Method.—The first stage of the flour-batter system is employed by creaming an equal weight of flour with the fat. The dried egg is sieved to eliminate lumps when it is mixed with the sugar, to which is added a weight of water to equal the weight of fat. This mixture is added to the fat/flour cream in two or more portions, the mixing to continue on medium speed for about 10 min. The mixing is finished in the normal manner.

A second modification combines the first two stages of the flour-batter method. The fat, together with an equal weight of flour, the sugar and the dried egg powder are brought to a crumbly mass on the machine, using low speed; the mass on no account to be machined to a continuous paste, but to have an appearance similar to that of ground almonds.

An amount of water, approximately the same weight as the fat, and at a suitable temperature to maintain the batter mix at about 70° F., is added and the mixture is beaten for seven minutes on second speed. The balance of the flour, together with the powder, the balance of milk and the fruit (if any) is added in the normal way.

Blending Method.—This method is used for a type of product developed before the war and known as high-ratio cakes. These cakes are produced from special flour and fats which enable the normal rules of formula balance to be amended so that a very high ratio of milk and sugar can be used based on the weight of flour.

The mixing is done in two stages. First the fat, salt, sugar, part of the milk and all of the flour, with the baking-powder, are blended together on medium speed for 6–9 mins. The eggs and the rest of the milk are added over 2 min. on low speed, then given a further 3 min. on the same speed. The speeds and timing must be adhered to strictly, and the bowl and beater scraped down thoroughly at least once during each stage.

This type of cake will be dealt with much more fully in a later chapter.

Continuous Batter System.—This process is entirely new and is in process of commercial experiment in the U.S.A. and in this country.

At present, two tanks are used, the first of which is used for the mixing of all the ingredients, both dry and liquid. The mixing is then passed to the second, or holding tank, as it is known.

It is from the holding tank that the 'slurry' as it is termed, is passed to the mixing chamber, where air under pressure is injected while the batter is rapidly mixed. In this way a constant and controlled flow of mixture is available.

Experiment is still in progress to perfect metering devices, so that the raw materials can be introduced to the mixing chamber in a controlled stream. In this way the whole process will be fully automatic, and the mixing and holding tanks can then be eliminated.

AERATION IN FLOUR CONFECTIONERY

The aeration of flour confectionery products is effected by the following means: (1) panary (yeast), (2) chemical (baking powder), (3) mechanical (whisking and beating), (4) lamination (rolling and folding), and (5) combinations of the above.

Panary.—Apart from bread, fancy bread and rolls, there are many types of fermented goods that are aerated by the use of yeast. These include the many varieties of buns, muffins, crumpets, babas, savarins, yeast and lardy cakes.

The aeration comes from the living yeast, which breaks down sugars and changes them to CO_2 and by-products. The gas is trapped by the gluten structure and the whole mass is aerated.

Panary fermentation is dealt with fully in Chapter 5.

Chemical.—Chemical aeration is effected by the production of CO_2 from the interaction, in solution, of an alkali and an acid in the presence of heat. The alkali and acid, in correct proportion, and harmless to human digestion is baking-powder.

With this method of aeration the greater amount of gas should be generated after the application of heat—that is, when the cake is in the oven. The gas generated leaks into air cells already created and is held by the gluten network of the cake; this generation and the consequent expansion causes an increase in the volume, which is maintained by the coagulation of the gluten and any other proteins that may be present. The baked cake thus becomes light and digestible.

Where baking-powder is the sole means of aeration, such as in scones, rock, rice and raspberry buns, the gluten should be of such quality that it will withstand the sudden generation and expansion of gas, and retain it during the initial baking period, until the structure of the cake is set, and so does not collapse.

Mechanical.—When fat/flour, fat/sugar, sugar/eggs or combinations of these are beaten or whisked together as already described in this chapter, the method of aeration, if there is no baking-powder used, is known as mechanical. In whatever way air is incorporated, whether by hand, hand-whisk or spatula, or by the whisk or beater on a machine, it is still mechanical aeration.

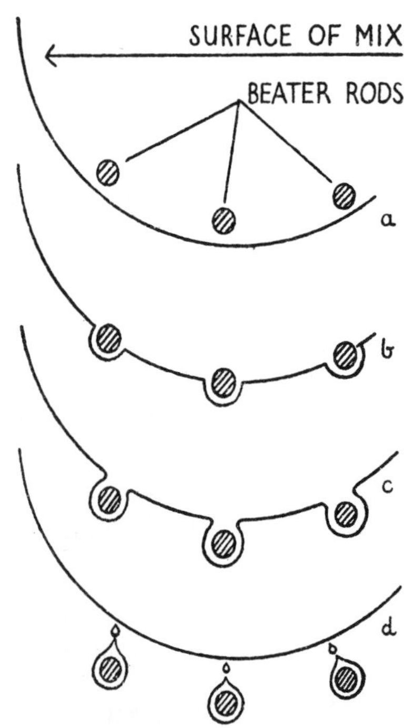

FIG. 55.—The mechanism of air incorporation.

All cakes, whether made on the sugar-batter, flour-batter, or modifications of these methods, and depending solely on the incorporation of air for aeration, are therefore mechanically aerated. Sponge goods of the highest quality are aerated by whisking the eggs and sugar together. Meringues and royal icing, being balanced mixings of egg-whites and sugar into which air is beaten, are excellent examples of mechanical aeration.

The mechanism of air incorporation is interesting, and if the student will watch closely, he will see that the surface of the mixture is continuously broken by the rapidly moving hand, whisk or beater. This is illustrated in Fig. 55. As the striking face of the implement being used enters the mix, the surface area is temporarily extended and increased (*b*).

A natural tendency to keep the surface area at a minimum has the effect of offering a resistance which drives the mix behind the implement as it penetrates still further into the mix (*c*). It is in this fractional moment of time before the extended surface is again at a minimum, and before the implement strikes again, that a bubble of air is drawn into the mix behind the beating instrument, and becomes incorporated and held by the fat or eggs, or both (*d*). In this way countless air bubbles are drawn into the mixing until it is thoroughly aerated.

Lamination.—This has been fully dealt with in Chapter 3.

Combinations.—Combinations of two of the above are used to produce different types or differing qualities of confectionery.

An example of this is the fermented scone. This was a product of war conditions, and was brought to perfection by the technical skill and research technique of a team sponsored by one of the companies supplying bakers with an essential raw material.

It was found that national flour did not make a satisfactory powder aerated scone because the gluten was inclined to harshness, the resultant scone being neither soft nor mellow. It was found that an initial yeast ferment, followed by the balance of the materials, including baking-powder, produced a scone that was not only beautifully soft and mellow, but did not stale quickly. It is probable that this type of scone has come to stay.

Danish pastries are a combination of aeration by yeast and by lamination. For this product a rich yeasted dough is made up, and butter or pastry fat incorporated as for puff pastry. In this way the pastry is given a lift because of the process of aeration by lamination, and at the same time the dough layers are softened and aerated by the action of yeast.

When the quality of cakes and sponge goods is reduced, it is necessary to re-balance the formula. This is done by reducing the proportion of egg and fat to flour, and introducing, or increasing, the baking-powder to assist in aeration. Because the proportion of egg is lower, then milk is added or increased to balance the moisture content.

Goods of this quality are thus aerated by both chemical and mechanical means.

26

Fats and Oils: Basic Types; Function of Fats in Bakery Products; Fats used by the Baker; Sources; Processing and Composition

FATS AND OILS

THE only difference between a fat and an oil is in the melting-point. Generally, any that are liquid at room temperature, or more precisely, at 15° C., are termed oils; any that are plastic or hard at that temperature are termed fats.

There are three basic types of oils and the differences should be clearly understood by the student so that he may distinguish between the edible and the non-edible oils.

Mineral Oils.—These are products of the petroleum and coal industries. They are hydrocarbons and have no food value. The human digestive system cannot split these oils into their component elements; in consequence the oils pass through the body unchanged. The danger however, is in the fact that passing through the digestive system, the oil absorbs the fat soluble vitamins from other foods, which are thus lost to the body. The use of mineral oils in foodstuffs is banned.

Mineral oil has its uses in the bakery as fuel oil for heating purposes and as a lubricating oil for machinery.

Essential Oils.—These are the edible aromatic oils such as orange, lemon, almond, peppermint, etc., used for flavouring purposes. They will stain a paper, but because they are volatile, the stain can be removed by heating. There is more information on this subject in Chapter 30.

Fixed or Greasy Oils.—These are the fats and oils of animal and vegetable origin. They are known chemically as tri-glycerides, consisting of glycerine and fatty acids in chemical combination. They are known as fixed oils because they do not evaporate or lose weight when distilled with water. They will stain a paper, the stain not being removed by heating. Fats and oils are insoluble in water, slightly so in alcohol, but readily soluble in ether, petrol, benzine and carbon tetrachloride.

A glyceride is a chemical combination of glycerine (known to the chemist as glycerol) and fatty acids. One molecule of glycerol is capable of combining with up to three molecules of fatty acids, which may be the same or different. If there are three and they are the same, then a simple tri-glyceride is formed. If the fatty acids are different, then the result is a mixed triglyceride. Most fats are mixtures of mixed tri-glycerides.

It is the combination of glycerides that determines the physical nature of the fat, i.e. a hard fat, a plastic fat, or an oil. In turn, the physical properties of the glyceride depend on the nature of the fatty acids of which it is constituted. The fatty acids are grouped under two main headings, saturated and unsaturated; these are respectively solid and liquid at ordinary temperatures.

The student will understand quite clearly that if three saturated fatty acids are combined with glycerol, then the result will be a solid fat of higher melting point. An oil will be the result of a combination of three unsaturated fatty acids with glycerol. Between the two, intermediates are formed depending on the physical properties of the fatty acids in the combination.

Here are six common glycerides occurring in fat:

Olein	Glycerol + Oleic acid
Butyrin	Glycerol + Butyric acid
Laurin	Glycerol + Lauric acid
Myristin	Glycerol + Myristic acid
Palmitin	Glycerol + Palmitic acid
Stearin	Glycerol + Stearic acid

The commercial process of hydrogenation or the hardening of oils can now be understood. In this process, soft fats and oils are introduced to hydrogen in the presence of a catalyst, usually finely divided nickel; in this way they take up hydrogen and become saturated, and the oils are converted into fats. The degree of hardening depends, amongst other factors, on the length of the process and the temperatures used.

Function of Fat in Bakery Products.—Fats are used in almost all bakery products. They add to the food value and are thus enriching agents. It is the quality and the amount of fat in a balanced formula that largely determines the quality of the finished product.

Fats have the power of preventing the development, or lessening the toughness of gluten, according to the method and the amount used; all fats therefore are shortening agents. Fats confer flavour according to the type used.

It is the fat which holds the air incorporated in the creaming process; again this is related to the quality. Eggs, when added, assist the fat in holding air.

To summarize, fats act as (1) enriching agents, (2) shortening agents, (3) air retainers (when creamed), (4) flavouring agents (butter, margarine and lard).

Fats used by the Baker.—The fats most useful to the baker are butter, shortening, cake and pastry margarines, pastry fat, and cooking oil. Emulsions are also in fairly common use. Bakery fats and oils can be composed of (1) animal fats, (2) animal oils, (3) vegetable fats, (4) vegetable oils.

Animal Fats—Butter.—Because of the presence of glycerides with a low melting-point and because of its unique flavour, butter, provided it is of good quality, and is suitable for the product being made, is considered to be one of the best fats for the making of cakes and pastry.

Here is a table showing the general average composition of butter:

Fat	82–85%	Curd	1·5–2%
Water	10–16%	Mineral matter	1·4–2%

The amount of mineral matter will include salt.

Butter is made by churning milk fat after it has been ripened. Ripening confers flavour and allows the formation of lactic acid which breaks down the emulsion. In the past, samples of sour milk held over from a previous churning were used to accelerate the ripening.

In the present-day large-scale commercial production of butter, this method has been replaced by the use of pure cultures of lactic organisms which are added to pasteurized milk. At a certain acidity it is then used as a starter.

During churning, the fat globules separate from the rest of the cream which is drained off as buttermilk. The butter is then worked to improve the consistency, during which colour may be added to improve its appearance. Salt is added for flavour and also to improve the keeping quality. The water content is generally adjusted at this stage; this is limited by law to 16%.

Butter contains the naturally occurring vitamins A and D.

The attributes of good butter are:

Flavour—the volatile fats, chief of which is butyrin, confer on butter its distinctive flavour. There should be freedom from oiliness and rancidity. Salt should be sufficient only to improve the flavour.

Aroma—should be delicate and pleasing. A strong odour is indicative of the commencement of rancidity.

Texture—should be firm and plastic.

Creaming quality—for cake-making, this should be such that it will cream easily and hold the maximum of egg without curdling, provided that creaming is carried out properly.

Flavour is of particular importance, for if cakes made from butter do not possess the distinctive flavour of it, then the greatest selling point is lost and money is wasted.

For cake-making a fairly soft butter is best. For puff and Danish pastries, a tougher butter is required. For butter creams an unsalted butter is necessary.

Butter should be stored in a cool, dark place; this will delay considerably the onset of rancidity. Slightly rancid butter can be reconditioned by melting in hot water and thoroughly washing.

Although milk fat is of animal origin, it is quite different from the fat obtained from animal tissues. These also differ and this can be clearly seen by an examination of pork, beef and mutton dripping. Pork dripping is soft, that of beef less so, while mutton dripping is quite hard. The physical differences are explained by the differing compositions of the various glycerides.

Lard.—This is the fat obtained from the pig. The legal specification of the grades and qualities of all lards is that 'Lard is the rendered fat from healthy hogs, free from rancidity and containing not more than 1% of substances other than hog fat'.

The greater quantity of lards are marketed as neutral and leaf lards. The highest quality neutral lard is produced by vigorously agitating the minced hot fat with water below 122° F. The best quality (No. 1) comes from the region of the kidneys, and the next quality (No. 2) from the back.

This low temperature treatment, however, melts the softer fats only, and because of the low temperature, certain enzymes remain active. It is considered that this is the reason why these higher quality lards are liable to rancidity more quickly than the lower grades.

After the extraction of the quality grades, the remaining fat is removed by the use of boiling water under pressure, producing the quality known as leaf-lard. All the rest of the fatty parts, including all trimmings and scraps, are rendered by steam pressure and sold as prime steam lard.

The composition and consistency of the various qualities vary according to the method of extraction and the part of the animal from which they are obtained. The best qualities are white in colour, have a granular texture, an agreeable flavour, low melting-point and are firm in consistency.

Lard has practically no creaming properties and its chief use in the bakery is for frying, for meat-pie pastes, such special products as lardy cakes, and for the enrichment of bread, especially Vienna bread. Lard is easily absorbed by the human digestive system and possesses a high food value, as do in fact all fats with a comparable melting-point.

Beef Tallow or Oleo.—This is obtained from oxen and is more familiar as suet. In its natural form its only use in the bakery is for mincemeat and Christmas puddings. The best suet comes from the region of the kidneys.

Commercially the fat is separated from the tissues in the same way as for the extraction of lard. It is sometimes referred to as beef tallow, although this term is best applied to the rest of the body fats which are rendered at low temperatures and known as premier jus. If suet and premier jus are subjected to high pressure, there is a separation into the fat oleo stearin and liquid oleo oil. The fat and oil are of high quality and can be used in the manufacture of margarine although it is not common in this country where other fats and oils of high quality are used.

Mutton Tallow.—This hard solid fat is obtained from the sheep. In its raw condition it is suet and can be used by the baker for mincemeat and Christmas puddings. It has a higher melting-point than beef suet and is less pleasant in flavour.

Animal Oil—Whale Oil.—Apart from lard oil, the only animal oil that can be used in bakery shortening is whale oil, which is a marine oil obtained from the blubber of whales. It is deodorized, and changed from an oil to a fat by hydrogenation. It can be used in the manufacture of margarine and shortening.

Vegetable Fats.—These are fats in some countries and oils in others, according to the prevailing temperatures. The list includes palm, palm kernel, cocoa and coconut fats and shea butter.

Palm and Palm Kernel Fats.—Both are obtained from a species of palm grown principally in West Africa. The fruit, resembling the plum, is firm and fleshy. It contains a kernel enclosed in a hard shell. The fleshy part of the fruit is pulped, and heated, and the oil is then extracted, either by pressure or by centrifugal machines. The oil, which is reddish in colour is bleached. The fat content of the fleshy part of the fruit is about 60%.

After the hard shell is removed, the kernels are either ground up and pressed to remove the fat, or it is extracted by solvents. The extractable fat content of the kernel is approximately 45%. The fat is white to pale yellow in colour. Both fats are used extensively in the edible fats industry for the manufacture of margarines and shortenings.

Cocoa Butter.—This is extracted from the cacao bean in the process of making chocolate and cocoa. It is a hard brittle fat, white to pale yellow in colour, with an odour and flavour of chocolate. Cocoa butter is not used in the manufacture of margarine or shortening.

Coconut Fat.—This comes from the fruit of the coconut palm, which grows in abundance on the seaboard of the Atlantic and Pacific tropical seas.

The fat is found in the flesh of the coconut and is formed as the nut ripens, the flesh containing up to 40% fat. High grade coconut oils are extracted at source. The flesh, after the removal of the hard shell, is heated and pressed, yielding an oil that is used in large amounts by the manufacturers of edible fats.

Vast quantities of the flesh, however, are dried in the sun to produce commercial copra. The drying is done as soon as the nut is harvested, otherwise the flesh would sour, and in consequence rancidity would develop very quickly. Commercial copra has an oil content of between 60 and 65% and is extracted by pressure.

Only the highest quality copra oils are used in the manufacture of edible fats, the rest is mainly used in the soap industry. The residue from the extraction process is known as cattle cake and contains about 20% protein.

Coconut fat is classed as a vegetable butter and has a low melting-point, approximately 82–84° F.

Shea Butter.—This is obtained from a tree grown in West Africa, the fruit of which yields a stiff butter which, when refined, is free of taste and aroma. It is used in the production of high quality pastry fats with a low melting-point.

Vegetable Oils.—These are classified under three headings; that is, by the capacity that they have of drying as a thin film when exposed to the air.

Non-drying Oils—Olive Oil.—This is extracted from the fruit and the kernel of the olive which is cultivated extensively in the countries bordering on the Mediterranean, in Australia, South Africa and the U.S.A. The olive is green in colour and about the size of a damson.

The finest oil is obtained by cold pressing the pulp and is one of the finest of all oils. The next grade is produced by hot pressing and the residue extracted by solvency; this is the lowest grade produced. Olive oil is used extensively for culinary preparations, such as food dressings. Olive oil is not used in the manufacture of margarine or shortening.

Groundnut, Peanut, or Arachis Oil.—Produced from the groundnut which is the fruit of the arachis plant, a native of South America and the West Indies. It is now cultivated in West Africa, Australia, India and the East Indies.

The plant grows to a height of about 20 in. After flowering, the stems bearing the pods bend over and the nut matures and ripens underground. The nuts are imported into this country in the husks or as decorticated nuts, the term used for husking. The undecorticated nuts produce the best oil because the keeping and transporting qualities of the nuts are better in the natural protection of the husks.

After the removal of the thin red-brown skin, the nuts are pressed, yielding a practically colourless oil. The nut contains about 50% oil which does not readily become rancid. The cake left after oil extraction is a valuable cattle food, containing about 2–8% oil and about 40% protein.

Almond Oil.—Although almond oil is not used in the manufacture of bakery fats, it is important for the bakery student studying the technology of raw materials.

There are two distinct types of almond oil, the first produced from sweet almonds and the second from bitter almonds. On pressure, both produce a fixed or greasy oil containing the enzyme emulsin. Bitter almonds also contain amygdalin a substance which, with emulsin and in the presence of water, is changed to the essential oil of almonds, which is used for flavouring purposes.

Semi-drying Oils—Rapeseed Oil.—This oil is on the border line between a non-drying and a semi-drying oil. It is produced from a very small seed very much like a mustard or a turnip seed. The best oil is produced by pressure. If carefully treated and processed, this oil can be used in the manufacture of edible fats.

Cottonseed Oil.—This oil can be considered a by-product of another industry. The oil is expressed after the removal of the fibres for textiles. The oil, which is a deep yellow to a reddish-brown in colour, is bleached, and the strong odour removed before manufacturing into edible fats.

Soya Bean Oil.—Soya beans under pressure yield an oil of excellent quality. It is deodorized and used in the manufacture of bakery fats. The bean has been cultivated for centuries in China, Manchuria and Japan. It is now grown extensively in Canada, South Africa, the East Indies and the U.S.A. The bean resembles a large yellow pea and contains about 25% oil.

There are many other vegetable oils used in the manufacture of edible fats, the more important of which are seasame, sunflower and maize oils.

Drying Oils.—These are not used in foodstuffs. An example of a drying oil is linseed, used in paint.

To summarize, here are the main sources of fats and oils:

(1) Animal body fat and oils.
(2) Vegetable fat and oils.
(3) Milk fats.
(4) Fish and marine animal oils.

There are four principal methods of extraction.

(1) Pressure.
(2) Solvency.
(3) Application of heat (wet or dry).
(4) Combinations of all three.

Before edible oils can be used in the manufacture of domestic and bakery fats, they must be carefully and thoroughly refined. All impurities or substances which confer an undesirable colour or flavour must be removed.

The principal operations in edible oil refining are:

(1) Water washing to remove impurities by precipitation.
(2) Neutralizing with alkaline solutions to remove free fatty acids. Other impurities are removed at the same time.
(3) Bleaching to remove or reduce colour.
(4) Deodorizing by means of steam distillation in vacuum.

MARGARINES AND SHORTENINGS

Because of the desperate shortage of butter in France in consequence of industrialization and the shift of manpower from the land to the factory, a shortage still further aggravated by the Franco-German war, the French government was led to offer a substantial award for a satisfactory butter substitute. It was won by the Frenchman Mége-Mouries, who had the idea that because cows produced milk, and butter was made from milk fat, it would be possible to make a butter from the fats in the body of the animal. The idea was further confirmed when he noticed that if the cow was kept from food for a while and given water only to drink, it still produced milk.

Mége-Mouries experimented with the body fats and with the digestive juices, until finally he succeeded in producing a butter-like substance that he called margarine. The name was probably derived from the Greek word, 'margarites', meaning pearly, and 'margaron', meaning a pearl; the references being to the appearance of the margarine during a stage in the original method of manufacture. Mége-Mouries obtained a patent for his discovery in 1869. The patent was acquired in 1871 by a Dutch butter factor, Henri Jurgens. Soon he and his brother Jan, together with their local rival Simon Van den

Bergh, who had learned of the secret, began the commercial manufacture of margarine.

Margarine was not popular before the first world war, but because of the scarcity of butter during the war years and the extensive use of margarine as a butter substitute, together with a progressive improvement in quality, prejudice was gradually broken down. Great strides were taken after the war and as a result of research and experiment, new methods of manufacture were adopted and new raw materials were used, until today margarine of excellent quality is made, equal in food value to butter and totally different from the butter substitute of Méges-Mouries.

Manufacture. Margarine is an intimate mixture of a blend of hardened and liquid oils, that may be either of animal or vegetable origin. The oils are mixed with ripened milk and other additions and processed to form the very stable water in oil emulsion that we all know as margarine.

Almost all the margarines manufactured in this country are made from vegetable oils, chiefly groundnut, cottonseed, soya and palm oils. To effect plasticity it is customary to balance the blend with approximately equal amounts of liquid and hardened oils. The fats and oils used are colourless, odourless, bland in taste and of the highest quality.

The milk used is reconstituted skim milk, which is first pasteurized and then ripened by the addition of a lactic culture, a process which is carefully controlled over a period of about 18 hr. at a temperature of 64–65° F. This souring process is responsible for the development of a flavour and aroma similar to that of butter.

The oil blend, soured milk, salt (as brine), colour and an emulsifying agent are all intimately mixed ready for the next stage. In the case of domestic margarine, concentrates of vitamin A and D are added.

The mixture is then fed into a holding tube, where it is continuously agitated, from which it is passed to a set of externally cooled tubes of the Votator type with rotating internal wall scrapers, where the mixture is rapidly cooled. It is then passed through a texturizing unit after which it is packed.

Pastry Margarine.—The student will remember that puff pastry is built up of alternate layers of fat and pastry, and it depends to a great extent on the stability of the fat used, whether the laminated structure is to be clearly defined. A soft fat will roll out and have a shortening effect on the resultant pastry; on the other hand, hard fat will not film easily and in consequence remains in hard pieces and breaks down the structure, eventually melting and running out of the pastry while it is in the oven. A tough plastic fat is therefore needed.

Pastry margarine is toughened by the addition of stearin or oils hardened up to the consistency of stearin, thus enabling the margarine to withstand the manipulation entailed in the manufacture of puff pastry.

Pastry margarine is still made on the old system where the liquid emulsion is converted to solid form by pouring on to large revolving cooling drums, through which ice-cold brine is passed. The solidified mixture is scraped off the drums in flakes which are conveyed to rolling and kneading machines. The flakes are thin and pearl-like; it is this similarity that probably gave margarine its name.

Rolling and kneading is necessary to bring the margarine to the correct texture. The process consists of rolling between several sets of rollers after which it is passed to the kneading machines where the texture is further improved. Before the Votator system was used, all margarines were made by this method.

Shortenings.—These originated as lard substitutes in the U.S.A. about the year 1871, and were widely used as a lard adulterant by lard refiners, the product being sold as 'refined lard'. As the result of legislation, it was then marked as 'compound lard' and became so popular that it virtually replaced lard for cooking purposes. Great improvements were made in the manufacture of this product, and it was soon seen by the manufacturers that compound as it was then known, was no longer a lard substitute but a cooking fat in its own right, and unlike lard, which had poorer keeping and creaming qualities, compound has a much longer storage life and creams easily.

The introduction of the commercial process of hydrogenation enabled the manufacturers to use the softer animal fats and a choice of hardened marine and vegetable oils, so that eventually compounds of the finest quality became available to the baker. There are many grades and two distinct types which are distinguishable by colour, they are white and golden. The finest grades are sold under trade names.

Compound, or shortening as it is now called, can be, and still is, made on the drum method already described. The modern Votator system, however, produces shortening with a much superior texture. By far the greater proportion of shortening is now produced by this method.

Shortening is the utility fat in most bakeries because it is used for many purposes. For this reason it must possess good creaming properties, be fairly soft in consistency, resistant to rancidity over a fairly long period and be free from any tendency to foam when used for frying.

Great care, therefore, must be used in the selection of fats and oils; this is complicated by the fact that those fats and oils which confer good creaming qualities also have a tendency to foam when used for frying. Such fats are those produced from the coconut and the palm kernel.

To promote better creaming properties, the oil blend is passed through small filters where air up to 10% by volume is drawn in before it passes through the Votator cooling tubes. Thus the shortening gets, as it were, a flying start as far as creaming is concerned.

The cooled fat is ejected through a special nozzle which gives a final blending, so improving the texture; it then flows directly into boxes after which it is stored for a short time to mature.

The student must remember that shortenings contain no salt and are therefore bland in taste conferring no flavour to the finished cake.

Special Cake Fats.—In 1938, high grade shortenings with high emulsifying powers were introduced for use in conjunction with special cake flours for making cakes with a high sugar/liquid ratio to flour. These fats are capable of holding a high level of egg/milk without curdling.

These shortenings owe their special qualities to the admixture of varying proportions of mono and di-glycerides which are excellent emulsifying agents. Not only do they confer on the shortening the special property of holding an increased amount of liquid, but they increase the stability of the batter so that it does not collapse during baking.

Because they have a higher glycerol content than ordinary shortenings they are also known as super-glycerinated fats.

Pastry Fats.—Pastry fats are now on the market for use as an alternative to pastry margarine. They have a lower melting-point than pastry margarine, but have sufficient plasticity to be ideal for the manufacture of puff pastry.

They are based on shea butter, which is unique in that it melts quickly at a temperature somewhat below that of the human body, and is plastic at normal temperature. As these pastry fats have a higher fat content than pastry margarine, less is used per pound of flour to produce the same lift in the finished pastry; 11 oz. being the equivalent to 1 lb. of butter or pastry margarine in the making of full puff pastry.

Cooking Oils.—These are 100% oils and because of their low melting-point are liquid at normal temperatures. They are used in cakes of cheaper quality, for frying and for tin greasing. Because they are liquid, they have no creaming properties.

Oil is particularly useful in the making of light genoese which requires the admixture of a liquid fat into whisked eggs and sugar.

Here is a summary in diagrammatic form of the manufacture of bakery fats.

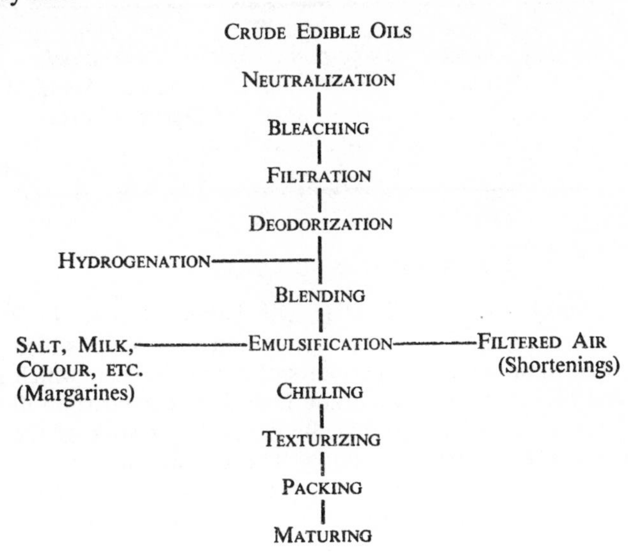

27

Baking-powders: Definition; History; Chemicals used; Reactions; Effects on Bakery Products; Some Experiments; Comparative Merits of Cream of Tartar and Cream Powders

BAKING-POWDERS

THE bakery student is familiar with baking-powder; he knows that it is a mixture of one part bicarbonate of soda, which is an alkali, and approximately two parts of cream powder, which is an acid. The two when moistened and heated produce carbon dioxide gas (CO_2), which is entangled in the gluten framework of the cake during the early stages of baking. The gas expands as the heat penetrates, until such time as the proteins in the cake coagulate. The structure becomes comparatively rigid and the cake does not collapse.

There are many chemical substances from which gas can be produced, but there are important considerations that must be kept in mind.

(1) That the finished product is intended for consumption as an article of food. This means:
  (*a*) The chemicals must comply with the provisions of the Food and Drugs Act.
  (*b*) After reaction, the residual substances remaining in the cake must be harmless and not be unpleasant in taste and aroma.

(2) The chemicals should be reasonably cheap and in good supply.

(3) They should not react together in the dry state.

(4) They should not readily react together when moistened in the cold state.

It is one thing to know what baking-powder is and what it does, it is another thing altogether to define it in writing should the question be asked in a written examination. Here is an excellent definition given by Daniel in *Bakery Materials and Methods*.

'A baking-powder can be defined as any substance or a mixture of substances, which may be purchased at an economic price, which, when moistened and heated, will produce a gas to aerate confectionery and which will leave a harmless and practically tasteless residue in the goods. For preference the chemicals should not react very readily when moistened with cold water, but should produce the greatest volume of available gas when mixed with warm water.'

Once the gas has been generated it cannot be replaced a second time.

An examination of old recipe books will show that chemical aeration was known and in use many centuries ago, certainly bicarbonate of soda has been in use for over 200 years, and before that 'pearl ash', which is a purer form of potash, was in use. This alkali was used in domestic cookery, where sour milk or buttermilk was the main moistening agent, and it is evident that reaction with the lactic acid of buttermilk effected a greater liberation of gas and in consequence a greater aeration of the mixture.

As home baking gradually decreased in favour of bakery products, so there was continual experimentation with other chemical substances, amongst which were alum and the carbonates of magnesia and lime.

One of the recipes in an old cookery book, dated 1886, is for ginger nuts to sell at 3*d.* per pound. The recipe contains three chemicals—'ash', 'hard' and 'volatile'. In faded ink by the side of the recipe a previous owner of the book has written—'ash means ordinary lump soda' and 'hard means ordinary ground alum'.

Old recipe books also refer to muriatic acid, now known as hydrochloric acid, in conjunction with bicarbonate of soda; the residue from this reaction, after the release of CO_2, is sodium chloride (common salt). There are also many references to 'vol' or 'volatile', the name given by the baker to carbonate of ammonia; this chemical when moistened and heated decomposed completely into CO_2 and ammonia gas, leaving no residual salt. Many were the bakery apprentices who had their first introduction to chemical aeration by being asked, with calculated nonchalance, to take a deep sniff at an un corked bottle of 'vol', which done, left the unfortunate boy gasping for breath.

Tartaric acid used with bicarbonate of soda then came into favour, tartaric acid in turn being superseded by cream of tartar, which became in general use. Cream of tartar, however, was much more expensive than tartaric acid, and in addition more of it was necessary to a given amount of bicarbonate of soda; this led to the introduction of cream of tartar substitutes, known as cream powders.

Unfortunately some of these substitutes had an adverse effect on the quality of powder aerated goods, resulting in a rapid decline in the popularity of such morning goods as scones, rock cakes, etc. Great strides, however, have been made, and are still being made, to perfect baking-powders, although there is still much to be learned on the subject before perfection is reached.

Bicarbonate of Soda.—Bicarbonate of soda ($NaHCO_3$) provides the necessary gas for aeration, either alone or mixed with a suitable acid. When moistened and heated it gives off CO_2, but the maximum is not liberated unless it reacts with a sufficient amount of a suitable acid.

When used alone as an aerating agent, the reaction is as follows:

$$\underset{\text{bicarbonate of soda}}{2NaHCO_3} \longrightarrow \underset{\text{sodium carbonate}}{Na_2CO_3} + \underset{\text{water}}{H_2O} + \underset{\text{carbon dioxide}}{CO_2}$$

The above reaction is not strictly accurate under baking conditions. It is only accurate after the prolonged boiling of a solution of the bicarbonate. Sodium carbonate is dehydrated washing soda, and is the residue of the reaction. It is a strongly alkaline substance with an objectionable taste. It has the added disadvantage of being able to bring about a partial dehydration of carbohydrates, probably the invert sugars present, and so causing crumb discoloration.

The use of bicarbonate of soda alone as an aerating agent is limited to such products as ginger cakes and gingerbread because of the treacle and spices that they contain. The alkaline taste is covered up by the spices. The main reason why bicarbonate of soda is used in these goods is that it does not react in the cold state, and, as mentioned, does not produce the volume of gas in the absence of the acid constituent as in baking-powder. This is of particular importance, for if baking-powder is used, the speed of gas evolution in such high sugar mixtures would probably cause collapse during baking, due to the softening action of sugar on gluten. Slow action is necessary in this type of product, and bicarbonate of soda will give this.

Cream of Tartar.—This acid constituent of baking-powder is a by-product of the wine industry. It is made from argol, which is precipitated in the form of a deposit in the wine vats as fermentation proceeds. It is crystallized and known as tartar. After further purification and re-crystallization it is potassium hydrogen tartrate, $KHC_4H_4O_6$, better known as cream of tartar.

Cream of tartar is sparingly soluble in cold water but readily so in hot. This is of advantage to the baker, because in contact with bicarbonate of soda in the cold state very little gas is evolved, whereas in the oven it is rapidly generated.

When mixed with bicarbonate of soda in the correct proportion, moistened and heated, the following reaction occurs:

$$\underset{\substack{188 \\ \text{cream of tartar}}}{KHC_4H_4O_6} + \underset{\substack{84 \\ \text{bicarbonate of soda}}}{NaHCO_3} = \underset{\substack{210 \\ \text{rochelle salts}}}{KNaC_4H_4O_6} + \underset{\substack{18 \\ \text{water}}}{H_2O} + \underset{\substack{44 \\ \text{carbon dioxide}}}{CO_2}$$

The numbers under each chemical formula are the total atomic weights of the elements concerned, and from these figures it can be seen that 188 parts of cream of tartar are required to neutralize 84 parts of bicarbonate of soda. The two to one ratio used in bakeries represents 168 parts of cream of tartar to 84 parts of soda, so that there is insufficient acid present. By weight, 11¾ lb. of cream of tartar to 5¼ lb. of bicarbonate of soda is correct. The residue left after the reaction is potassium sodium tartrate, the commercial name of which is Rochelle salts. It is harmless and practically tasteless.

Tartaric Acid.—This was first isolated from argol by Scheele in 1769, although argol was known to the Greeks and Romans.

Tartaric acid ($H_2C_4H_4O_6$) is readily soluble in cold water and reacts with bicarbonate of soda immediately in the cold state, giving an exceedingly rapid generation of gas, most of which would be lost before the dough could be worked off. With tartaric acid a large quantity of bicarbonate of soda is necessary for complete neutralization, as much as 168 parts of soda to 150 parts of tartaric acid. The reaction is as follows:

$$\underset{\substack{150 \\ \text{tartaric acid}}}{H_2C_4H_4O_6} + \underset{\substack{168 \\ \text{sodium bicarbonate}}}{2NaHCO_3} = \underset{\substack{194 \\ \text{sodium tartrate}}}{Na_2C_4H_4O_6} + \underset{\substack{36 \\ \text{water}}}{2H_2O} + \underset{\substack{88 \\ \text{carbon dioxide}}}{2CO_2}$$

It will be seen that for complete neutralization, 150 parts of the acid to 168 parts of soda is necessary.

Because of the rapid generation of gas in the cold state, when used with bicarbonate of soda, tartaric acid is not of great interest to the baker as an aerating agent. It is excellent, however, for use in puff pastry, if a weak acid is necessary, because being so readily soluble it exerts its beneficial action on the gluten far more quickly than most other baking acids. It is used also in sugar boiling, and as the acid complement in cold-set jellies.

Ammonium Carbonate.—(Volatile or 'Vol') Vol, as it is best known to the baker, was an essential aerating agent in bakeries of the past; it is used far less today except in the manufacture of biscuits.

Commercially, ammonium carbonate varies in composition. It

may be considered a mixture of ammonium hydrogen carbonate and ammonium carbamate. It has a pungent ammoniacal smell and an acrid burning taste. When moistened and heated alone, it volatilizes completely into ammonia gas and CO_2, and if reasonably pure leaves no residue in the product manufactured.

The objection to its use, however, is that unless all the gas is driven off, the taste is most objectionable. This is even more pronounced if undissolved particles remain in the goods, which slowly continue to volatilize.

'Vol' is excellent for biscuits which are thin and for other types of confectionery from which the gas can be rapidly dispersed. For this reason, and also because it gives practically all its gas in the oven, it is used to give added bulk to cream buns, although its use is not essential in these goods.

'Vol' can be obtained either as a fine powder or in lump form. When used it is important that it is completely dissolved in a little of the moistening agent. It should be stored in air-tight containers, or it will lose its strength by slow decomposition.

Alums: Potash Alum, Sodium Alum, Ammonia Alum.—These have all at some time been used in baking-powders.

Dehydrated soda alum—sodium aluminium sulphate—known generally as S.A.S., does not react with bicarbonate of soda in the cold, but does so rapidly in the oven. The residue from the reaction is sodium sulphate (glauber salts) and aluminium hydroxide which is insoluble.

In the U.S.A., its use is permitted, but in this country the presence of aluminium, other than that naturally occurring in foodstuffs is considered an adulterant and therefore not desirable.

Cream Powders.—Cream of tartar, although an excellent baking acid, is expensive; for this reason many substitutes have been available to the baker, and given the name of cream powders. Because most of them are of greater acid strength than cream of tartar, they are diluted so that they can be used in the ratio of 2 : 1 with bicarbonate of soda to give complete neutralization.

The substance most commonly used to dilute this acid strength is starch. The diluent also helps to keep the cream powder dry and free-running.

Cream powders are available to the baking industry under various well known trade names. Amongst the compounds that have been used are acid calcium phosphate, mono-sodium phosphate and sodium acid pyrophosphate. The last-named, however, is the acid now generally used in high-grade cream powders.

Acid Calcium Phosphate.—A.C.P., as it is commonly called, reacts very slowly with bicarbonate of soda in the cold but increases steadily in the oven. The reaction with bicarbonate of soda is approximately as shown:

$$\underset{\text{acid calcium phosphate}}{CaH_4(PO_4)_2} + \underset{\text{sodium bicarbonate}}{2NaHCO_3} = \underset{\text{di-hydrogen ortho-phosphate}}{CaNa_2H_2(PO_4)_2} + \underset{\text{water}}{2H_2O} + \underset{\text{carbon dioxide}}{2CO_2}$$

There is a great diversity of opinion as to the reactions taking place between these two chemicals, partly due to the variable character of the A.C.P.

If used by the baker in the pure state, the correct proportions of the chemicals would be 234 parts A.C.P. and 168 parts bicarbonate of soda, which is a little less than a ratio of 1½ : 1. When sold as a cream powder its strength is reduced by the addition of a 'filler' which is usually starch.

A.C.P. also can be used as a flour improver, because of its action on gluten, which is to confer a certain stability. It is used also as the acid constituent in baking-powders for self-raising flours, and as the means of increasing the acidity of a dough to inhibit the development of 'rope'. For this latter purpose A.C.P. is used at the rate of 1½–2 lb. per sack.

Acid Sodium Pyrophosphate.—A.S.P. as it is generally known, has the property of making gluten more extensible. More gas is thus held, and the cakes have a greater volume. From the reaction with bicarbonate of soda, the residual salt is sodium pyrophosphate, the formation of which causes the 'after-taste' in cakes in which it is used. There is no crumb discoloration.

In the pure state, the correct proportion is 1·36 lb. of A.S.P. to 1 lb. of bicarbonate of soda. As a cream powder the acid strength is diluted with a filler so that it can be used in the bakery in the proportion of 2 : 1. The reaction is as follows:

$$\underset{\text{sodium acid pyrophosphate}}{Na_2H_2P_2O_7} + \underset{\text{sodium bicarbonate}}{2NaHCO_3} = \underset{\text{sodium pyrophosphate}}{Na_4P_2O_7} + \underset{\text{carbon dioxide}}{2CO_2} + \underset{\text{water}}{2H_2O}$$

The chemicals mentioned are only a few of those used in cream powders, either alone or as mixtures, the manufacturers being ever anxious to provide a product of the highest purity and efficiency.

Here is a summary of this important subject:

Bicarbonate of soda: When used alone and moistened and heated, produces CO_2. The residual sodium carbonate leaves an objectionable taste and causes crumb discoloration. It is useful for ginger cakes where a rapid generation of gas is not desirable, and where taste and discoloration is masked by spices and treacle.

Used in correct proportion with a suitable acid, produces gas more efficiently.

Cream of tartar: The residual salt after reaction with bicarbonate of soda is practically tasteless and is harmless. Cream of tartar is slightly soluble in cold water and readily so in hot; some gas therefore is generated and lost before the goods are placed into the oven which must be done fairly quickly. Cream of tartar is not in good supply in large quantities and is expensive.

Tartaric acid: This acid reacts at once with soda in the cold state and most of the gas is thus lost. Because of its solubility it is useful for use in puff pastry and in sugar boiling.

Alums: Almost perfect with bicarbonate of soda except that the residue, aluminium hydroxide, is considered undesirable in foodstuffs. Use is therefore undesirable in this country.

Ammonium carbonate: Used alone produces its volume of gas in the oven with no residual substance. Unless used in biscuits or where the objectionable ammonia gas can be dispersed, its use is not commended.

Acid calcium phosphate: Confers stability on gluten, which, offering a greater resistance to gas expansion, reduces the volume of the finished product. Used in baking-powders for self-raising flours, as a bread improver and to inhibit the development of 'rope' in bread. Sparingly soluble in the cold state.

Acid sodium pyrophosphate: Confers resilience on gluten, thus allowing greater expansion and an increased volume. The residual salt has an 'after-taste'; no crumb discoloration. Readily soluble in hot water and sparingly so in cold.

Some Experiments.—To assist in the study of baking-powders, the student may like to try some experiments by making up four small mixings of scones, all of them exactly the same except for aerating additions. Here is the formula: 8 oz. of flour, 1 oz. of compound fat, 1 oz. of sugar and 5 oz. of milk.

To No. 1 make no addition.

To No. 2 add ½ oz. of bicarbonate of soda.

To No. 3 add ½ oz. of cream powder.

To No. 4 add ½ oz. of baking-powder.

Make each mixing up into two rounds of scones and let each pair lay for exactly the same time to recover from the manipulation. Bake off at 460° F. After baking, when cool and ready to handle, it will be noticed that there has been no increase in the volume of the scones from mixing No. 1. When cut it will be seen that there is no evidence of aeration; this will not be unexpected as there has been no addition of aerating substances.

The scones from mixing No. 2 will be found to have a fair volume, but are dark and unattractive in colour. When cut, the crumb will be found to be discoloured, with a pronounced alkaline taste. The aroma will be unpleasant. If the crumb is spotted with phenol red there will be a cherry red colour reaction, proving alkalinity. The increase in volume will prove that aeration has taken place from the soda alone.

No. 3 will not have risen at all, being exactly the same in volume as No. 1, showing that no aeration has taken place. When cut, the crumb will be white and close, with a pronounced toughness; when spotted with phenol red there is a yellow colour reaction, proving acidity.

The last set will have a good volume and be light and well aerated with a bright crumb colour; spotting with phenol red should give an orange colour reaction, proving neutrality.

The student will thus see quite clearly that it is the soda which evolves gas, but which, used alone has a bad effect on colour and flavour. There is no aeration from acid alone, but the crumb colour is very white. The best scone will be the one that is aerated by a properly balanced baking-powder.

Here is another interesting experiment, the details of which are often given to students by Mr. W. E. Spencer, the well-known teacher and demonstrator.

Take seven 1-lb. glass jam jars and pour in cold water until each is three parts full. Into each put eight grams of bicarbonate of soda, weighing carefully and accurately. With the same precision, weigh amounts of cream powder so that, starting from No. 1 there will be proportions of acid to soda from 1 : 1, 1¼ : 1, 1½ : 1, 1¾ : 1, 2 : 1, 2¼ : 1 and 2½ : 1. Thus there will be eight grams of both acid and soda in No. 1, 10 grams of acid to eight grams of soda in No. 2, and so on. Add a few drops of phenolphthalein solution to each jar, and keeping them in the same order, place them on a baking-sheet and then into the oven and let them boil.

On removal from the oven, the student will notice that some of them have changed in colour; in all probability the first three will be red, the next one or two will be pink and the rest will be colourless.

The explanation is that in water, and heated, a reaction takes place in which CO_2 is generated, leaving a residue in the water. Phenolphthalein is an indicator which by colour reaction reveals alkalinity, therefore those that show a red reaction are alkaline, the pinks are faintly alkaline and the colourless are either neutral or acid.

It is considered that the first colourless one, next in order to the last pink, will show the proportions of the chemicals most suitable for baking purposes. This applies only to the baking acid under test; a similar experiment will be necessary for a different cream powder.

Although this is interesting and instructive, one cannot draw accurate conclusions, because baking-powder is used with other raw materials, all of which may differ in their *p*H value. It will, however, reinforce in a visual way the necessity for care in the balance, and in the weighing and preparation of baking-powder.

Cream of Tartar v. *Cream Powder*.—A question may be expected on a City and Guilds paper on the relative merits of cream of tartar and cream powder. Assuming that they are used in correct proportion with bicarbonate of soda, and that the cream powder is of good quality, here is a short summary:

Cream of Tartar

Advantages	*Disadvantages*
No 'after taste'.	More expensive.
	More soluble in cold water, therefore some gas lost during mixing.
	Unless cakes are put into the oven quickly there is a further loss of gas and in consequence a loss of volume.

Cream Powder

Advantages	*Disadvantages*
Uniform in strength and quality.	Possible 'after-taste'.
Regular in supply.	
Less expensive.	
Less soluble in cold water.	
Goods can recover from the effects of manipulation before baking, without loss of volume.	

It must always be remembered that cakes are made to eat and enjoy; the extent therefore of any after-taste is of great importance.

For the purpose of City and Guilds examinations in flour confectionery, only a general knowledge of this subject is necessary. The student will be well advised, however, to study the subject of chemical aeration with diligence in his study of bakery science, for not only will questions on the subject be expected in greater detail on the bakery science examination paper, but the study will reinforce his knowledge for possible questions on the examination paper in flour confectionery at the final level.

He will be well advised also to take every opportunity of revising his notes in the light of fresh available knowledge. There is still much to be learned on the subject of chemical aeration.

28

Formula Balance: Construction of Formulae; Basic Formula and Rebalance; Effects of Basic Ingredients; Cake Faults: Diagnosis and Causes; Changes during Baking: Faults in Baking; Fruit Ratios

FORMULA BALANCE

WHAT is a cake formula? It is an accurate record of the quantities of certain raw materials necessary to make a particular type of cake. If the formula contains ingredients in correct balance it will produce a good cake, provided that care is taken in manufacture, baking and packing. It will do this time after time, always bearing in mind the possible variability of the materials used.

What is a good cake? A good cake is one showing no faults, either in appearance or in the eating. It will be light, with even aeration, and with a thin golden crust. It will have an agreeable flavour and aroma. If it contains fruit this will be of good quality and evenly distributed. The quality of the cake can vary according to the materials used, but if the formula is balanced, then it will still produce a good cake. Plate XXXII illustrates good Madeira and Genoa cakes.

What is balance? There are four main ingredients necessary in the construction of a cake formula: they are flour, fat, eggs and sugar.

Balance can be divided into four parts:

(1) Ingredients which provide strength and structure; they are flour and eggs.
(2) Ingredients that have to be carried, such as sugar, fat, milk and fruit.
(3) Ingredients that have a lifting or opening effect—sugar, baking-powder, egg and fat.
(4) Ingredients which have a closing effect; these are milk, water and to a certain extent eggs reconstituted from dried egg-powder.

Therefore a balanced formula contains sufficient materials from Group 2 as can be carried by Group 1. These should be balanced between the effects of Group 3 and Group 4.

Basic Formula.—This is probably the oldest consistent formula for a cake known to the baking industry, and is more familiarly known as 'a pound all round'.

1 lb. sugar } creamed
1 lb. fat } together
1 lb. egg—moistening and aerating
1 lb. flour—dry ingredient

In this formula there is sufficient strength provided by the eggs and flour to carry the sugar and fat. The closing effect of the water in the eggs is balanced by the lifting effect of the fat and the air holding quality of the eggs. The sugar has an opening effect on the structure.

It will be seen from this formula that it requires 1 oz. of egg to assist in aerating 1 oz. of flour (remembering that fat is holding air from the initial beating) and 1 oz. of egg is required to moisten 1 oz. of flour.

It is known that the maximum ratio of egg to fat is 1¼ : 1; any more egg will tend to toughen the cake. With this knowledge it is possible to make a change in the balance of the basic formula.

Formula Re-balance No. 1

lb.	*oz.*	
1	0	Sugar
1	0	Fat
1	4	Egg
1	4	Flour

The proportion of egg to flour is the same as in the basic formula, so that the moistening and aerating effect is the same. There is, however, an increase in the strength and structure materials, which would be useful in the case of a genoese for dipping purposes. The result in a cake would be a bolder crown, with possibly a slight break, according to the strength of the flour and the amount of manipulation given.

Formula Re-balance No. 2

lb.	*oz.*	
1	0	Fat
1	4	Sugar
1	0	Egg
2	0	Flour
	½	Baking-powder
	14	Milk

Here it is seen that 1 lb. of eggs will moisten 1 lb. of flour, leaving

1 lb. of flour to be moistened. This is done by introducing milk. As milk contains 90% water (reconstituted milk powder) against the 75% contained in egg, 14 oz. of milk is the approximate equivalent of 16 oz. of egg in moistening power. Baking-powder is added to aerate the balance of the flour not affected by the egg, and the rule is as follows:

Cake ½ lb. or less: 1 oz. of powder for each 1 lb. of flour in excess of weight of egg.

Cake ½ lb. to 2 lb.: ½ oz. of powder for each pound of flour in excess of weight of egg.

Cake 3 lb. or over: ⅓ oz. of powder for each 1 lb. of flour in excess of weight of egg.

It will be noticed that in this formula the sugar has been increased; this is to maintain the sweetness of the cake due to the addition of the non-sweetening materials—the milk and the extra flour. The general rule is, that the weight of sugar should be approximately 25% of the total weight of fat, eggs, flour and milk.

Formula Re-balance No. 3

lb.	*oz.*	
1	0	Fat
2	0	Sugar
1	4	Eggs
3	12	Flour
	1¼	Baking-powder
2	0	Milk (approx.)

With this formula there is a further increase of flour based on the weight of fat. The ratio of egg to flour is widened, so that more powder and milk is used to effect balance. The sugar is increased in proportion.

Fat controls the quality of a cake. The lower the proportion of fat used in a cake formula, then the cheaper the quality of the cake. The quality of the fat used is important; a good quality fat, be it butter, margarine or compound has excellent creaming properties and will take the maximum of 1¼ egg to 1 of fat without curdling, under proper conditions. The weight of fat should never exceed the weight of flour.

Due to a greater knowledge of raw materials and the interaction of them in the manufacturing and baking processes, there has been a re-assessment of the rules of formula balance. It is now felt that the old rules were far too rigid, for it is seen that by a greater flexibility, a much wider range of good cakes can be made. Furthermore the old rules made no provision for differences in method and the influences of bakery conditions on the finished cake.

Three simple considerations govern the new system of formula balance. The levels for fat, sugar and total liquid (egg/milk) in relation to flour are selected subject to the following:

(1) The weight of fats should not exceed the egg.
(2) The weight of fat should not exceed the sugar.
(3) The weight of sugar should not exceed the total liquid.
Baking-powder is used for the final adjustment.

Based on flour as 100 and using normal materials, fat can be anything between 20/80, sugar 45/90 and total liquid 80/110. Using high-ratio flour and special shortenings, the sugar may be as high as 130 and the total liquid 145/150.

The student will know that a good cake is one showing neither the 'X' nor the 'M' faults. Between these two limits, bearing in mind the considerations given above, a greater range of cakes can be made, each with a perfectly balanced formula, each different in degree one from the other. In this way a greater flexibility in formula balance is attained, and there is a wider field for experimentation.

A great deal of valuable work has been done on formula balance and cake faults by the bakery research establishments of Craigmillar and British Creameries Ltd. and Thomas Hedley and Co. Ltd. The bulletins issued by these firms during and after the war have been of great assistance to craftsmen and students alike. The author has drawn freely on the data so readily offered to the baking industry by these research workers.

The Effect of Sugar.—Sugar obviously sweetens. It is important also because it has the power to lift and lighten the cake, and confer crust colour and bloom. It increases the eating and keeping qualities of the cake and the food value. All this assuming that it is used in the right amount in a correctly balanced mixing.

Fig. 56 A shows the outline of a cake made from a correctly balanced formula. The sides are straight, the shoulders nicely curved and to finish the symmetrical outline, the top is slightly domed. The crust colour will be an even golden brown with a healthy bloom. The interior will show an even coloured bright crumb, with a regular grain, showing neither cores nor streaks.

B. In this example the lifting effect of the extra sugar has been too much for the strength of the batter. As a result, it has expanded to such an extent that the protein structure (gluten and albumen) has collapsed. This is known as the 'M' fault, because the outline of the top and sides is similar to the outline of the letter 'M'. The crust will show sugar spots, and the crumb will be open and sticky.

C. The outline of this cake shows a decreased volume, with a peaked crown. The crust will show a lack of bloom. The crumb will tend to be close and harsh to the touch according to the amount of sugar deficiency.

Not only is there a decrease in the lifting or opening effect but the

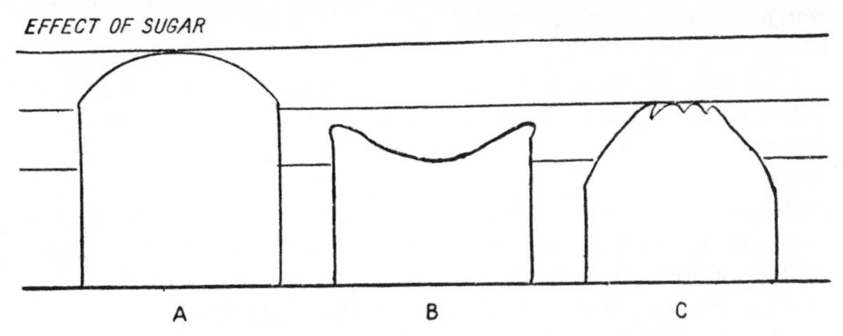

FIG. 56.—Formula balance. The effects of sugar.

softening action of sugar on gluten is also decreased; in consequence there will be a greater resistance to expansion, showing itself in a peaked top.

The Effect of Fat (Fig. 57). The amount of fat in a balanced formula

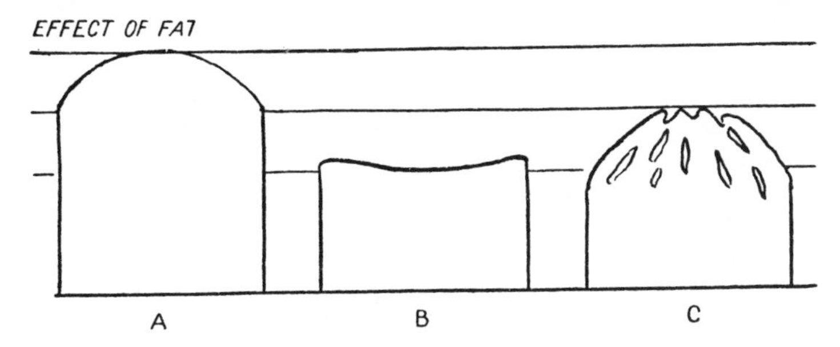

FIG 57.—Formula balance. The effects of fat.

is the measure of the quality of the cake. (Obviously the quality of the fat itself is of importance also.) Fat imparts a pleasant and rich eating quality and increases the food value of the cake. Good butter confers flavour also. Fat also improves the keeping quality. Because of its shortening properties, it prevents toughness. It holds the air incorporated during the initial creaming process.

A. This again is the control cake and has the correct quantity of fat.

B. This cake has too much fat, which has to be carried by the structural materials. The volume is small; the top crust will be thick and greasy; there will be a closeness at the base of the cake and the crumb will feel decidedly greasy.

An increase of fat must be balanced by an increase in the structural materials, egg and flour. It is clear that eggs and fat must bear some relation to each other, and the rule is to keep the egg weight equal to the weight of fat, or slightly in excess. (1 pint (20 oz.) of egg to 1 lb. of fat.)

C. A cake made with too little fat will have a poor crust colour, and will stale rapidly. The cake will be tough, show a loss of volume and the crumb structure will show tunnel-like holes, pointing to the centre of the crown of the cake. Because the shortening effect on the gluten is less, there is more resistance within the cake to the expansion during baking. The expansion being irresistible, the steam escapes more violently, tearing its way to the crown of the cake, causing the long-shaped holes, and 'peaking' the top.

The Effect of Milk (Fig. 58).—Milk confers bloom on the crust

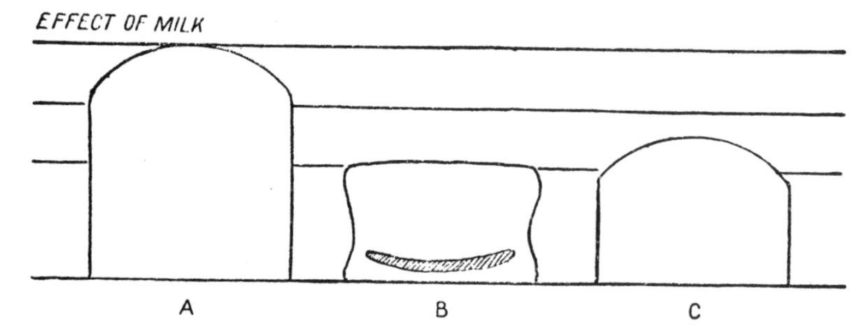

FIG. 58.—Formula balance. The effects of milk.

and adds to the food value of the cake when it is used instead of water. It has a closing effect on the crumb.

A. The control.

B. A cake containing too much milk will seem to have no fault until it leaves the oven, when it will contract as soon as it commences to cool. Volume is maintained as long as steam is in the cake, after which it drops, the structure closing up, the sides collapse and the paper band round the cake falls away. When cut, a heavy solid core is seen at the base of the cake. If the student studies the drawing, he will note that if the lines of the contracted sides are brought together, they form a letter X. This fault is therefore known as the 'X' fault.

C. This cake has too little milk. It lacks volume, it is dry eating and will stale rapidly.

The Effect of Baking-powder (Fig. 59).—Baking-powder is used for aerating; it thus increases the volume of the cake. The student will know that baking-powder consists of approximately two parts acid and one part bicarbonate of soda. He will know also that it is the bicarbonate that produces the gas, but with the correct proportion of acid, a greater volume of gas is produced.

Weight for weight, bicarbonate of soda has a greater freeing action than baking-powder; it is, however, used alone only in ginger goods, where the flavour can be masked and where the off-colour that it imparts actually improves the appearance.

Baking acid can be used alone in puff pastry, because it confers resilience on the gluten. In meringues, a little acid in solution introduced during the whipping will increase the stability of the egg whites. Used in excess, however, it has a solvent action on proteins, breaking down the strength. In addition it will confer a sour taste on the finished goods.

Used in excess in a cake mixing, baking-powder will have the same effect as an excess of sugar, producing the 'M' fault. In this case there has been a generation of gas, beyond that which the strength and structure materials can maintain, with the result that the cake fabric collapses.

When examined it will be noticed that the crust of the cake is darker than normal and the crumb is open, and is discoloured, especially near the base of the cake.

The outlines (Fig. 59) show clearly the results of variation in baking-powder content in one formula.

A. This is correctly balanced.

B. This shows the collapsed cake with the 'M' outline.

C. The outline shows quite clearly the loss of volume when insufficient baking-powder has been used.

It will be noted that according to its action on proteins—gluten and albumen—baking-powder can be included in the strength and structure group of raw materials. The student will find it particularly interesting and instructive to make small mixings with formulae out of balance, reproducing faults for himself. It will not be long before he will note that it is impossible to produce the 'M' and 'X' faults in one cake.

From this knowledge he will find that it is possible to rebalance a formula and vary the quality of a cake. If he experiments carefully, basing the tests on the balance of materials from Group 1—the strength and structure group—and Group 2, the materials that have to be carried, with due regard to the opening effect of some and the closing effect of others—he will be well on the way to a complete control, not only of the materials used but of the manufacturing process also.

From his experiments he will notice that the 'M' and 'X' faults to a certain extent will cancel each other out; for example, if a cake has the 'M' fault from an excess of sugar, then apart from the obvious remedy of reducing the amount of sugar in the formula, it can be corrected by a careful increase in the amount of milk, the result being a good cake but of a slightly different quality.

It must be clearly understood, and this observation is made with due emphasis, that the data given on this subject, while basically correct, is nevertheless general in character, for like the many faults and their remedies met with in breadmaking, the diagnosis of cake

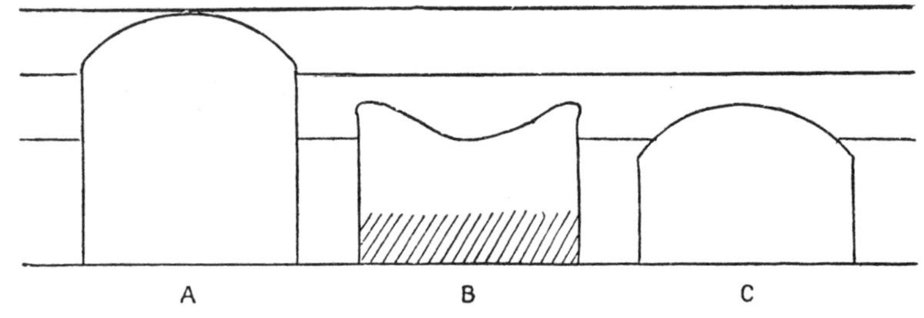

FIG. 59.—Formula balance. The effects of baking-powder.

faults can prove difficult because there can be different causes and remedies for the same apparent fault.

It sometimes happens that a tendency to a particular fault can be corrected, not by re-balancing the formula, but by altering or slightly adjusting the method of making, or by an adjustment in the quality of one or more of the raw materials. For example, a cake may show a tendency to the 'M' fault, which can be corrected by a little more machining, thus developing the potential strength of the flour. On the other hand, the fault can be remedied by using a proportion of flour with a greater strength.

Streaks.—These can be caused by insufficient mixing, especially if the flour is not cleared properly through the batter. Another source of streaks is from failure to scrape the mixing bowls thoroughly during all the stages of manufacture. Baking-powder with a low gassing power, especially a powder that has been allowed to deteriorate by faulty storage, will cause streaks. Sometimes dense streaks are found at the base of a cake, similar to the streak caused by the over use of milk or water. This can be due to the use of flour below the usual strength, there being insufficient support for the materials to be carried. Conversely, too strong a flour will lead to this fault.

'Cauliflower' Tops.—This fault can be due to several causes. A flour that is too strong, or one in which the gluten has been developed by overmixing, are general causes. An oven too hot will cause this fault, because there is a rapid formation of crust which bursts as the cake batter begins to expand. This fault may be accentuated if there is a lack of humidity in the oven.

Patches and Seams.—Sometimes a 'sad' patch is seen just under the centre of the crown of the cake. This is a clear indication that the cake has been underbaked. This is the last part of the cake to bake, and the extent of the patch is the measure of the deficiency in baking time. A ring-shaped seam in the crumb structure usually points to a sharp knock during baking, causing a partial collapse of the semi-cooked interior. Bearing in mind that the cake is only cooked when the heat has penetrated to the centre, some indication of the time of the knock can be estimated by the diameter of the seam.

Holes.—These are indicative of faulty formula balance, in which the strength and structure materials are proportionately too high, or the strength has been increased by the use of an unduly strong flour, or one in which the gluten has been developed by over mixing.

When the structure of the cake is too strong, it offers a greater resistance to the expansion within the cake, with the result that there is a violent series of ruptures in the cake structure, in the direction of the crown of the cake, resulting in tunnel-shaped holes.

Horizontal holes are caused in cakes, especially in slab cakes, by carelessness in depositing the batter in the frames. If the scale pan is wetted with water and the batter is put into the frame in two portions, a film of water will be left between the two. This will change into steam in the oven, causing expansion; the weight of cake above will flatten the hole and so extend it. A pocket of air trapped between two additions will cause the same fault. Similarly a portion of unmixed fat/sugar will result in a long hole, although not necessarily horizontal.

Finally it must be emphasized that although the cake may be perfect when leaving the oven, it can be spoiled by careless handling and packing. Eventually the cake will be sold and probably be expected to grace the table. If it does not look appetizing and inviting, even although the formula is balanced and the materials are of the best quality, then the result is a failure, and those responsible are not craftsmen.

CHANGES DURING BAKING

Not a lot of thought is given to the wonderful changes that take place in a cake batter during the baking process. The oven is opened, and provided that the formula is properly balanced, and reasonable care has been exercised, a good cake is expected.

Nevertheless, great physical and chemical changes have taken place, and the cake has become an appetizing and highly nutritious article of food.

The student will do well to study these changes, for apart from the interest that can be derived from it, there comes also an understanding of the necessity for care in correct baking temperatures, sufficient humidity and correct baking times.

The aeration of cake depends on many factors, chief of which are fat, eggs and/or baking-powder. The air incorporated in the fat during the initial creaming, and held there with the assistance of the eggs, expands within the cake during baking. As the heat penetrates, water is changed to steam which exerts pressure. The gas generated by the action of water and heat on the baking-powder, also expands and exerts pressure. In the oven, the temperature rises as it penetrates the cake. The fat melts to oil, and as the heat penetrates still further, an expansion takes place and the cake begins to rise. After a time a skin gradually begins to form on the surface of the cake, as the moisture is slowly evaporated. This skin will form slowly, giving time for maximum expansion, provided that the baking temperature is correct and there is enough humidity in the oven. A skin will form more slowly on a large cake than on a smaller one, partly because the oven temperature is lower and partly because of the greater evaporation of moisture, going on for a longer time, from the surface of the cake.

It is here that the importance of sufficient humidity in the oven becomes obvious, for if the oven atmosphere is unduly dry, more moisture is taken up from the surface of the cake, and a hard dry skin is quickly formed. Then the expansion, which cannot be denied, bursts through the top crust, forming what is known as a 'cauliflower top', with long tunnel-shaped holes in the crumb of the cake. If, on the other hand, humidity is correct, the maximum expansion can take place, as the heat penetrates to the centre of the cake, bringing about the fullest volume and a cake of good shape.

With expansion at its maximum, and with crust forming on the outside of the cake, the centre is still in a molten condition. As the temperature increases, some of the starch takes up moisture and is gelatinized. Not all the starch undergoes this change because there is not sufficient moisture present. The proteins—gluten and albumen—start to coagulate and form the framework or girderwork of the cake. While this is going on, more water is driven off in steam, the crust takes on a higher temperature and begins to colour as it approaches the temperature of the oven. As the temperature within the cake rises, more moisture is evaporated, and the protein strands dry and begin to absorb the oiled fat.

The crust colour deepens as the sugars caramelize, until at last the cake is baked, and the wonderful change becomes visible.

It sometimes happens that a batch of cakes is forgotten in the oven, and then still further changes take place. More and more moisture is driven off and the crust thickens. Slowly the temperature of the whole cake increases; the crust deepens still further in colour and gradually turns black; the crumb slowly begins to darken; all the time the crust gets thicker until there is hardly any crumb left, until at last the cake is completely black right through and the whole of the materials calcined, giving off the acrid smell of burning.

Baking Cakes too Slowly.—When a cake has been baked too slowly it is dry, it has a thick crust, and if the oven temperature is very low it has a badly discoloured crumb. The dryness is explained by the fact that as the cake is longer in the oven in order to bake it, more than the normal amount of moisture is driven off.

At the same time the crust thickens, but does not colour unduly. In an attempt to get sufficient crust colour, the cake is left in the oven, with the result that the temperature of the crumb will rise to above the boiling point of water (212° F.) and the sugar in the crumb will commence to caramelize.

Baking Cakes too Quickly.—If the oven temperature is excessive for the type of cake being baked, then a thick, hard crust is rapidly formed, which quickly takes on more colour. The 'cauliflower top' is formed as already explained, and the volume and appearance of the cake suffers. The crust begins to blacken before the cake is baked inside. The unbaked part of the crumb will be shown as a damp patch under the crown of the cake. The cake will be altogether unappetizing.

Fruit Sinking.—Some years ago there was some controversial correspondence in the trade press on the subject of cherries sinking in a cake. It arose from a simple request from a baker for assistance and advice.

Almost all the replies advised washing the cherries to free them of syrup; some suggested that they should be rolled in flour after washing, others suggested rice flour, while others more quality minded, advised rolling in ground almonds. Other bakers joined in by saying that not only cherries but currants and sultanas dropped to the bottom of their cakes. As is usual in such correspondence, a baker wrote to say that he took the cherries, loaded with syrup straight from the box, and they did not sink in his cakes.

We know now, from our knowledge of raw materials and formula balance, that if any fruit sinks, then the cake batter is not stable enough, in relation to the size and weight of fruit, to keep it up—it is as simple as that.

There are degrees of instability, for a batter that will just support currants and sultanas may not sustain the weight of cherries. A batter may be just tolerant enough to maintain the weight of washed and dried cherries, but not cherries thick with syrup.

The correspondent who used cherries straight from the box, obviously used a cake formula with materials, in quantity or quality, of such strength that the other materials were easily carried.

The fault is one of degree in relation to the size and weight of fruit. An adjustment of the two groups is the obvious remedy. If the fault is slight, a little extra mixing after the flour is added, will develop the gluten strength a little and so increase the stability of the batter. Similarly, the replacement of a small proportion of the flour with an equal weight of one stronger, will give the necessary strength to the batter.

Fruit Ratios.—The question is often asked, 'What are the differences between a heavily, medium and lightly fruited cake?' Here is a guide.

(1) Heavily fruited cake—1 lb. of fruit to each pound of the total mix.
(2) Medium fruited cake—½ lb. of fruit to each pound of the total mix.
(3) Lightly fruited cake—¼ lb. of fruit to each pound of the total mix.

For example, if the following formula is used:

lb.	*oz.*		
1	0	Fat	Heavily fruited cake—4 lb. of fruit
1	0	Sugar	Medium fruited cake—2 lb. of fruit.
1	0	Egg	Lightly fruited cake—1 lb. of fruit
1	0	Flour	

For bride, birthday and similar cakes, fruit can be used at the rate of up to 1½ lb. per lb. of total mix.

29

Creams: Types; Dairy Creams: Definition and Standards; Composition and Preparation; Other Creams: Formulae and Manufacture; Sponge Goods: History; Principles of Manufacture; Basic Formulae; Marbling a Gateau; Jellying Agents: Sources and Manufacture; Slab Cakes: Preparation of Frames; Formulae; Faults; The use of Cake Crumbs

CREAMS

THE types of cream used by the baker are legion, varying from fresh dairy cream—even in normal times used too rarely—to a mixture of fat and some sweetening agent. This latter is generally misnamed 'butter cream' unless, of course, the fat used is really butter. There are also imitation creams available and proprietary creams that are ready for use. The baker can still further add to the variety by incorporating other substances to his creams such as egg white, gelatine or marshmallow cream during the whipping or beating, or he may even blend two types of cream together.

Dairy Cream.—This cream as far as the confectioner is concerned is, without doubt, the acme of all creams and was probably the first cream used for the purpose of filling or decorating cakes. Almost all other types of cream are, to a certain extent, substitutes either because of the cost or the limited keeping qualities of fresh cream, although modern refrigeration has increased the shelf life of confections containing fresh dairy cream.

If the student will look at a bottle of milk that has been standing for a few hours he will note that the cream has risen to the top. The quality of milk is determined, amongst other things, by the amount of cream in a given amount of milk. If he will pour the milk into a shallow pan and allow it to stand, the cream can be skimmed off quite easily. Commercially it is done by separators, when the cream is separated from the milk by centrifugal force. If the cream is allowed to stand after separation for about 12 hours at a temperature between 36 to 40° F. it will mature, after which it can be sweetened, flavoured and whipped to a fairly stiff consistency.

The baker normally sells cream in its whipped form only. The ideal butter-fat content for whipping dairy cream lies within a range from 38 to 42% butterfat with 40% butterfat as an optimum. Where it is possible to obtain cream of this butterfat content, it is obviously the most satisfactory for the baker. When, however, it is only possible to obtain 48% butterfat cream, this may be adjusted by mixing the double cream with milk in the ratio of four parts of cream to one part of milk. Care must be taken that this ratio is adhered to, otherwise the whipped product may not stand up satisfactorily after piping.

Cream for whipping should be cool—an ideal temperature is 40° F. It is best not to guess the temperature but to use a thermometer. If the temperature is too high the cream will become buttery. Equally it is important to carry out whipping in a cool place, for whipping in a hot atmosphere will cause a considerable rise in the temperature of the cream. It is not advisable to whip cream if the temperature is above 53° F. Once whipped, cream will stand up to higher temperatures, but cream goods look more attractive and keep better if kept cool—they are at their best displayed in a refrigerated counter.

Whipping can be effected by either hand whisk or by machine. Some mechanical methods claim expansion of cream from 3 to 4 times but most satisfactory results should be obtained with an expansion of 2 to 2½ times. In either case, where actual whipping is involved, it should not be too fast an action or the cream will not stand up well after whipping.

The flavour and sugar are added before whipping commences. Sugar is used at the rate of about 1 oz. to 1 pint of cream; this will vary according to the opinion of the confectioner and the taste of his customers. If cream is over whipped, the fat globules separate out from the water and so coalescence is broken down. This in effect is how butter is made. Even if the cream is only slightly over whipped its smoothness and homogeneity is spoiled for moisture from it will percolate through the savoy bag and the cream itself will have a buttery look and consistency.

Hygiene Precautions.—In using dairy cream the baker can be assured that every precaution possible has been taken by the dairyman to ensure that cream as near sterile as possible has been delivered to him. Nevertheless, most modern bakeries set aside a special area of their premises in which to deal with the cream whipping operation. Churns or cans should always be wiped down before opening and lids should be replaced when not actually in use.

All equipment used for cream whipping should be sterilized daily, either by boiling water or live steam immediately after the equipment has been washed down with a suitable detergent to remove the grease.

Savoy bags which will boil are preferable, e.g. cotton or nylon fabric. They should be turned inside out after the removal of the tube, thoroughly washed in detergent and then should be boiled for at least 15 min. If the bag is not suitable for boiling, then it must be soaked in a solution of hypochlorite and then thoroughly rinsed in clean, cold water before re-use.

Cream Standards.—Under the Public Health (Preservatives, etc., in Food) Regulation, cream is defined as that portion of milk rich in milk fat which has been separated by skimming and it is specifically forbidden to add any thickening substance to cream such as gelatine, starch paste or any substance which, when added to cream is capable of increasing its viscosity and then to sell the mixture as cream. If the confectioner does use such substances, then he must not sell the goods containing such a mixture as 'cream' goods.

The composition of cream is governed by the Food Standard (Cream) Order, 1951. This divides fresh cream under two main headings of 'single' and 'double' cream. In effect, it means that no cream may be of less than 18% butterfat and if described as 'double cream' it must be not less than 48% butterfat. This makes it possible to sell cream containing more than 18% butterfat, but it must not be described or sold as 'double' or thick cream unless it contains 48% or more of butterfat.

The Food and Drugs Act also provides for the use of the word 'cream'. It is now illegal to sell for human consumption any substance resembling cream in appearance but is not cream, or under a description which includes the word 'cream'. The terms 'imitation cream' and 'reconstituted cream' as defined are allowed.

Clotted Cream.—This cream is inevitably associated with Devon and Cornwall. It is prepared by allowing milk to stand for about 12 hr. in shallow pans. It is then scalded for a sufficient time, so that water is driven off and the milk proteins (casein and albumen) coagulate. The scalded milk is left to stand and cool for 24 hr., when the clotted cream is skimmed off. About 1 part cream is obtained from 23 parts milk.

The composition of clotted cream is approximately:

Fat	63·0%	Protein	4·03%
Water	29·5%	Lactose	2·8%
Ash	0·67%		

The legal standard for butterfat in clotted cream is 48%.

Jellied Cream.—It sometimes becomes necessary for the confectioner to increase the stability of cream so that it will set. Jellied cream is used for such table sweets as charlotte russe, and is an example of a stabilized cream. It is prepared by the addition of gelatine at the rate of 1 oz. of gelatine to 1½ pints of cream; the gelatine is heated in water and the cooled suspension added to the cream during whisking.

Gelatine soon sets when in contact with the cool cream so that it must be rapidly dispersed and thoroughly mixed. The cream may be coloured and flavoured before whisking commences.

Butter Creams.—These should, as the name implies, be made with butter and it is almost certain that in the future, it will be necessary by law to use butter as the fat constituent, if it is to be termed butter cream.

Butter cream is a light, well-beaten mixture of a fat and a sweetening agent in varying proportions. The fat can be butter, margarine or a high quality shortening, or mixtures of these. The sweetening agent can be icing sugar, fondant, or sugar syrups made from boiled solutions of lump, granulated or castor sugars. Butter cream can contain milk, water or additions such as honey or ginger syrup; either to alter the consistency and/or to impart a particular flavour. Melted chocolate can be added both for colour and flavour.

Butter cream, being a water in oil emulsion, is not an ideal medium for the multiplication of harmful bacteria. This, however, does not absolve the baker from being scrupulously clean in its preparation, as in fact he should be in the manufacture of all bakery food products.

Formulae for butter creams are many and various. Here are two that can be considered as basic, the second having a particularly smooth texture.

No. 1

lb.	*oz.*	
1	0	Butter (unsalted)
1	0	Icing sugar
	1¼	Egg white or milk
		Colour and flavour as desired

No. 2

lb.	*oz.*	
1	0	Butter (unsalted)
1	0	High quality shortening
2	0	Fondant (warmed)
		Colour and flavour as desired

Here are two formulae from the book *All About Pastries* by Harris and Borella, which will give the student some idea of the butter creams in use in high-class bakeries 50 years ago. The student will notice the use of the word 'finest' as applied to butter.

No. 1			No. 2		
lb.	*oz.*		*lb.*	*oz.*	
1	0	Shell eggs	2	0	Finest fresh butter
1	0	Castor sugar	2	8	Icing sugar
1	0	Finest fresh butter		6	Egg yolks
		Colour and flavour as desired			Colour and flavour as desired

No. 1: Whip the egg and sugar to a stiff sponge. Add the butter (which is melted), a little at a time, stirring all the while.

No. 2: Beat up the sugar and butter lightly, adding the yolks by degrees. Boiled custard can be used instead of egg yolks.

Butter creams can be mixed or blended with other creams and mixtures such as, fresh cream, meringue, marshmallow cream, lemon curd and custard. Here are details of some of these mixtures.

Butter Cream with Marshmallow

No. 1			No. 2		
lb.	*oz.*		*lb.*	*oz.*	
1	8	Fresh butter	1	4	Fresh butter
1	0	Marshmallow		6	Marshmallow
1	0	Icing sugar		6	Fondant
		Colour and flavour as desired		6	Icing Sugar
				4	Glucose (warmed)
				5	Evaporated milk
					Colour and flavour as desired

The second formula is softer and will spread more easily.

Butter Cream with Lemon Curd

lb.	*oz.*	
1	0	Fondant
1	0	Fresh butter
	8	Lemon curd
	8	Icing sugar

Butter Cream with Eggs

lb.	*oz.*		*lb.*	*oz.*	
	15	Eggs	2	0	Fresh butter
	12	Castor sugar	1	4	Icing sugar
		Whip to a stiff sponge			Colour and flavour as desired

Beat until very light. Add the sponge to the butter/sugar mixture in portions and beat thoroughly.

Butter Cream with Custard

lb.	*oz.*	
1	8	Fresh butter
	12	Icing sugar

Beat thoroughly and blend in

lb.	*oz.*	
1	12	Cold boiled custard

Here is a suitable formula for custard:

lb.	*oz.*	
1	4 (1 pint)	Fresh milk
	5	Egg
	3	Sugar
	1½	Cornflour

Mix the cornflour with a little milk. Boil the rest of the milk with the sugar and pour on to the cornflour, stirring all the time. The eggs are added to the cornflour/milk suspension.

Marshmallow Cream.—Manufactured marshmallow cream of excellent quality can be bought from allied traders and is readily available. It is not really worth the time and the trouble for the baker to make it himself. Nevertheless the student should know how it is made, and even make up a small batch for himself so that he may more readily understand the nature of the cream, and the process of manufacture.

Marshmallow cream is a mixture of sugar, water, egg whites, and agar-agar, the last named being a powerful jellying agent obtained from an edible seaweed, found particularly in Southern Asian seas. Here is a formula for marshmallow cream:

lb.	*oz.*	
1	0	Lump sugar
	8	Corn syrup
	6	Egg whites
	10	Water
	¼	Agar-agar

The agar-agar is soaked in the water for some hours and then brought to the boil so that the agar is properly dispersed. To make certain of this dispersal, the suspension is passed through a fine sieve; this is important for if pieces of agar are left undispersed, the smoothness of the cream is spoiled. The sugar is then added and when properly dissolved, the mixture is taken to a temperature of 225° F., when the warmed corn syrup is run in; on no account should it be stirred or the whole mixture will grain.

The mixture is then boiled to 245° F., the pan being washed down with water repeatedly. Just before this figure is reached, whip the egg whites with a pinch of cream of tartar to a stiff snow. While the machine is running at fast speed, pour the boiling sugar/agar solution carefully into the machine. When all is in, change from the whisk to the beater and beat well for about 15 min. There is a tremendous increase in volume during the whipping and beating, so the student should allow for this by having a large enough mixing bowl. The finished cream should be stored in tins or pails and when cold covered with wax paper or polythene.

To use marshmallow cream, take 2 lb. of the stock marshmallow and whip it to a stiff meringue with 10 oz. of egg whites. It may be coloured and flavoured as desired.

Cream Fillings.—In the years immediately before the last war, a new type of fat was introduced to the baker. It had high emulsifying properties and was used for the new type of high ratio cake that became very popular and has since maintained that popularity. By using this type of fat a new type of filling cream was evolved.

Here are examples:

Stock Mixture

lb.	*oz.*	
5	0 Fondant	
1	4 Water	
	1 Salt	
	10 Milk powder	
2	8 Special fat	

The fondant is thinned with the water to a mixture free from lumps. The mixture is added to the rest of the materials and beaten on fast speed for 10 min. The cream can be coloured and flavoured as desired.

From this plain stock mixture, many excellent creams can be made. Here are some examples.

Chocolate Filling Cream.—To each pound of the above, beat in 2 oz. of melted chocolate and a little chocolate colour.

Honey Filling Cream.—To each pound of stock cream add 5 oz. of honey and beat thoroughly.

Orange or Lemon Filling Cream.—Add 8 oz. of either orange or lemon curd to each pound of stock cream. Colour may be used as an adjustment according to the colour intensity of the curd used.

Jelly Filling Cream.—To stock cream, piping jelly may be added in sufficient quantity to give the desired flavour and colour. Jams can be used for the same purpose.

Mocha Filling Cream.—To each pound of stock cream add about ¼ oz. of coffee essence and also a little vanilla extract.

Ginger Filling Cream.—To each pound of stock cream add 2 oz. of chopped preserved ginger and 4 oz. of the preserving syrup. Blend in thoroughly.

Filling Cream using Dairy Cream.—An excellent filling cream can be made by blending equal parts of whipped dairy cream and the stock filling cream. The mixture, of course, must not be sold as dairy cream.

Nut or Fruit Filling Cream.—All kinds of finely chopped nuts or fruits can be added to the stock cream for variety.

Reconstituted Cream.—This is produced from a mixture of unsalted butter together with milk which can be fresh, reconstituted, dried, or condensed. The average proportion is one part by weight of butter to one and a quarter parts of milk. It is particularly important to ensure that the butter is free from salt or the flavour of the resultant cream will be completely spoiled.

The reconstitution is effected as follows:

First of all the milk and any emulsifying agent is carefully warmed and the butter added in small pieces. The mixture is then heated to 140° F. and held at that temperature for not more than 30 min. It is then passed through an emulsifier and cooled as quickly as possible. Stability is greatly increased if it is allowed to stand for at least 8 hr. at about 40° F. before use.

It is advised by the Food Standards Committee of the Ministry of Food that the term 'reconstituted cream' be used to describe the product and not 'artificial cream' as it has been referred to in the past.

Reconstituted cream is now legally defined as a substance not being cream, resembles cream in appearance and contains no substance not derived from milk, except:

(*a*) water, or (*b*) ingredients (not added fraudulently to increase bulk, weight or measure, or conceal inferior quality) which may lawfully be contained in a substance sold for human consumption as cream.

The legal standard for milk fat in reconstituted cream is 18%. For reconstituted double cream it is 48%.

To produce a gallon of cream the following may be used:

lb.	*oz.*	
5	0	Water
4	12	Fresh unsalted butter
	8	Spray dried milk powder

The emulsion can be stabilized by the addition of 3 oz. of G.M.S. 1 : 5 emulsion (page 143).

The method is as described above.

Synthetic Cream.—The legal definition of synthetic or imitation cream is a substance not being cream or reconstituted cream, resembles cream in appearance and is produced by emulsifying edible oils or fats with water, either by themselves or with other substances which are neither prohibited by regulations made for the purposes of this section, or added in quantities so prohibited.

There are no legal standards for imitation cream in relation to its composition, other than the description given in the Food and Drugs Act. In 1951, the Food Standards Committee recommended that a standard should be proscribed for imitation cream, which it is considered should contain a minimum of 25% of fat and oil in the form of triglycerides.

Imitation cream when received from the manufacturers, has a very low bacterial count, being virtually sterile. It has a greater potential volume increase than has dairy cream. There is also less seepage into the cake, which in consequence has a longer shelf life.

SPONGE GOODS

Sponge goods have always been popular with the baker. Firstly because they are easy to make; secondly because they have a high volume to weight ratio; and third because the basic mixings are capable of such variety in shape and finish, from small fancies, Swiss rolls and sponge sandwiches to the gateau base. Plate XXXI shows excellent chocolate rolls.

They have always been popular with the baker's customers, mainly because they are light and tasty for afternoon tea, and as a basis for trifles and such articles of dessert. Years ago the sponge cake and sponge finger were given to newly weaned babies, because not only was the sponge cake good food, but it readily softened in the mouth so that there was little danger of the child choking.

The traditional sponge cake is a mixture of eggs, sugar and flour. Aeration for this type of product is mechanical, and is effected by whipping the eggs and sugar to a foam, after which the flour is carefully mixed in. This type of aeration can be helped by the use of baking-powder under certain circumstances.

It is during whipping that air is incorporated, and held by the egg protein, in the form of tiny bubbles. As whipping proceeds, more and more air is incorporated, and the bubbles get smaller and increase in numbers while the mixture takes on an increased stability.

It has been known for hundreds of years that eggs and sugar, whipped to a light foam and then reinforced carefully with flour, will retain the structure after the gentle expansion of the air bubbles under the influence of heat, because of the coagulation of the proteins (egg albumen and flour gluten) during baking. It seems probable that the fine yellow coloured structure and soft texture so resembled that of the commercial sponge that the name has been retained throughout the centuries. There is in existence an old recipe for sponge cakes, printed and in use over 250 years ago, and in essentials it is the same as the basic formula used today.

Almost all bakery textbooks dealt very briefly with the sponge-making process, the authors evidently believing that it was simple enough to whisk eggs and sugar together and mix in the flour. Practical craftsmen of the day saw to it that the shell eggs that were used were of the best possible quality, that the sugar was of the correct granularity and the flour of the correct strength. They saw to it also that the bakehouse boy knew how to prepare the sponge cake frames and moulds correctly. The rest was in the very competent time-experienced hands of the confectioner himself, and very fine sponge goods were turned out.

If at that time it had been suggested that the confectioner should experiment with other materials and with formula rebalance, he would have been horror-struck. The basic formula of 1 lb. of sugar and 1 lb. of flour to 1 pint of eggs for ordinary sponge goods, and a similar formula with the flour and sugar dropped to 10 oz. to a pint of eggs for Swiss roll, were used unfailingly. But despite this rigidity of purpose the standard of production was high, especially as the technical principle of mechanical aeration and the technical knowledge of raw materials was almost unknown.

There being no added fat in sponges, staling was fairly rapid, so that for certain types melted butter was carefully added with the flour after the initial sponging of the eggs and sugar. This was essentially a craftsman's job, for in inexperienced hands overmixing took place, the aeration was lost and the gluten developed, resulting in a tough rubbery sponge with little volume.

The advance of technical knowledge, together with the introduction of new materials and methods, however, wrought many changes in the age-old conception of sponge cake manufacture. Chief of these were the introduction of semi-automatic machines and the advent of special cake flour. As a result of technical experiments it was found that an adjustment of the basic formula, that allowed for the addition of a little warm milk or water, increased the palatability of the sponge.

When the special cake flour was introduced it was found to be ideal for sponge goods. This flour is of very fine granularity, so that a far greater ratio of water or milk can be used. This necessitated an increase in the sugar content and the possible addition of a little baking-powder, resulting in soft and tender sponge goods with first-class eating qualities.

It was the exigencies of war and the acute shortages of some of the essential raw materials, together with the introduction of others hitherto unknown, that created a minor revolution in sponge cake manufacture. Shell and frozen eggs were unobtainable and spray dried egg took their place. This egg, because the foam producing quality has been largely destroyed in the processing, was unsuitable for whipping. Technical knowledge coupled with experiment, however, resulted in the use of this egg in a flour-sponge method that was quite new. As the reconstituted spray-dried egg was incapable of forming air cells when whipped, an amount of flour not exceeding 25% of the total weight was added to the egg/sugar and whipped for 25–30 min. on high speed, the air incorporated being held by the gluten of the flour. Baking-powder was added to help volume, and if special cake flour was used, extra milk or water was added.

All this new data, gained in the hard times of shortage and necessity, has resulted in a new conception of the quality standard of sponge goods, so that we now have, not only better materials in the form of shell and frozen eggs and good quality flours, but also more valuable technical knowledge.

It is now possible to make sponge goods to an exceedingly high standard of quality, with an amazing tenderness and delightful eating qualities, by using new materials and rebalancing formulae in the light of increased technical knowledge.

Because there is still a measure of craftsmanship necessary in the making of sponge goods, the student may be expected to make them in some form in his practical examinations. It will be well therefore to practise making them so that the finished product will earn him satisfactory marks. Here are some sponge recipes for goods that he may be expected to make.

Sponge cakes

lb.	*oz.*		
1	4	Eggs	Whipping temperature 70–75° F.
1	0	Castor sugar	Baking temperature 400° F.
1	0	Soft flour	Yield six frames.

The eggs and sugar are placed in a clean bowl that is free from grease, and whipped to a stiff sponge. The flour, which has been well sieved, is then carefully folded in by hand. From a savoy bag with a ¾-in. plain pipe the mixture is carefully piped into the prepared frames. The frames are prepared by cleaning thoroughly, greasing with lard or compound, dusting with castor sugar and finishing with a dusting of flour, the surplus being carefully tapped out. The sponge cakes are well dusted with castor sugar before being baked.

Sponge Sandwiches.—If eight 7-in. sandwich plates are prepared in exactly the same way as the sponge frames, the above mixing can be equally divided between them and baked at the same temperature.

Sponge Gateaux.—Continuing with his practice in making sponge goods, the student may like to make and finish his first gateau. First make up the same mixing as for sponge cakes and sponge sandwiches, and divide equally between five greased and floured cottage pans, baking them carefully at about 380° F. This mixing should be flavoured with vanilla.

When sufficiently cool, they should be turned out of the pans, with the smaller surface uppermost. When cool they are sliced through the middle, and spread, either with a good raspberry jam or with vanilla flavoured butter cream.

Some sieved apricot purée is boiled until it sets when tested on a cold plate. Brush this purée thinly over each gateau. While this is setting and cooling, make up some water icing and flavour it with vanilla; colour a little of this with chocolate colour and place it into a paper icing bag.

Carefully coat the top of one gateau with the white water icing, and immediately and quickly pipe parallel lines across it with the chocolate icing, then quickly draw the point of a knife across the lines at right angles, alternating each stroke in opposite directions. This operation is known as 'marbling', and if quickly and neatly done is most effective. Plate No. XXXIII.

Marble each gateau in turn, and carefully cover the sides with either roasted coconut or roasted flaked almonds. It completes the finish if a tiny sprinkle of chopped green almonds is placed in the centre of each marbled top. Coconut looks much brighter and better if it is tinted yellow before it is roasted.

When the student is proficient at marbling he can vary the design by piping concentric circles instead of parallel lines; then starting from the centre of the gateaux, draw the point of the knife outwards, or from the edge of the cake draw the point inwards, care being taken to make the strokes equidistant round the circles.

Again the sprinkle of green chopped almonds enhances the colour harmony.

It often happens at examination time, that the student will be asked to make two gateaux bases and to decorate one only with a simple finish.

The one undecorated, will be cut by the examiner to assess the care and workmanship given to the manufacture, and it will be marked accordingly, while the other will earn marks according to the artistry and simplicity of the finish. Marbling is both simple and artistic if carried out quickly and carefully.

Plates XXXIV, XXXV, XXXVI, XXXVII and XXXVIII, show further examples of marbling.

JELLYING AGENTS

Gelatine.—This is a protein extracted from hide, skins, bones and the connective tissues of animals. Collagen is the principle constituent and is converted on boiling to gelatine.

The hides and skins are treated with lime for seven weeks after which they are washed and then treated with acid to neutralize the excess lime.

A process known as 'melting' follows when the hides and skin are cooked in water at 140° F. and the solution drawn off to produce first quality gelatine. Lower grades are produced from successive boilings at progressively higher temperatures.

The bones are treated to remove fat followed by treatment with hydrochloric acid to remove mineral matter. Bleaching with sulphur-dioxide follows after which gelatine is extracted with water at about 170° F.

The gelatine liquors from both sources are filtered, partially evaporated, and run out on to tables to set. It is cut into oblong sheets after setting, stretched on wire frames and passed through a drying tunnel where the remaining water is evaporated.

Gelatine is marketed either in sheets or in powder form. It is used as a jellying agent at the rate of 1 oz. to 1 pint of water.

Agar-Agar.—This is a powerful jellying agent from a marine growth found in the seas of the far East and many other parts of the world including those around Britain. It is available in two forms; as semi-transparent strawlike stems, and in powder form.

It is necessary to soak agar-agar in water, in which it swells considerably. To complete the dissolution it is boiled and then passed through a sieve.

It is used in jams, piping jellies, marshmallow cream, and for jellying meat pies. One ounce of agar will set one gallon of water.

Pectin.—In water, and in the presence of sugar and acid, pectin will produce a jelly. It is this combination that causes jam to set after it had been correctly boiled.

Pectin is available in powder form, extracted from citrus fruits, or is produced from the apple.

GUMS

There are two gums that the student may be expected to use in his practical work either in confectionery or in cake decoration.

Gum Arabic.—A product of a species of acacia. It is known alternatively as gum acacia.

In powder form it is readily soluble in hot water and is then used as a glaze for Parisian rout biscuits, marzipan fruits and on ganache shapes before they are dipped in couverture or fondant.

To make the solution, soak 1 oz. of gum arabic in 10 oz. of water until the gum is dissolved. Heat over a water bath and use while the solution is hot.

Gum Tragacanth.—This gum has a long history in connection with cooking. Very old cookery books refer to it as gum dragon. It is a product of a species of shrub—Astragalus—which flourishes in Persia, Syria and Kurdistan. It is available either as a powder or in the form of hard, horny flakes.

Gum tragacanth is used in the manufacture of gum paste, which in the past was used extensively by the confectioner for fashioning into ornamental decorative pieces for use on bride cakes. Gum paste was used also for window show-pieces and for pieces montées for table decoration.

Bride cake ornaments are now manufactured by large firms able to employ specialists in modelling and mould-making.

Sugar paste, which contains gum tragacanth, has largely replaced gum paste in bakeries today. It has the added advantage that it is much more tolerant in use, in that it does not dry so quickly or so hard; in addition it is pleasant to eat.

SLAB CAKES

Slab cake, as its name implies, is cake of various kinds in bulk. When properly made and baked, slab cake is a delightful addition to the table. It is easily transported from the bakery to the shop, and from the shop to the home. It is easily cut, and is ideal for those whose taste is not for rich and highly decorated confections.

Slab cake can be made plain or with additions such as coconut, caraway seeds, cherries, ginger, currants, sultanas and peel or a mixture of some of these. It can be either light or dark in colour and can vary in quality. Slab cake can be sliced and sandwiched with jam or cream and the top can be decorated with almonds, almond paste, fondant and preserved fruits.

It is one of the minor tragedies of our time, that the greater bulk of slab cake manufactured is not made in the smaller bakeries but in larger plants, most of which is sold in grocers' shops or in departmental or chain stores. There can be little doubt that this is because not enough thought and care was given to formula balance, to the choice of raw materials, to the manufacture, and above all to the baking, which is of the greatest importance.

In recent times, the trend is for the sale of slab cake in predetermined weight and wrapped in transparent paper. This is ideal, for not only can the cut surface be seen, but the wrapping retards staling and the pieces are easily handled. Furthermore the slab cake so sold is of uniformly good quality.

There are many things the student must know on the subject if he is to make slab cake successfully, or be able to answer a question on the subject in a written examination.

Slab Tins and Frames.—Slab cakes can be baked either in metal tins or wooden frames. On balance the metal tins seem to have more advantages. They last longer, are easily set in the oven, are easily handled when preparing and filling and when the slabs are baked, they can be stacked for cooling.

They have two disadvantages. They are more expensive than wooden frames and they need plenty of paper for lining.

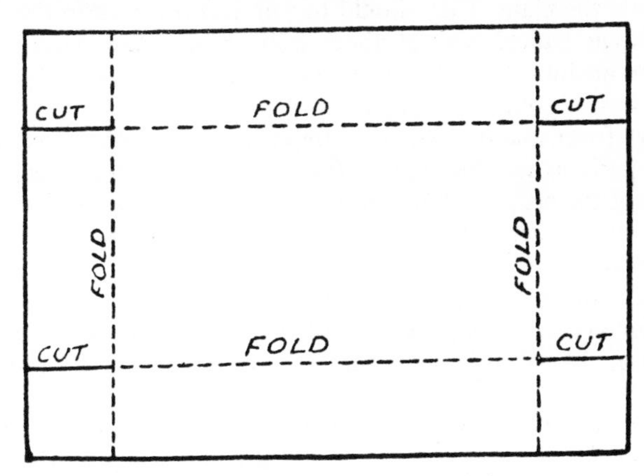

FIG. 60.—Slab frames. Paper lining.

Wooden frames have two advantages. As wood is not a good conductor of heat, wooden frames need less protection and they are definitely better in use for the high-ratio type of slab cake. The disadvantages are loss of room in the oven due to the necessity for using baking-sheets and the fact that they quickly wear out.

All new tins should be baked off, or seasoned, before use unless they are made with dark metal. Before filling with slab cake mixing they should be lined with several thicknesses of newspaper (according to whether they are wooden or metal, and the type of oven used) and a top lining of white paper. All the papers should be cut as illustrated (Fig. 60).

The average size is as follows: 12 in. by 8 in. (inside measurements) with a depth of about 3 in. This will have a capacity of about 4½ lb. of plain slab and 6 lb. of fruit.

It is important that scaling should be done properly or faults will be seen in the finished product. The batter should be put into the frame by holding the scale pan in one hand and guiding it into the container, in one piece, with the other. If the batter is put into the frame in several portions, there is a danger that air will be trapped, which during baking will expand, causing holes that will run horizontally. For the same reason, the scale pan should never be wet, or water may be trapped in the cake, which changing to steam during baking will cause a similar fault.

If a small bakery is doing a mixed trade and several types of slab cake are being made, and are to be baked together in one oven, then the heavily fruited cake should be made first, followed by the medium and lastly the plain. They should be put into the oven in that order.

A heavily fruited cake of about 6 lb. should take about 3 hr. to bake. A medium fruited slab of the same weight about 2¾ hr. and plain slabs of about 4½ lb. 2¼ hr.

Apart from quality, which is important, the appearance of the slab is perhaps its chief selling feature, and in this connection the quality of the crust is all important, for if it is thick, overbaked and overcoloured, then the standard is immediately debased and flavour and eating quality is lost. In baking, slab cakes must be properly protected and baked in an atmosphere that is sufficiently humid to allow for maximum expansion, with a consequent lack of top crust distortion. The ideal is the naturally created steam from a full oven of cake.

When cut and displayed, slab cake should be about the same depth, so that no matter whether they are plain or fruit, the display will look neat.and harmonious; therefore the weight of batter in a frame to get this uniformity of depth, should be a subject of experiment. The appearance of the cut surface is also of importance; the colour should be rich and attractive and the grain of the cake even. The fruit in the slabs should be evenly distributed, bright and fleshy and of good colour. Plate XXXIX shows a good slab cake.

Faults in Slab Cakes.—Apart from the faults which are the result of improper scaling and careless baking, there are others that will occur if care is not taken.

Streaks.—These are the result of insufficient mixing, or failure to keep the mixing bowl scraped down. In either case there is not a proper dispersal of ingredients.

Cores.—If near the centre of the crown of the slab, it shows that the cake is insufficiently baked. Elsewhere in the cake it is due to incomplete mixing.

Long Vertical Holes.—These are due to (*a*) flour too strong, (*b*) gluten development by overmixing when adding flour, (*c*) or oven too hot. These holes are invariably accompanied by a 'cauliflower top' with an unsightly break. The holes clearly show the passage of the collected expanded gases when forced at last to break through the increased resistance offered by the toughened structure, or the prematurely thickened crust. Lack of oven humidity will cause this fault.

Fruit Dropping.—This is a fault common to all fruited cakes of any size, and is the result of faulty formula balance. This fault has been fully dealt with in a previous chapter.

Here are some formulae for first quality slab cake:

	Madeira		*Sultana*		*Currant*		*Cherry*		*Genoa*	
	lb.	*oz.*	*lb.*	*oz.*	*lb.*	*oz.*	*lb.*	*oz.*	*lb.*	*oz.*
Butter		12		12		12		12		12
Compound		4		4		4		4		4
Sugar	1	0	1	0	1	0	1	0	1	0
Eggs	1	4	1	4	1	4	1	4	1	4
Flour	1	8	1	4	1	4	1	6	1	2½
Scone flour	—			4		4		3		1½
Powder		¼	—		—		—		—	
Essence	Vanilla & Lemon		Vanilla & Almond		Vanilla & Lemon		Vanilla		Vanilla. Lemon & Almond	
Cherries	—		—		—		2	4		8
Currants	—		—		1	12	—		1	0
Sultanas	—		2	0	—		—		1	0
Peel	—		—			4	—			4
Colour	q.s.		q.s.		q.s.		q.s.		q.s.	
Top decoration	—		Strip almonds		Flaked almonds		—		Split almonds	
Oven temperature	370° F.		350° F.		350° F.		350° F.		345° F.	

USING CRUMBS

Stale, broken or sub-standard cakes are a by-product of the baking industry, and provided that they are clean, edible and of good flavour, they are of value. If they can be used successfully then they have a greater potential value. It is not wise to use them in lowering standards of quality with the attitude of 'out of sight, out of mind'.

All crumbs should be graded into three categories, firstly sponge and plain cake crumbs free of crust particles, secondly, all other crumbs free from fruit, and lastly, fruited debris.

The most outstanding use for crumbs in high-class work is probably in frangipan, which when properly made is a delightful product in its own right, quite apart from its value in using up crumbs. The filling is usually piped into sweet paste lined plain or fluted tins, or flat patty pans. Larger frangipan flans are made by lining sandwich plates and then adding the filling. Baking sheets can be lined with sweet paste on which the frangipan filling is spread. In all cases there should be a spot or spread of raspberry jam before the addition of the filling.

The small tarts are finished in many delightful ways using all kinds of decorative materials (Plate XL). The larger flans and sheets are invariably finished as they are removed from the oven by brushing with well boiled apricot purée and then with soft, vanilla flavoured water icing which gives a translucent glaze. The sheet is then cut into fingers. Here is a formula for frangipan filling:

lb.	*oz.*		*lb.*	*oz.*	
1	0	Butter		6	Light sponge crumbs
1	0	Sugar		6	Ground almonds
1	4	Eggs		4	Flour
		Colour			

Baking temperature 360° F.

The darker crumbs can be used successfully in some types of ginger bread, the dark syrup and spices masking the crumb particles very well. Here is a formula for a light gingerbread:

lb.	*oz.*		*lb.*	*oz.*	
2	0	Flour		6	Sultanas
1	0	Crumbs		4	Peel
	8	Butter		½	Spice
	10	Sugar		½	Ginger
1	0	Liquid milk		4	Ginger chips
	¾	Bicarbonate of soda	1	4	Syrup

Baking temperature 400° F. Yield one tray 16 in. × 16 in. Cut into 49 squares.

When the gingerbread is removed from the oven it is immediately glazed with sugar wash and when cold cut into squares. Care must be exercised in the use of crumbs for gingerbread for if they are rich in fat and sugar, then the fat and sugar content in the formula must be lowered or the gingerbread will flow over the sides of the tray and sink in the middle.

A sparing addition of good crumbs to a high-class mincemeat will make a first-class filling for banbury cakes, which although not the real thing is far better than a concoction of low quality crumbs, spice and some jam.

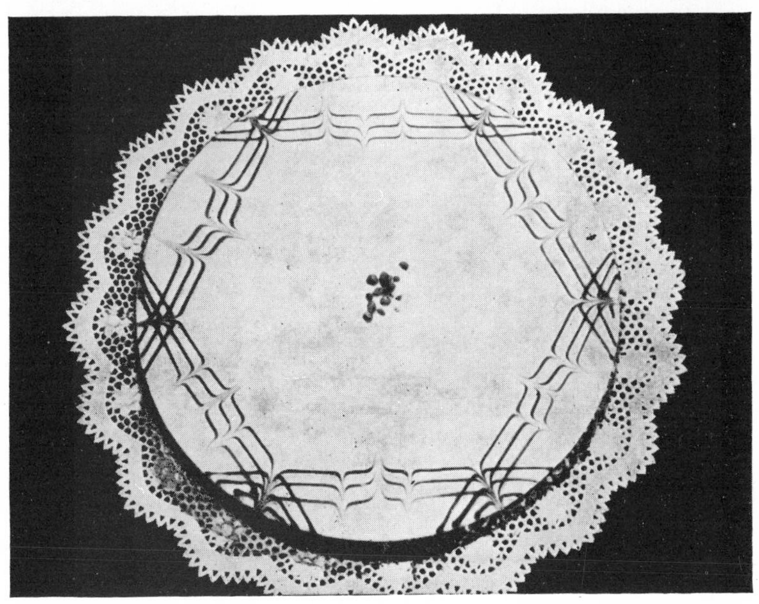

XXXV and XXXVI Examples of marbling

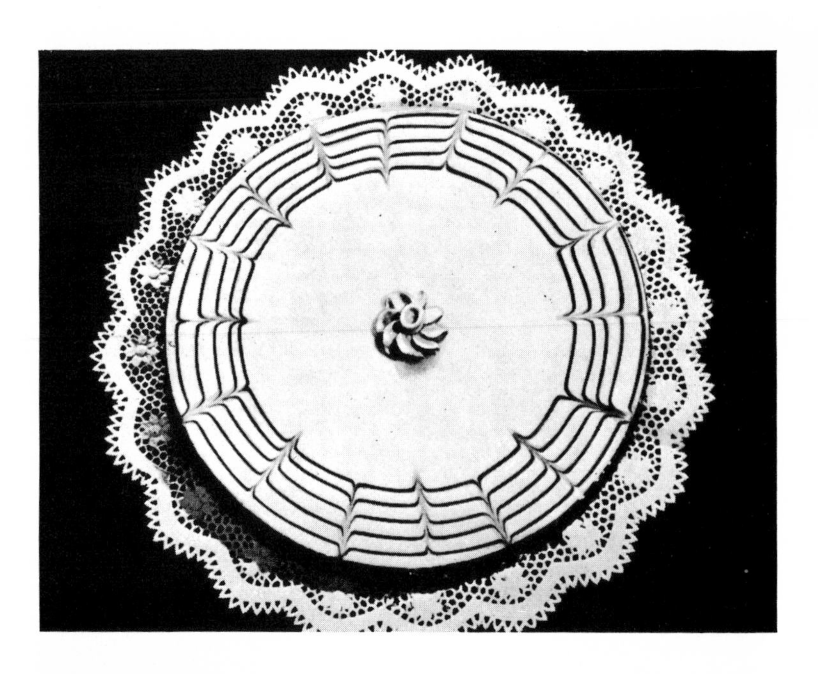

XXXVII and XXXVIII Examples of marbling

XXXIX A good Genoa slab

XL Frangipane tarts

XLI The simnel cake. An example of marzipan 'flashing'

The fruited crumbs or debris can be used in fruit squares. The crumbs with a little cinnamon or spice and mixed with sultanas or raisins are moistened with milk or water and spread on to a tray lined with sweet paste; this is covered with another sheet of sweet paste, then washed with diluted egg and dusted with castor sugar. When baked and cold, it is neatly cut into squares.

Cuttings of coloured genoese can be used for Russian slices and gateaux. For these a wooden frame is required which is placed on a lightly sugar dusted sheet of greaseproof paper placed on a baking-sheet. The base of the frame is then lined with a sheet of sponge which has been spread with apricot jam—the jam is uppermost. The frame is then filled with cubes of varied coloured genoese which have been carefully mixed with well boiled, rum-flavoured, apricot jam. The blending is done in a mixing-bowl and in such a way that the small cubes of genoese are not pulped or unduly broken.

When the jam-covered cubes have been spread evenly in the frame, another piece of sponge, jam side down, is placed on top. The sponge is sugared and a piece of board which fits just inside the frame is placed on it. Weights are placed on the board and the slab is left for some hours. When pressed, and after the removal of the board, paper and frame, the top is spread with white or chocolate fondant, which is marbled in a contrasting colour. When the fondant is set, the slab can be cut into fingers for Russian slices or into larger pieces for Russian gateaux.

The student will find that there are many ways of using crumbs if he will study recipe books, trade journals, and the bulletins published by the bakery service establishments, always remembering that care is necessary in the use of crumbs if quality standards are to be maintained.

30

Flavour in Confectionery: Taste and Aroma; Essential Oils; Vanilla Extract; Fruit Juices; Liqueurs; Synthetic Flavours; Other Flavours; Aromatic Dried Fruits; Spices: Sources and Processing

FLAVOUR IN CONFECTIONERY

TASTE and aroma combined produce the sensation we know as flavour. Taste alone is not enough, for the buds in the tongue respond only to sweetness, bitterness, acidity and saltiness. There is, however, a liaison with the olfactory nerves at the back of the nose, and the dual effects of taste and smell are in evidence as flavour.

First of all the student will note that there are quite a number of bakery raw materials that will give a taste reaction; sugar will give sweetness, fruits a certain acidity, the addition of salt will relieve blandness. It is rare that there is a bitterness except perhaps in an almond or in burned crust.

Flavour is evident when using a good butter, in fact a properly made shortbread is dependent on butter alone for flavour. Again the distinctive flavours and aromas of honey, jam, almonds, peel, fruit, cocoa, spice, seeds, etc., all combine with one or more of the basic tastes to give many excellent and pleasing flavours to confectionery products.

Combinations of different raw materials will produce confectionery with quite distinctive flavours; for instance, the flavour produced in a rich Dundee cake where there is butter, demarara sugar, fruit and almonds. Sometimes the combination of raw materials that are out of balance will produce flavours that are far from pleasant, for instance, an excess of bicarbonate of soda in a cake rich in fat, will produce the flavour of soap, due to the reaction of the alkali on the fat. Faulty raw materials will produce unpleasant flavours, a musty egg or flour infected with mould are two examples. Cheap plain slabs with a low sugar content can become infected with 'rope' the result of the action of a soil-borne bacteria introduced to the cake with the flour. 'Rope' gives an unpleasant smell of decaying pineapples; this infection in cake, however, is extremely rare under normal conditions.

It is the additional flavouring substances that are of interest to the baker, and the student should have some knowledge of the source, manufacture and the use of them.

Flavourings can be listed under two broad headings:

Natural	*Synthetic*
Roots	Acids
Stems	Alcohols
Buds	Aldehydes
Barks	Esters
Fruits	Ethers
Leaves	Ketones
Seeds	Phenols
Flowers	

Many flavours are blends of both.

The student will note from the list of natural flavours that they can be produced from any part of different plants. He will note also that research into the chemical nature of these aromatic substances has led to the chemist being able to synthesize many of them in such a way that they resemble closely, or in some cases they are identical with the flavouring substances found in the natural product.

Flavour is of the greatest importance to the confectioner, for while appearance attracts, it is in the eating that the decision is made to eat more or less. The British confectioner could learn much from his continental colleague, who places flavour in a high position in his scheme of confectionery production, using natural products in season, far more than is done in this country.

Flavour must be treated in the same way as all raw materials and carefully weighed or measured. It is also important that the right type of flavour should be used, for example, flavours produced for use in creams or icings would be quite useless in any product that would be subjected to heat.

Reputable firms who manufacture flavours will gladly advise the confectioner on the correct amount of flavour to use. It must always be borne in mind that the finest quality flavours are the cheapest in the end. It must be remembered also that all flavours used in foodstuffs must be pure and wholesome, and comply with the provisions of the Food and Drugs Act.

ESSENTIAL OILS

These are extracts prepared solely from a fruit or a plant, and consist of the natural flavouring in the most concentrated form. They are extracted from fruit or plants by force, i.e. pressure, or by steam distillation. Although harder to obtain, they are better to use than essences. The oil may be found in practically any part of the plant or fruit, e.g. the stem, roots, buds, leaves, etc.

A good essential oil should be bright and be free from any foreign matter. It should have also a sound characteristic bouquet. The oils are highly inflammable and give off a dense smoke. They have no connection with the fixed or greasy oils, and, as mentioned in the chapter on Fats and Oils, they will stain a paper, but unlike the fixed oils, the stain can be removed by heating, because the oils are volatile.

All essential oils undergo oxidation rapidly, consequently they should be kept in dark bottles, well stoppered or corked and in a reasonably dark place. The main points to remember concerning essential oils are as follows:

(1) Although insoluble in water, the oils are more or less soluble in alcohol or ether for the purpose of making essences.
(2) They are volatile when pure and will evaporate leaving only a slight stain.
(3) They should not be overheated as this tends to destroy some of the flavour; this is the reason why the distilled oil is slightly inferior to the forced oil.

Fresh Lemons.—The flavouring is contained in the oil glands immediately beneath the thin yellow skin surface and in the juice.

The yellow skin, together with the oil glands are known as the zest and can be removed with the use of a grater or a special tool known as a zester.

The flavour of fresh lemons is sharp and pleasantly refreshing. The zest and/or the juice is used in a variety of high-class cakes, creams, fillings and icings.

The comparatively weak acid content makes the juice particularly useful in puff pastry for rendering the gluten more extensible; in sugar boiling and in the making of croquant for the inversion of some of the sucrose to glucose, and in lemon sponges when the juice can be added to the whisking sugar and eggs to confer a greater stability on the egg albumen as well as flavour. A little lemon juice has the same result in the making of royal icing.

The zest and juice of oranges and the juices of other fruits can all be used for flavouring purposes.

Oil of Lemon.—The consumption of this oil is very large, in the region of 1,000 tons annually. Because it is expensive, there is a great deal of adulteration of the pure oil, together with the use of many substitutes. The lemon oil industry is chiefly centred in Sicily and California and is a by-product of the citrus fruit industry. The best oil is virgin hand pressed.

This oil is obtained by pressing and squeezing the ripe lemon caps on to sponges; this is the top quality oil and the most economical, although the most expensive. It is 20–30% stronger in flavour than the other oils of the same type. It is composed of terpenes, citral, and other naturally occurring aromatic substances. It will leave a white deposit on standing, but this can be filtered out in many cases.

The proportion of citral in the oils controls the strength of the flavour. This varies from 3·5–5%. All classes of lemon oil should be kept away from the light, moisture and heat and stored in full, well corked bottles or cans. They will deteriorate on standing for a long period.

Machine pressed oil is essentially a product of machinery. The oil is extracted by squeezing the whole fruit between the corrugated lining of the machine and a moving belt. Jets of water are sprayed into the machine while it is working, in this way the oil is washed from the fruit. The mixture of water and oil is separated in a centrifuge. The oil, after separation, is run into drums, cans, or bottles. This oil is chiefly used as the base for the preparation of lemon essences.

Terpeneless oil is prepared by the distillation of the straight oil and is very expensive, being about 20 times as concentrated as virgin oil. It is used in jellies and syrups, etc., where it is essential to have a transparent liquid. Terpeneless oil is considerably more soluble in aqueous media than straight lemon oil. It can be dissolved in alcohol or other suitable solvent and is then normally termed an essence.

Sesqui-terpeneless oil is prepared from a terpeneless type and possesses almost the same qualities, except that it is more readily soluble in water.

Orange Oil.—Is a product chiefly of Sicily, Italy, Israel and U.S.A., and is produced in a similar manner as for lemon oil. Both sweet and bitter orange oils are available, manufactured from the sweet and bitter orange respectively. Fruit which is slightly under-ripe will produce a greater amount of oil, but it will possess an inferior flavour to that which is produced from fully ripened fruit.

Oil of Almonds.—Sweet and bitter almonds contain a fixed or greasy oil which has no flavour. Bitter almonds contain also a glucoside known as amygdalin and an enzyme known as emulsin. After the oil has been expressed from bitter almonds, the press-cake is ground to a fine powder and boiling water added to it. When cool, freshly ground bitter almond press-cake is added and allowed to stand for twelve hours. The unscalded emulsin from the fresh press-cake hydrolyses the amygdalin to benzaldehyde, glucose and hydrocyanic acid, better known as the poisonous prussic acid. The prussic acid is removed by the use of lime during distillation. Peach and apricot kernels both contain amygdalin and emulsin and are used for producing a cheaper type of almond oil.

Benzaldehyde has a bitter burning taste with a distinct almond flavour, Benzaldehyde is now prepared commercially from the coal-tar hydrocarbon, toluene; it is not identical with the essential oil of almonds manufactured from bitter almonds, but is often used as a less expensive substitute. As it does not contain hydrocyanic acid it is probably safer to use. Essential oil of almonds must be stored in tightly stoppered bottles and kept under the same conditions as other essential oils.

Almond essence is prepared by making a 1% solution of oil in alcohol or other suitable solvents.

Peppermint Oil.—This is used extensively in sweet making. It is manufactured by the distillation of the peppermint plant, mentha piperata. The commercial oil is a 3% solution of the pure oil in alcohol and has a slight green colour with a penetrating odour.

Vanilla.—This is never an essential oil, always an extract and essence. It is prepared from the vanilla bean which is the seed pod of a species of orchid, which flourishes in Mexico, West Indies, South America and in the French colonies in the tropics. The beans are gathered when they are yellowish-green in the upper part, that is, when they are slightly under-ripe. They are then immersed in warm water to facilitate the action of enzymes. The period of immersion is under strict control, after which they are drained and packed in wool-covered boxes for 24 hours. They are then removed and placed between blankets. This treatment is repeated until the correct degree of enzymic activity is reached, taking from 16–60 days.

After grading and tying into bundles, they are stored in tins where crystals of vanillin appear on the surface of the cured pods. These crystals are responsible for the flavour of vanilla, one of the most popular of flavours. The cured beans develop a rich brown colour, with a waxy feel when touched. The vanillin will be found to be present to the extent of 1·5 to 2·5%.

The flavouring matter to a certain extent will depend on the size and variety of the bean—Mexican beans being considered the best. The beans contain all the usual plant substances such as gums, resins and enzymes, all of which add to, and develop the flavour.

Genuine vanilla extract is produced by mincing the pods and mascerating the pulp in alcohol, which dissolves the vanillin crystals, and some of the aromatic resins present, all of which gives true vanilla essence an exclusive bouquet. It is a very expensive product and cannot compete commercially with the synthetic vanillin produced by the oxidation of the eugenol of clove oil. This vanillin, chemically, is exactly the same substance as that produced from the vanilla bean, except that the synthetic vanillin has a bouquet that is less pronounced.

Vanilla Essence.—Because the true vanilla extract and essence is so expensive, synthetic essences are freely available on the market. One such, obtained from the eugenol of clove oil, has already been mentioned.

Vanilla Sugar.—The student may, from time to time, find a recipe containing vanilla sugar, especially if the recipe is contained in an old cookery book. Here are two ways of preparing vanilla sugar:

(1) Take 1 oz. of vanilla beans and chop them finely; pound them up with 2 lb. of castor sugar in a mortar until smooth. Pass through a fine sieve and keep in a perfectly air-tight container.

(2) Heat 1 oz. of vanilla crystals and 4 oz. of rectified spirit to 95° F. and pour it over 14 lb. of castor sugar, the whole being thoroughly mixed together. The alcohol evaporates and the sugar is then ground down, sieved and stored in air-tight bottles. It possesses a very strong flavour.

Orange and Rose Flower Waters.—Here again the student will find these waters mentioned in old bakery recipe books. They are manufactured by steeping the orange or rose flower petals in water and distilling. The distillate is concentrated and the essential oils of orange flower (neroli oil) and rose separates out. The water from the separation, however, contains the aromatic flavours of the flowers. Orange flower water used to be added to almond paste and to good quality fruit cakes. Both are still used in sweets, especially chocolate centres.

Fruit Juices.—Apart from sweetness and acidity, all fruits contain a distinctive flavour. These flavours are due to essential oils which are rich in esters, alcohols, volatile acids and other aromatic compounds, all of which are found in solution in the fruit juices. The flavours are so very powerful that they are immediately recognized by taste and aroma, even though they are contained in such minute quantities in the fruit juices.

Concentrated fruit juices have a great commercial value, and they are prepared by pulping the fruit and treating with pectin-destroying enzymes to assist in the pressing and the subsequent clarification.

The juice is extracted by hydraulic pressure, clarified either by filtration, sedimentation or centrifugal machines, after which it is concentrated by heating at low temperature in vacuum pans or film evaporators. The concentrated juices are canned, bottled, refrigerated, or a preservative may be added.

Concentrated fruit juices can be combined with synthetic flavours in a suitable solvent, and sold as blended flavours.

Liqueurs.—These are strong sweetened alcoholic beverages, flavoured with aromatic substances. They are used extensively for flavouring purposes by the Continental confectioner. Liqueurs are used for flavouring creams, ices, and almond pastes, and are sprinkled over baked genoese and sponge bases before finishing for fancies, gateaux and torten.

There are many liqueurs, chief among which are, crème-de-menthe, which has the essential flavour of peppermint; kummel, from caraway; kirsch, from the wild cherry; curaçao, from bitter orange peel; maraschino, from the small black cherry of that name; and noyeau from the bitter almond. Benedictine and chartreuse are liqueurs invented and made by the monastic communities of that name; they are flavoured with aromatic herbs.

Synthetic Flavours.—Natural flavours are due to organic compounds composed mainly of esters, aldehydes, ketones and alcohols; they can be reproduced in the laboratory and by careful blending flavours can be produced similar to the genuine extract. The aromatic esters used in food flavour are produced by the interaction of organic acids and alcohols. Here are some examples:

Amyl alcohol + acetic acid = amyl acetate + water
Amyl acetate has the flavour of pear drops.
Ethyl alcohol + butyric acid = ethyl butyrate + water
Ethyl butyrate has the flavour of pineapples
Ethyl alcohol + benzoic acid = ethyl benzoate + water
Ethyl benzoate has a flavour reminiscent of raspberries
Ethyl alcohol + formic acid = ethyl formate + water
Ethyl formate has the flavour of rum

Synthetic flavours, however, are generally compounded from a complex mixture of esters so that the product is as near as possible to the flavour of a particular fruit or flavouring substance. Sometimes the flavour has to be modified by the addition of such organic acids as succinic, acetic or tartaric. The compounds are dissolved in alcohol with sometimes the addition of glycerine. Here, for example, is a possible combination for a cherry flavour:

Chloroform	5 oz.	Oil of bitter almonds	2 oz.
Ethyl benzoate	15 oz.	Amyl acetate	1 oz.
Ethyl acetate	15 oz.	Alcohol	6 pts.

There is an observed code of practice under which, where the flavouring materials are derived wholly from natural products the product is termed 'essence' irrespective of whether the essential oil or other natural extract is in solution or suspension. Where, however, the flavouring materials are derived partly or wholly from artificial ingredients, then the product would be termed 'Flavour', 'Flavouring', 'Artificial or Synthetic Essence'.

Salt.—Common salt has a flavouring value that is very often forgotten in confectionery. Quite apart from relieving blandness when unsalted shortenings are used, the addition of salt serves to bring out other flavours and effect a marked improvement in the flavour combination.

Coffee.—Coffee was originally found in Abyssinia and Arabia, but has been introduced into many parts of America and Central Africa, until it is now extensively cultivated in the tropical belt north and south of the equator. Brazil produces about four-fifths of the world's annual crop.

The beans are put on to mats and sun dried; after the impurities are removed they are put into bags for export. The quality and price depend to a large extent on the care expended during preparation. The beans must be freshly roasted and ground, and used at once if the distinctive flavour of real coffee is to be enjoyed. The flavour may be retained by storing the freshly roasted and ground coffee in sealed containers.

Another type of coffee which is ideal for flavouring purposes is coffee extract, which is made from coffee and sometimes a blend of coffee and chicory, the latter being the dried powdered root of a wild endive. A further type now available is the finely powdered coffee which is immediately soluble in hot water.

Coffee imparts both colour and flavour to icings, creams, and cakes. Coffee and vanilla make a delightful flavour combination known as mocha.

Chocolate.—The genuine flavour of chocolate can only be imparted by using cocoa or one of the many types of chocolate available. A Code of Practice lays down that if a cake is described as a chocolate cake, then it must contain at least 3% fat free cocoa based on the moist crumb of the cake. Care must be given to the assessing of the fat content of the cocoa and the moisture content of the cake.

For the purpose of flavouring and colouring a cake, cocoa is more suitable, for it can be sieved with the flour. It is usual to delete an equal weight of flour from the mix when using cocoa, and add an equal weight of milk or water. The usual proportion of cocoa to flour is 2 oz. to 14 oz., thus making 16 oz., which for the purpose of formula balance is counted as flour.

A good method is to mix the cocoa with the equal weight of water necessary, and to make a paste. It is considered that a better colour is obtained by this method. Melted sweetened or unsweetened block chocolate is ideal for creams, fondants and icings (royal icing excepted). It must, however, be used with care and at the right temperature.

Aromatic Dried Fruits.—Included under this heading are caraway and coriander, pimento and pepper. The first two are almost always incorrectly referred to as seeds, whereas in fact they are the fruit of their respective plants.

Caraway.—This is the most common of the dried aromatic fruits. It is grown in Europe and is the product of the plant, carum carvi. The seed-like fruit is about a quarter of an inch in length, slightly curved and nearly black in colour, possessing a pungent stimulating odour. Caraway oil is the essential oil present, the main constituent being carvone. The cheaper types of caraway essence have this oil dissolved in a suitable solvent.

The caraway used to be used extensively by the baker for making what was known as 'seed' cake, which seems to have gone out of favour. It is used by the bread baker in special types of rye bread and this is finding an increased popularity amongst those who like a distinctive flavour in bread. Caraway is also used in the manufacture of the liqueur, kummel.

Coriander.—This is the fruit of a plant grown in the Mediterranean region known as the coriandrum sativum. It is round shaped, and is light brown in colour. It is hollow, which makes it easy to crush. The flavour is similar to sage. Coriander is used in jellies and ginger cakes.

Pimento.—This is also known as Jamaica pepper and sometimes as allspice since its flavour resembles a combination of cinnamon, cloves and nutmeg. It is the fruit of a species of myrtle grown in Jamaica and India. The berries are almost the size of blackcurrants. Flavour is more abundant in the berries that are slightly underripe. In its powdered form it is subject to adulteration.

Pepper.—This condiment is the dried berries of a climbing shrub grown in the East and West Indies. If the smaller berries are picked under-ripe, dried and ground, the product is black pepper. If ripened, dried and the outer shell removed and then ground, it is the less pungent white pepper. Pepper is used in the baking industry for seasoning meat pies and the fillings for savoury vol-au-vents.

SPICES

These are aromatic vegetable products, which, usually in powder form, are used to flavour various types of confectionery, savoury pastries, and as a condiment for various types of foodstuffs.

The vegetable tissue of certain plants is dried, then ground by heavy machinery; the strong aromatic flavour of the spice is caused by the essential oils which are present in them.

Many cheaper types of spices may be adulterated by the addition of ground-up nut shells and stones of some of the fruits; others have some of the flavour extracted with alcohol.

Spices have no food value. They are added to foodstuffs to stimulate the palate and appetite, thus aiding complete digestion. Indiscreet use of spice may prove harmful to the digestive system. Certain spices are considered to have a narcotic effect on yeast action.

Ginger.—This is a popular and greatly used spice, and is cultivated in India, China, America, Australia and South Africa. It is the product of the herb *zinzibar officinale*. It is the roots that supply the material for the processing of the various types of commercial ginger. The succulent roots, or rhizomes as they are called, are carefully washed and dried, and then ground into a fine powder. This is the ground ginger of commerce.

Black Ginger.—This type of ginger is obtained by boiling the cleaned roots to prevent germination. They are then dried as sticks and bars.

White Ginger.—Another variety of ginger which is from the centre or core of the root. It is produced by scraping the outside and leaving the white centre. Sometimes it is bleached to give a whiter effect.

Stem or Preserved Ginger.—This type of ginger is produced by boiling the rhizomes and placing into concentrated sugar solutions. Preserved ginger is used for decorative purposes and for inclusion in ginger slab and some types of ginger cakes. This product can be minced to make the familiar ginger crush which is used by high-class confectioners. The syrup from stem ginger is useful for flavouring icings, fondant and creams. The smaller pieces of preserved ginger can be crystallized and sold as a sweetmeat, or used for decorative purposes.

Cinnamon.—The finest cinnamon comes from Ceylon and is the product of a species of laurel. The trees are allowed to grow normally for five years, after which they are cut almost to ground level. After about eighteen months, the long straight shoots growing out from the base are cut and the bark peeled off with a brass knife. Each strip of bark is then sprung over a stick so that the outer cork layer can be carefully removed. When partially dry the 'quills' are fitted together one over the other into what are known as compound quills. After cutting into uniform lengths the quills are wrapped and exported. The debris is ground to a fine powder and marketed as ground cinnamon. Essential oil of cinnamon is also distilled from the debris.

Cassia.—This spice is similar to cinnamon, but definitely inferior in flavour and aroma to the product from Ceylon. Cassia is grown in China and India. It is easier to grow and therefore cheaper to produce. The buds and flowers of the cassia tree are also ground to a powder. Cassia is used as one of the components of ground spice.

Cloves.—These are grown in Zanzibar and the East Indies, being the product of a species of myrtle. The trees produce large masses of small buds which are gathered and sun dried, which turns them black. They possess a hot, strong flavour and contain the essential oil of cloves. As the student will now know, the eugenol in clove oil is used to synthesize vanilla essence. The flavour of cloves has an affinity with that of apple and they are used in apple-pies, tarts and dumplings. This delightful spice is sadly neglected in the baking industry. It is delicious in properly made Banbury and Eccles cake fillings.

Nutmeg and Mace.—These spices come from the same tree, grown in the East and West Indies and Malaya. The fruit is like a peach, which when ripe is split open, giving a skin and a stone. The skin is sun dried, turning to a buff colour. This is mace, which is ground to a powder. The stone is stripped of its covering, leaving a hard nut which is the commercial nutmeg. The nut when ground is the correct finish for the custard tart, and the only permissible flavour addition to plain scones.

Cardomom.—The fruit of a shrub closely allied to ginger. The fruit, generally-termed seeds, are dark brown in colour and are contained in capsules from which they are extracted and dried. When ground they are used as a flavouring in Danish pastries.

The essential flavouring constituents of all the above spices can be obtained in a much more concentrated, and in some ways more convenient form, as essential oils, extracts or essences.

31

Nuts used in Confectionery: Sources and Processing; Almond Paste and Marzipan; Cocoa and Chocolate: History; Processing and Manufacture; Its uses in the Bakery; Tempering; Easter Eggs; Ganache

NUTS USED IN CONFECTIONERY

NUTS are an important raw material for the confectioner, not only for decorative purposes, but for inclusion in cake, adding to the food value and also to the flavour. The biological importance of nut protein is recognized, supplying valuable tissue building substances together with heat and energy. They contain also, mineral salts and vitamins of the B complex.

Almonds.—Almonds are perhaps the most important of all the nuts used by the baker. In their various forms they make excellent decorative materials, providing flavour and enhancing quality whether they are used on or in the cake. In addition, a whole range of attractive high-class goods can be made in which almonds play a major part. Almond paste and marzipan, apart from their traditional uses, are wonderful media for artistic creative work.

The almond is the seed of a tree known botanically as the *Prunus Amygdalus.* The main growing areas are the Mediterranean basin and California, the Mediterranean area producing an annual average crop of 85,000 tons and the U.S.A. 20,000 tons.

The almond tree was first recorded in ancient history in the Middle East, growing along the valleys of the Euphrates and the Tigris, later being transplanted in the Mediterranean countries, where they are carefully cultivated after first grafting a bud of the sweet almond on to a bitter almond tree about 3 years old. The tree begins to bear fruit after 7 years, reaching maturity in about 20 years.

Bitter almonds are used for the production of natural almond essence and for other commercial purposes; they are smaller in size and because of their limited commercial value are less expensive than the sweet varieties. There are many types of almond, of which the Jordan, Palm, Malaga, Valencia and the Girgenti are the largest; Sicilian and Bari are smaller, while the North African, Berber and Jaffi are generally of poorer commercial quality.

Almonds are purchased by British buyers of repute on what are known as Almond Trade Association Terms, which is a standard of quality honoured by the exporter.

Almond Processing.—When the almonds arrive at the factory, they are automatically weighed, graded and sorted into large hoppers. A visitor to a factory will not fail to notice in the almond store, printed notices exhorting the staff to watch for the almond moth and weevil. Failure to exercise insecticide control, and failure to maintain high standards of cleanliness may well result in great financial loss, for almonds are an expensive commodity.

From the hoppers, the almonds are taken for sorting, which is done on a moving band, all extraneous material being removed, such as pieces of broken shell, stones, pieces of metal, etc., after which they are conveyed to the blanching machines for the removal of the skins. For this operation the nuts are immersed in water at a temperature of between 180–210° F. for 2 to 3 min. They are then passed through a series of rubber rollers which remove the skin. After a wash in cold water and a further sorting to remove sub-standard nuts they are passed to a dryer where at 150–170° F., surplus moisture is removed over a period of about 2 hr. until the moisture content is normal.

From the dryers, the almonds are fed into graders, which are fitted with metal screens containing a series of holes of differing size. These screens are inclined, and vibrate, causing the almonds to stand up and move forward briskly until they drop through into the appropriate large, medium or small holes; broken pieces are first removed and passed to grinding machines where ground almonds are produced.

Some of the graded almonds are packed as whole blanched, the rest being processed in various machines into split, flaked, strip, nib and ground almonds. All of these grades will be familiar to the student, as will nib and ground almonds that are coloured for cake decoration purposes.

Almond Paste and Marzipan.—The difference in the constituent parts and in the manufacture of almond paste and marzipan is one that is often the subject of a question on a written examination paper, and for this reason, and also because the knowledge is valuable in practical and commercial work, the student will do well to be well informed on the subject.

Marzipan is a cooked mixture of almonds and sugar after refining, the recognized standard being two-thirds almonds and one-third sugar. The almonds direct from the blanchers and still wet from washing, are chopped and mixed with granulated sugar and refined to a paste through granite rollers. The paste is put into copper, steam-jacketed pans, similar to an open pan dough mixer, where it is cooked at a temperature of about 212° F. During cooking all excess moisture is removed. After cooking and cooling, the marzipan is packed into cartons.

Almond paste is a mixture of ground almonds, sugar and glucose, with a little yellow colour, the standard being one-third almonds and two-thirds sugar. Almond paste is not generally cooked. Cheaper grades of almond paste have a higher proportion of sugar and glucose. To make almond paste from marzipan, equal weights of marzipan and sugar are taken and with a little yellow colour the whole is carefully blended together; the student is advised to do this by hand, using the fingers rather than the palm to avoid undue warming of the paste which may cause oiling.

Both almond paste and marzipan are packed in wax-lined cartons, and the student will notice that there is a perforated cover of the same material in each carton. If the contents are to remain in good condition it is essential that the cover is replaced to prevent drying. Apart from the fact that these materials are expensive, it is plain common sense to take the same care of the product as does the manufacturer, if the highest quality goods are to be produced.

Another useful raw material for the baker is prepared macaroon paste, which is a mixture of ground almonds, coarse granulated sugar and egg whites; the almonds and sugar in the ratio of 30 to 70.

Coconut.—The coconut is the fruit of a species of palm found in most tropical countries, growing to perfection in sandy soil near the sea. The tree is prolific on Pacific Islands, no doubt because of the sea-borne nuts that have been carried by currents from isle to isle. The nut is enclosed in a thick fibrous outer husk which, when removed, reveals the hard shell that surrounds the white fleshy kernel, which in turn surrounds a milky fluid.

The flesh, which has great commercial value, is known as copra when dried. It is exported to oil refineries all over the world. Commercial copra contains about 70% oil, which after refining is used in the manufacture of shortening and margarine.

Coconut is used by the baker as an addition to cakes, conferring both food value and the pleasant characteristic flavour of the nut to the product. All coconut should be pasteurised. For decorative work it can be delicately coloured, but more generally it is toasted; incidentally the student may like to know that if it is coloured with a little yellow before toasting, a much brighter golden colour is attained. The baker can buy coconut in many forms.

Coconut Flour.—This is coconut ground to a fine powder. It is used as an addition to cakes and biscuits, for certain fillings, and in cheap substitute 'almond' pastes.

Desiccated Coconut.—This may be bought in three grades, fine, medium and coarse. By far the greater consumption of coconut in bakeries is in these grades, for in this form it is ideal for inclusion in cakes and biscuits and for decorative purposes, whether put on the cakes before baking, or added afterwards as a decoration either toasted or coloured. In desiccated form it is used in the manufacture of coconut ice.

Thread Coconut.—One cannot think of thread coconut without thinking of the modern form of cheese cakes. Most of the thread coconut in bakeries is used for that purpose.

Walnuts.—There are two distinct varieties of this popular nut, the light and the black. The former is extensively cultivated in Central and Southern Europe, while the black variety is grown in America. The light nut has a greater commercial value and bleaching has become a regular practice.

The walnut is rich in oil and phosphates, it also contains vitamins A and B. They may be purchased for use in the bakery either as complete halves, broken halves or as walnut debris which are small pieces. The unbroken halves are graded in respect of size and colour. The unbroken light coloured halves are excellent for decorative work, while the broken walnuts are used in cakes and sponges. Chopped very fine they can be used in filling creams.

Pistachio.—These are very expensive. They are grown in temperate zones, usually along the Mediterranean coastline. The nuts are small and oval in shape, being enclosed in a purple skin which is easily removed by the hot/cold water process, revealing a delicately coloured green nut with a flavour similar to that of the almond. The nut can be used for decorative purposes either whole, split, or chopped. Pistachio nuts are also used in high-class nougats, especially nougat Montélemar.

Groundnuts.—Better known perhaps as peanuts, they are cultivated all over the world where climatic conditions are ideal for the purpose. Arachis oil which is extracted from the peanut is a valuable commercial commodity, being used, after refining and hardening, in the manufacture of margarine and shortening.

After blanching, the nuts may be ground or flaked and treated with almond flavour to form a cheap substitute for almonds, although the true craftsman baker would be unlikely to use them for such a purpose. Nevertheless the groundnut has a high food value.

Hazelnuts.—These nuts are popular with the Continental confectioner, mostly in the ground form. When lightly roasted the flavour is superb and makes an excellent nougat or hazelnut praline paste. Although grown in this country, they are not exploited by the British confectioner. Spain, Italy and Turkey are the main exporting countries to the world's markets.

Chestnuts.—This is another nut popular with the Continental confectioner, especially for the well known delicacy, marrons glacé which are the blanched and cooked nuts preserved in a super-saturated sugar solution.

Brazil Nuts.—These nuts grow inside a hard round shell about 6 in. in diameter, within which are compactly packed the familiar hard shell nuts. They are grown along the rivers in Brazil and in the Guianas. The nuts are rich in oil of a type which makes them difficult to store for any length of time because of rancidity. It is probably for this reason that they are not popular in the bakery. Crushed and ground down with sugar, they make an excellent type of nougat paste.

COCOA AND CHOCOLATE

It was Columbus who first brought cocoa beans to Europe in 1494, although he did not understand the value of them. In 1519, Cortez, who conquered Mexico, noticed that the Aztecs made a preparation from the roasted ground beans which they called chocolatl from which word, chocolate was derived. Cortez brought the recipe to Spain where it was kept secret for over a century.

The secret was eventually learned in France and from France the knowledge gradually spread to other countries. In 1657, a Frenchman opened a 'chocolate house' in Bishopsgate in London. During the latter half of the seventeenth century, chocolate houses opened all over the Metropolis and were frequented by the politicians, gamblers, wits and writers of the day.

The cacao tree, which has the botanical name Theobroma Cacao, is cultivated in most of the tropical countries. World production in 1939 was in the region of 1,600,000 lb., of which 60% was produced in the British Commonwealth, some of the finest quality coming from West Africa. South America and the West Indies also produce fine quality beans.

The fruit of the cacao tree consists of thick skinned pods, each containing about 25–75 seeds surrounded by a soft juicy pulp. After the pods are harvested, the seeds or beans are, with the pulp adhering, removed from the rinds, and placed into 'sweating boxes' for a period up to 12 days, during which time the pulp ferments, probably as a result of the action of wild yeasts which change the pulp sugar to CO_2 and alcohol. Acetic acid bacteria oxidizes the alcohol to acetic acid, the liquid draining off from the boxes.

The beans are frequently turned during this fermentation, because aeration has an invigorating action on yeast activity, at the same time preventing the development of anaerobic organisms. (Anaerobic organisms are those that cannot live in the presence of oxygen.) During the fermentation the temperature rises to 120° F., which destroys the embryo or germ of the bean. As a result of this activity also, sugars and dextrins are produced within the bean.

After fermentation is finished, the beans are dried as soon as possible to reduce the moisture content to 5%. This is done by sun drying or by a combination of sun drying and artificial heat, the process taking about a week. The beans are now packed ready for shipment.

Sorting and Cleaning.—On arrival at the factory the beans are sorted and cleaned to remove all extraneous materials; this is done as in the case of wheat by screening, aspiration and the use of magnets. The beans are then ready for roasting, which is probably the most important operation in the whole art of cocoa and chocolate manufacture.

Roasting.—Roasting has a twofold aim, firstly to develop the full characteristic flavour of chocolate, and secondly to render the skin easy to remove. Roasting is an exact art and calls for great skill and experience if perfection is to be reached. The beans are roasted in revolving drums; the temperature varying between 203–248° F.; the lower temperatures are usually adopted for chocolate and the higher for cocoa.

Husking.—When roasting is finished, the husks must be removed. As the skins are now light and friable, this is easily effected by air currents.

Blending.—The roasted beans, now broken up into 'nibs', are next blended with a view to obtaining a desired result in the finished product, such as flavour, colour and eating quality. The purpose is similar to that of the miller who will blend wheat to produce certain types of flour.

Milling.—The blended nibs are next milled so that the particle size is considerably reduced. This is done in machines which consist of two grooved horizontally revolving stones, the nibs being fed into a hole in the upper stone.

During grinding, because of friction heat, the temperature rises to about 100° F., which causes the cocoa butter in the nibs to melt, reducing the mass to a thick, brown, viscous liquid known as crude chocolate. If after sufficient milling the mass is allowed to cool in block moulds, it is known as unsweetened block chocolate. It is used in the bakery for flavouring and colouring creams, fondants and in cake batters, or it may be stored by the manufacturer for future processing into cocoa or chocolate.

Particle size is of importance during milling, for if the mass is to be processed into cocoa, then the milling must be as fine as possible, because no further grinding is given to it. As will be learned later, cocoa powder consists of the finely ground nibs minus some of the cocoa butter, while chocolate contains the full cocoa butter content plus extra cocoa butter to compensate for increased bulk due to the inclusion of sugar, and for the various uses to which it is put.

Crude chocolate, therefore, must be finely milled if cocoa is to be produced, firstly because the particle size must be such that it does not precipitate in milk or water, forming a fairly stable suspension, and secondly, so that the fat cells are ruptured making the cocoa butter more easily removed by pressure.

Cocoa.—There are two methods of processing the nibs to cocoa, the natural process and the Dutch process. In the natural process the finely milled chocolate liquor is pumped into hydraulic presses, where at a pressure of up to 6,000 lb. per square inch, some of the cocoa butter is removed depending on the temperature and the pressure used; generally the press cake contains about 18–28% fat. When cool, the cakes are broken into smaller pieces and reduced to powder form either in pulverizing machines or by reduction rollers; the powder is then sieved through silk and packed.

The only difference in the Dutch process is in the pre-treatment of the beans, usually during roasting. Here the nibs are treated with an alkaline solution. This results in the elimination of all traces of acetic acid, giving a richer colour, a less bitter flavour, and resulting in a more stable suspension. Grinding and pressing is the same as in the natural process. An analysis of cocoa powder could read as follows:

Fat	18-28%	Protein	9–18%
Ash	5%	Carbohydrates	30-34%
Moisture	6- 7%	Cellulose	4- 5%

Chocolate.—The cocoa butter removed by pressure from the beans during the manufacture of cocoa, when cooled, sets as a hard yellowish fat with a strong odour of chocolate. It is a valuable by-product, for it is used in the manufacture of chocolate to adjust fluidity according to the type of chocolate being made, and to the use to which it is to be put.

Chocolate is a mixture of cocoa solids, sugar and cocoa butter; if the finished product is to be milk chocolate, then milk solids are also added. The manufacture of chocolate can be described under four main headings, and is a long and complicated process taking many hours.

Mixing.—The blended and processed nibs are mixed with cocoa butter, sugar and small quantities of flavouring materials—with milk solids in the case of milk chocolate—in a mélangeur, a machine fitted with a granite roller under which the chocolate is directed continuously. This mixes it to a thick heavy paste.

Refining.—From the mélangeur, the chocolate is directed to the refiner. This is a machine containing a series of smooth steel rollers each set progressively closer together. The rollers are water cooled. During the process the particle size of the chocolate is reduced to about 0·0008 in. Because of the chilling, the chocolate is scraped off from the final rollers in the form of a flaky powder. Refining is of great importance, for the quality of chocolate is usually assessed by its smoothness, which in turn makes the flavour more readily discernible.

Conching.—After warming, the chocolate is passed from the refiner to the conche for further processing. In this machine the molten chocolate is rolled and buffeted for up to 100 hours to ensure perfect smoothness and flavour. The conche is a heated tank with a concave granite bottom, over which a small granite roller runs backwards and forwards.

The tank is so made that the chocolate agitated by the roller is constantly directed back so that it is continuously being rolled and beaten. The process is slow but most necessary, if blending is to be complete and the full flavour of the ingredients are to be brought out.

Moulding.—The chocolate, now known as couverture, is run into storage tanks where, if it is necessary, the viscosity is adjusted by adding cocoa butter. It is then run either into moulds, in which form it is ready for packing and distribution, or transferred to temperature-controlled storage tanks where it is constantly agitated while awaiting despatch in liquid form.

The amount of cocoa butter in couverture is critical. The greater the percentage, the more easily will the chocolate particles slip over each other and the lower will be the viscosity. Particle size is another consideration, for as it decreases, so the aggregate surface area is greater. This means that the finer the milling then the more cocoa butter becomes necessary.

Bloom.—There are two types of bloom. A grey bloom which is generally caused by dampness or condensation dissolving the surface sugar which recrystallizes on drying. This is known as sugar bloom and the remedy is obvious. There is also a yellowish-white fat bloom which is almost always the result of carelessness in the tempering of couverture. This operation is of the greatest importance.

Tempering.—If the student will study some well made chocolates, either with plain or milk chocolate covering, he will notice that they are attractive in colour and in the beautiful surface gloss. If he will stand one in a warm place and let it melt slightly and then cool, he will note, on comparing it with the others, that there is a marked difference in its appearance. It will have a fat bloom which is quite unattractive.

The student can consider that the change in the appearance between the one and the other is the difference between experienced craftsmanship and either carelessness or a lack of technical knowledge on the subject.

If the best results are to be obtained, then the greatest care must be given to the important operation of melting and tempering, for the appearance and the keeping quality of the finished products are largely dependent on the success of these operations. For melting and tempering on a small scale, the couverture is broken up and put into a double-jacketed pan, taking care that it is of such a shape that steam cannot condense on the chocolate. On no account must chocolate be in contact with direct heat for the fine flavour will be lost and the chocolate will burn.

Place the pan on the gas and keep the heat low, stirring the chocolate from time to time until the temperature reaches 115–118° F. (milk couverture 110° F.). Take the pan out of the water, taking care to wipe the moisture from the bottom, for water or steam must on no account come in contact with the chocolate, then pour half of the molten couverture on a clean, dry marble slab.

Here it is spread to and fro with a palette knife until it begins to thicken, without allowing it to crust. The cooled couverture is then returned to the warm mass in the pan, and stirred gently and carefully until it reaches a temperature of 88° F. (84° F. for milk). It is then ready for working.

If the temperature exceeds the figures given, then the operation of tempering must be repeated. Chocolate must always be stirred gently and never beaten or air bubbles will be incorporated that will spoil the appearance of the finished products.

An explanation of the need for tempering is not easy, for technically it is quite complicated. First of all cocoa butter is a mixture of fats, each having a separate melting and setting point. When the chocolate is taken to the higher figure, it is liquid enough to be well stirred and the fats to be properly distributed. As the mass cools on the marble slab, partial crystallization of the fat takes place. When the mass is carefully re-heated to the lower figure the fat crystals remain to act as nuclei on which the complete crystallization can take place after dipping and moulding has been finished.

In this way the lighter fat fractions are fixed, and will not float to the surface of the semi-liquid chocolate and then set, causing a fat bloom. To simplify the explanation it can be said that the higher figure ensures fat distribution, the rapid cooling fixes the dispersion and the lower figure makes certain that there is no separation.

Chocolate couverture is used for dipping centres, biscuits, etc., and for figure moulding such as animals and Easter eggs. It is not entirely satisfactory for covering gateaux and fancies, for it sets hard and splinters on cutting; in addition it has to be tempered. A new chocolate product, bakers' chocolate compound, was evolved for flour confectionery many years ago. It is easily prepared, simple to use, requires no tempering and is entirely satisfactory for this type of work.

Bakers' Chocolate Compound.—This product can be bought either as plain or milk. It has the same composition as couverture, except that most of the cocoa butter has been removed and replaced by hydrogenated vegetable fats together with a stabilizer, such as lecithin, which prevents the added fat from separating. The stability and the type of fat used make certain that little or no bloom can develop, therefore bakers' compound needs no tempering.

Plain compound is melted in the same way as couverture, to a temperature of 130° F. (milk 110–125° F.). The temperature should then be allowed to drop until the compound is of such a consistency that it will easily cover the article to be dipped. Generally speaking, the bigger the article the thinner the consistency. For smaller fancies, a dipping temperature of between 105–110° F. is advised (milk 100–105° F.). It is possible to use bakers' compound at a dipping temperature range of between 90–130° F., with good results.

Easter Eggs.—To produce Easter eggs, moulds are necessary; these may be either of plastic or metal. Provided that they are properly cared for, both are excellent for the purpose. Moulding couverture is also necessary, either plain or milk, and the student will be advised to secure this from a reputable firm; the use of cheap, low grade couvertures is not advised.

To commence, the moulds are carefully and thoroughly polished with cotton wool or a soft cloth. Never wash moulds or subject them to excessive heat. Never on any account scrape the interior surfaces with a sharp metal instrument. If traces of chocolate are present, gently warm the moulds and wipe the melted chocolate off with a cloth.

If the moulds are scratched, the furrows will be filled with chocolate particles and they will probably cause sticking. If they do come out of the moulds, the scratch will show as a mark on the surface of the chocolate. When moulds are not in use, they should be wiped clean, wrapped individually in soft tissue paper and stored away in a dry, clean place until required.

Easter eggs may be made by one of two methods:

(1) Some tempered chocolate is run into the moulds. When about six have been dealt with, the first one is inverted over the pan and with a rotary movement of the hand, the surplus chocolate is shaken out, leaving a shell of chocolate in the mould. It is then inverted on to wax or greaseproof paper and left to set in a cool place.

(2) With a perfectly dry soft brush, the tempered chocolate is brushed over the surface of the mould. When the chocolate is set, the operation is repeated and the moulds inverted on to paper. A third brushing with chocolate can be given if necessary.

If the room is quiet, and the couverture has been correctly tempered, and the moulds properly prepared, the student may hear faint but sharp cracks coming from the moulds. He should be pleased, for it is the sound of the egg and the mould surfaces parting company. The explanation lies in the different co-efficients of expansion and contraction of the metal or plastic and the chocolate.

If properly tempered, the chocolate on cooling contracts more than the mould, so that the egg has merely to be taken from the mould without force being applied. Before removal, however, surplus pieces of chocolate are removed from the edge of the mould; for this purpose a stout plastic scraper is ideal. Care must be taken not to remove the flange of chocolate formed on the inner edge when the mould is inverted on to paper; the flanged surface is needed when assembling the egg.

The correct method of assembling is by piping some molten chocolate on to the flange, and pressing the two egg halves together. Another method is to take an egg half in each hand and rub the flanged surfaces on a hot tray, then sticking the two together. This is not advised for chocolate is wasted, and somebody has to clean the trays!

The eggs are finished by piping a shell design round the join with piping chocolate, used according to the makers' instructions. The student can make a piping chocolate for himself by adding a quarter of a teaspoonful of glycerine to half a pound of melted chocolate, stirring carefully until piping consistency is reached. Piping chocolate must never be mixed with couverture or bakers' compound.

Piping chocolate can be used to pipe a design on the egg, together with the word Easter or a particular name. Piped or cutout flowers, crystallized violets or rose petals can be used for decorative effect. The new nylon ribbons are excellent for giving an attractive finish. One further hint. Handle the eggs with care. Fingerprints do not add to the artistic effect!

The student will note the constant insistence that on no account should water, either direct or as condensed steam, be allowed to come in contact with chocolate.

The fluidity of chocolate depends on the ease of movement of sugar and cocoa particles (also milk if it is milk chocolate) past each other in the liquid fats, i.e. cocoa butter.

When water is added to the chocolate it dissolves the very fine sugar particles and also the surfaces of the larger fractions. The syrup thus formed coats all the particles present and as they move about and touch each other, the syrup surfaces link together and slow down the general movement of the particles. The fluidity of the chocolate is therefore reduced and the chocolate has become thick.

Ganache.—In the past, ganache was quite familiar to the high-class confectioner, but as sweet and chocolate making were gradually lost to the baking industry, ganache was rarely made and used and so it was almost forgotten.

At the present time, however, due no doubt to a greater interest in Continental confectionery, ganache is now being made and used in bakery schools and in the establishments of high-class confectionery craftsmen.

Here is a formula and the method of making:

Gently warm 12 oz. of sweetened block chocolate (either plain or milk). Bring one pint of cream to the boil with a vanilla pod that has been split. When the fierce heat has subsided, take out the vanilla pod and add the cream a little at a time to the chocolate, stirring all the time. When all is added flavour with rum and let the paste get cold and set. It can be hand rolled for chocolate centres or cut out in various shapes; for the latter the paste is spread on to wax paper to about ½ in. in thickness, and kept in shape with a square of metal fondant bars.

This paste will need to be coated with hot saturated gum arabic solution before dipping in either chocolate or fondant, or the covering will not adhere to the greasy surface.

Ganache can be thoroughly beaten in a machine and used as a spreading cream.

32

Dried Fruits: Growth and Climatic Conditions; Types; Crystallized Fruits and Flowers; Candied Peel; Fruit Preserving: Storage; Dehydration; Freezing; Bottling; Canning; Jams: Manufacture; Standards; Fruit Jellies; Cold-Set Jellies; Piping Jellies; Lemon and Orange Curds

DRIED FRUITS

THERE are several types of dried fruit used by the baker in bread-making and flour confectionery. They are enriching agents used to give variety, to confer flavour and to improve appearance. The three common types of dried fruits are currants, sultanas and raisins, all of them being the product of the grape vine.

They are produced in countries bordering on the Mediterranean, and in other parts of the world where similar climatic and soil conditions prevail, i.e. Australia, South Africa, South America and California.

There are three essentials for the production of good fruit in abundance.

(1) Suitable soil conditions, preferably of a chalky nature and rich in potash salts.
(2) Sufficient rainfall for adequate watering.
(3) A warm semi-tropical climate with plenty of sunshine.

The vines are usually grown on the slopes or sides of hills facing the midday sun, for the following reasons: good drainage, plenty of sunshine and protection from cool winds.

Currants.—These are produced from the small black grape which is a native of Greece, where some of the finest currants are still produced, the Vostizza being world famous. There are many other well known brands of currants among which are Patras, Amelias, Gulf, Pyrgos and the Australian Crown.

The vines do not produce grapes of commercial value until they are seven years old. When ripe, bunches are cut and placed on fibre mats in the sun, which evaporates the moisture and concentrates the sugar and other solids. The drying takes from 10–12 days, the bunches being turned from time to time. After the removal of stalks and all other extraneous material, either by hand or by machine, the currants are sieved and packed for shipment.

High-class currants such as the Vostizzas, are shade dried in open sheds where the bunches are hung on strings. Drying takes much longer, but the texture and appearance of the fruit is much better, the process giving a beautiful blue-black colour to the fruit.

Currants contain about 63% sugar, 0·5% fat, and 2% protein. For bakery purposes the best currants are of medium size, bold and fleshy and of even colour. They should be clean and free from stalks before use. The small stalks are best removed by rubbing the fruit in a currant sieve.

Washing should be done in lukewarm water, the fruit being well stirred by hand, after which they are turned out into the sieve. When the water has drained off, repeat the washing and drain again. Over-washing or the use of hot water will dissolve out some of the natural sugar with a consequent loss of flavour.

To dry, the currants are spread thinly on clean cloths and left at bakery temperature for a few days when they are carefully picked over to remove large stalks and stones. The best way to do this is to sort them on clean baking sheets; stones will be heard to rattle on the metal as they are moved and the stalks will be clearly visible against the black colour of the metal baking sheet. Washed fruit should be used up in strict rotation, and fairly soon, because of the risk of mould and fermentation.

Sultanas.—These are produced from seedless yellow grapes. When ready for drying the bunches are cut and dipped into vats containing potash, lye and sweet herbal flavours such as rosemary or lavender, and with a surface layer of hot olive oil.

The object of the dipping is to soften and clarify the skins and to sterilize the fruit, so removing all yeast spores that would eventually set up fermentation. After this treatment, the bunches are dried in open sheds, in sunlight and warm air currants.

Some of the pale coloured sultanas are bleached with sulphur-dioxide gas, which results in a loss of flavour; the gas, however, acts as a preservative.

Sultanas for bakery purposes should be bold and fleshy, with a fine flavour and light even colour. The best quality sultanas are clean and do not require washing; others must be washed to remove dirt and grit, then dried and picked over to remove stalks and stones.

Sultanas contain about 65% sugar, 1% fat, and 2% protein.

Raisins.—Raisins have a fine flavour and a high food value. They contain about 65% sugar, 2% fat and 2% protein. The most popular are imported from Valencia, Alicante, Syria, Italy and Australia. The famous Muscatel raisin is partly dried on the vine, the sap being retained in the branches by twisting and cutting; in this way the food value of the raisin is increased. Apart from the Muscatel, raisins are treated in the same way as for sultanas.

The seeds of raisins are quite large and have to be removed before the raisins are used; this is done by machinery before sale to the baker. Large quantities of seedless raisins are imported yearly from California, these, however, should not be confused with the seeded raisins.

Apple-rings, apricots, pears and plums are also dried.

CRYSTALLIZED FRUIT

Crystallizing is a process by which various fruits and flowers can be preserved for long periods. By the addition of sugar in concentration, preservation, together with freedom from bacterial action is assured. Sugar in small quantities acts as a food to yeast and other micro-organisms. When, however, the concentration rises above 10% then progressively, bacterial action eventually ceases.

Crystallized Fruits.—The following fruits are used for crystallizing: apricots, plums, cherries, pears and various gages. The fruit must be ripe and perfectly sound, with any stones taken out with as little damage as possible to the shape of the fruit. The process follows more or less the same pattern as for glacé cherries except at the end, when they are placed on wires and exposed to dry heat, which changes the coating to a fine crystalline mass.

Crystallized Flowers.—The petals of the rose, lilac and the violet are used for crystallizing. They are placed on wires and warm, strong sugar solutions are allowed to cover them repeatedly until they are saturated. They are then dried by sunlight or by artificial heat, which produces the crystalline effect.

Crystallized Ginger. The root ginger is cleaned and boiled in a weak sugar solution until soft. It is then packed in barrels or earthenware jars with syrup and sold as preserved ginger. For crystallizing, the prepared ginger is processed as for fruits and flowers.

Angelica.—Angelica is neither fruit nor flower, but is included because it is an excellent crystallized decorative material. It consists of the stems of the plant Angelica archangelica, which grows wild in swampy places. For crystallizing it is specially cultivated. The processing is similar to that for fruit and flowers.

Angelica and crystallized fruits can be soaked in hot water to remove the sugar crystals, when they can be cut into slices and shapes and used for decorative purposes, the bright colours being particularly attractive, on gateaux and fancies.

Glacé Cherries.—The cherries are first graded and all unsound fruit discarded. They are then placed into containers and covered with a solution of sulphur dioxide with a little calcium carbonate in water. The solution bleaches all colour from the fruit and cures the flesh, the process taking several weeks. The stones are then removed with a special instrument, so that as little injury as possible is done to the fruit.

After washing in cold water, they are cooked in a dilute sugar solution, or in fresh water, then rapidly cooled. The cherries are drained, then packed into vessels and covered with a hot coloured sugar solution. After a time the fruit and syrup is brought to the boil for one minute. Then follows a succession of boilings over many days, each in a syrup that gets progressively more dense. The cherries are finally packed, with sufficient syrup, into the familiar boxes for export. Most of the glacé cherries come from France. If the glacé cherries are to be crystallized, they are drained, rolled in fine sugar and dried in a warm atmosphere.

Candied Peel.—There are three types of candied peel—lemon, orange and citron. All of them are from citrus fruits and the processing is part of the citrus fruit industry, chiefly centred in Sicily and Southern Italy.

Lemon Peel.—Thick skinned lemons are used for this purpose, the pulp being scooped out after they have been cut in halves transversely. To condition them so that the pores will open, and they will absorb sugar, and also to kill off any undesirable flavours, the caps as they are now called are placed in brine for several days. After thorough washing and draining they are placed into warm sugar solutions.

The caps are fully saturated by passing them progressively through stronger and stronger solutions, after which they are dried on wires. If the peel is to be sold as candied caps, they are dried in hot cupboards so that the sugar is crystallized and the caps thickly coated. If they are to be marketed as cut lemon peel, then the caps are machine cut. Cheaper qualities of peel may have some of the essential oil extracted before processing.

Orange Peel.—Thick skinned oranges are prepared, processed and marketed in the same way as for lemon peel.

Citron.—The familiar green citron is prepared in the same way as for lemon and orange peels, except that the fruit is generally cut lengthways.

Citron is available to the baker as drained or candied caps, sliced or cut. Sliced citron was commonly used up to the last war to decorate the tops of Madeira cakes; speedier production is probably the reason for its continued absence. The use of citron peel, however, should be re-introduced into exhibition work. Cut citron is used in high-class genoa and cherry cakes.

By far the greater proportion of peel used in the baking industry is in the form of cut mixed peel. It imparts both colour and flavour to fruited slabs and cakes. It is for this reason that care should be exercised in purchasing, for the colour and flavour of peel should be of the highest standard. The good craftsman will buy cut lemon and orange peel separately and mix them if and when required.

FRUIT PRESERVING (1)

A point made clear by nutritional scientists is that we need fresh fruit or vegetables every day if we are to be fit and well. They are more valuable in the fresh state, but if they can be preserved in some way that the food value is unimpaired, then not only is waste avoided but variety given to diet, especially during the time when fresh products are not available. There are many methods used for the preservation of fruit.

Cold Storage.—Fruits such as bananas, oranges, lemons and apples, can be kept for reasonably long periods at temperatures between 34–57° F. according to the type of fruit being stored. The micro-organisms responsible for decay are not destroyed at these figures, they are merely inactivated. Fruit is a living organism subject to chemical changes which leads to decay. Cold storage slows down these changes considerably.

Drying or Partial Dehydration. This method has been used for centuries in places where there are long periods of sunshine. Drying under such conditions removes most of the moisture, thus concentrating the sugars, so that micro-organisms such as yeast and moulds are unable to develop. In addition, the rays of the sun have a powerful germicidal effect.

Artificial heat can be used, and in this case air heated to 240° F. is circulated through the fruit. In another process drying is effected by introducing cold, dry, compressed air to the fruit, which is in a container with calcium chloride, or some other hygroscopic substance which will assist in the removal of moisture.

Pears,.apples, apricots and peaches are preserved by either of the above methods. The methods employed for drying currants, raisins and sultanas have already been explained.

Gas Storage.—The principle of this type of fruit storage lies in the fact that fruit exhales CO_2 and water vapour. It follows that if this respiratory activity is slowed up, then other chemical changes will be slowed also. To effect this the concentration of CO_2 is increased in the storage chamber by the introduction of more of the gas. By this means vast quantities of fruit are transported from different parts of the world to the home market.

Freezing.—Refrigeration is an excellent means of preserving fruit in bulk for subsequent canning, cooking and jam-making. Frozen fruit in packets is now available all the year round for dessert and for home cooking.

Freezing stops all ripening changes and completely inhibits the action of moulds and bacteria. Great care has to be taken with some fruits, which include ripe cherries, plums and strawberries. The first two may be partly cooked in syrup before freezing, while strawberries are successfully frozen by taking them rapidly to a very low figure (−50° F.). Other fruits, including rhubarb, are frozen about 14° F. without any deterioration in colour and flavour, and without special preparation.

FRUIT PRESERVING (2)

There are two further methods of preserving fruit, bottling and canning. Fruit deteriorates rapidly, particularly soft fruits, due to fermentation set up by enzymes and yeast organisms, by moulds and by bacterial action. All of these micro-organisms can be destroyed by heat, some easily at temperatures in the region of 160–170° F., and others only after longer heat treatment. The process of decay in the latter, however, is to a certain extent delayed by the fruit acids which have a germicidal effect.

Bottling.—The principle of bottling is to subject selected fruit to heat treatment in suitable glass containers, which have been sterilized. The heat is maintained to effect complete sterilization of the fruit. When this is done the bottles are sealed. After cooling has taken place, a partial vacuum is formed in the bottle.

Heating can be effected by water bath or by dry heat. In the former method the sterile bottles are filled with sound, firm, fruit which is covered with water, or a 40% sugar solution (8 oz. sugar to 1 pint of water). A sugar solution is considered to be the best, because during sterilization the fruit takes up sugar and the flavour is preserved. The bottles of fruit are placed in a suitable container, with a false bottom, and cold water poured in until the bottles are immersed to the necks. The temperature is taken, very slowly, over a period of 1½ hr., to between 165–190° F. according to the type of fruit being preserved.

It is important that the heat is allowed to rise very slowly, or the fruit in the centre of the bottle will not be warmed through; in consequence the fruit will rise, and furthermore the bottle may crack. Time and temperature are both important if bottling is to be successful. When the correct temperature is reached it must be maintained for at least 10 min. The bottles are then taken out one by one, and the screw tops tightened immediately.

With the dry heat method, the bottles, packed with fruit, are placed in an oven at a temperature of between 240–300° F. The bottles are filled either with water or syrup, or the fruit can be sterilized without addition. They can be placed in the oven in a water bath or without. Sterilization takes place between 45–90 min. according to the type of fruit, the density of packing and the size of the container. If water or syrup is used the bottles are taken from the oven and sealed immediately. Those sterilized without liquid are filled with boiling water or syrup and sealed at once.

There are several methods of sealing. The most popular is the glass lid, which together with a rubber ring is placed on the rim of the bottle at the commencement of sterilizing, with an untightened metal screw band to keep it in place. It is the screw band which is tightened when the bottles are removed from the water bath or the oven.

Sometimes a spring clip is used to keep the glass lid and rubber band in place; this allows the expanding air to escape during sterilization, but keeps the air out during cooling, when the partial vacuum is formed. There are other types of lid used, all designed for the purpose of maintaining the vacuum inside the container.

Chemical Method.—A new method of bottling fruit used successfully during the last war, is by means of fruit preserving tablets which are sulphur compounds. This method requires no heat; the tablets according to instruction are dissolved in the water which is used to cover the fruit. The bottles are then sealed with the rubber band, glass lid and screw cap. Not all fruits can be preserved by this method. The fruit must be cooked after removal from the bottle, for at least 15 min. in an open pan—an iron pan must not be used. In this way the preservative is removed.

If properly sterilized and sealed, bottled fruit should keep in perfect condition for many years, provided it is stored in a cool, dark, dry place. For the student who would like to bottle some fruit in season, a chart for guidance is given at the top of the next page.

Canning.—Canning is another method of preserving food by heat treatment. Obviously, most of the canning is done in the countries

Method	*Temperature*	*Fruit*	*Time over*
1. Water bath	From cold to 165° F. in 1½ hr.	Most acid fruits	10 min.
	To 180° F. in 1½ hr.	Cherries; red and blackcurrants	15 min.
	To 190° F. in 1½ hr.	Pears and tomatoes	30 min.
			Total time
2. Oven method with water or syrup	300° F.	Most fruits	60 min.
		Pears and tomatoes	90 min.
3. Oven method —liquid added after	240° F.	Most fruits	45–60 min.
		Pears and tomatoes	90 min.

where the particular food is plentiful; in the case of fruit, where it is grown extensively. Vast quantities of peaches, apricots and pears are canned annually in Australia, South Africa and the U.S.A. Pineapples are canned in Malaya and apples in Canada. Plums are the chief fruit canned in this country.

The principle of canning is the same as in bottling except that a lacquered metal can is used as a container instead of a glass bottle. The golden coloured lacquer inside the metal container makes it suitable for all fruits. Sometimes un-lacquered cans are used with a tinned surface to the steel, these are suitable only for colourless, green or yellow fruits such as apples, pears, peaches, apricots or gooseberries, but never with red fruits.

The sound fruit is packed into the cans and covered at once with boiling sugar solution or water and sealed immediately. The cans are then placed into sterilizers where the fruit is cooked and all organisms that could cause putrefaction are destroyed. The time taken depends on the type of fruit, size of can, and the density of the pack. After removal from the sterilizer, the ends of the can will be convex, having the typical appearance of the 'blown' can. This is due to pressure within from the heating of the contents.

Cooling is effected by plunging into cold water; this is necessary, otherwise the fruit may be over-cooked by the stored heat within. As the cans cool they will contract into the normal shape. If the student will examine a tin of fruit, he will notice that on the ends there are circular rings. These ensure expansion and contraction without damage to either lacquer or metal.

If properly stored in a cool dry place, canned fruits will keep for many years. If a can of fruit becomes 'blown' within a few weeks of canning then it will be due either to faulty processing or poor quality fruit. If 'blowing' takes place after about six months, then this can be due to the reaction of fruit acid with the metal of the can, forming hydrogen gas.

Compared with bottling, canning has the following advantages:

(1) The cans, packed and sealed, can be placed into boiling water without the slow preliminary warming up; time is therefore saved.

(2) Sealing is done before sterilizing. In this way the processing is completed much more quickly.

(3) Cans are lighter in weight, more easily packed and cheaper than bottles.

(4) Provided that the process is correctly carried out, success is more certain.

Generally speaking the nutritional value of canned goods, taking into account that there is little or no waste, is approximately equal to that of fresh fruit. A special committee of the British Medical Association, reported in 1933, that 'tinned goods', especially tinned fruit and tomatoes, offered a convenient and not too expensive means of obtaining certain vitamins and minerals during the season when fresh fruit is unobtainable or expensive.

Canned fruit is useful in the bakery, for tarts and flans. Canned apples are particularly popular because they are ready for immediate use, the labour of peeling and coring being eliminated.

JAMS

Vast quantities of fruit are made into jam each year. A fair proportion of this is used by the confectioner for filling, sandwiching and for decorative work. In the past jam-making was an art; it has now developed into a highly scientific process, although expert practical jam boilers are still necessary in the jam factory.

An analysis of fruit shows that it contains water, sugar, fibre, fruit acids and pectin. Pectin is a gum substance that is responsible under certain conditions for jam setting as it cools. Setting depends not only on the maximum amount of pectin being extracted from the fruit during boiling, but also on the presence of fruit acids. In addition, fruit acids improve the flavour and colour of the jam and prevent graining.

Fruits such as plums, gooseberries and currants, contain large proportions of acid and pectin and therefore can easily be made into jam. Strawberries and cherries are deficient in both, so that an acid such as lemon juice, citric or tartaric is added, together with the pectin of other fruits; an alternative is to make jam with a combination of fruits such as, for instance, strawberry and apple.

The fruit should be chosen with care. Fruit that has attained full size without over-ripeness is best, for in this condition, the pectin and acid contents together are at their maximum. It is important that the fruit be free of fermentation and moulds, or trouble may develop later.

There are four classes of fruit that can be used for jam-making, all of which have been described: fresh fruit, frozen or chilled, canned and sulphur dioxide (SO_2) preserved. Large stocks are preserved for commercial jam-making by the last method.

The varieties of some fruits are better for jam-making than others, so that selection and blending is important. Raspberries and strawberries are blended in different varieties so that uniformity is attained. Blackcurrants are not used for jam-making until they are just ripe, whereas gooseberries are best before they are fully ripe. The red and yellow Victoria plums are the best for jam-making. A proportion of the stones is removed, unless of course the jam is sold as stoneless, then all of them are sieved out.

All fruits have a preliminary cooking before the sugar is added; the time depending on the type and size of fruit. Currants, for instance, are cooked longer to soften the skins, Preliminary cooking breaks down the cell walls, thus facilitating the extraction of pectin.

A good quality, unblued, cane or beet sugar is used. The amount is calculated so that 60% of the final weight of jam is sugar. A proportion of glucose up to 25% of the total sugar weight is used by some manufacturers to prevent graining.

Quite apart from the natural pectin in varying quantities in fruit, commercially prepared pectin is used to make up any deficiency. It is used either in powder form or as a 5% solution. Most of it is apple pectin.

Any colours used in jam-making should be bright and fadeless and subject to the permitted list issued by the Food Standards Committee. Acids such as citric or tartaric can be used to make up any acid deficiency in the fruit.

Boiling.—This operation is most important if subsequent graining, fermentation and mould formation is to be avoided. Correct boiling will ensure that the jam sets and is of good flavour and colour. After the preliminary cooking of the fruit, the sugar, colour and the acid is added together with a little oil to prevent frothing. The pectin is added a few minutes before the end of the boiling.

There are three tests to ascertain whether the setting point has been reached. Thermometer—if the jam is boiling at 220° F. the sugar is in the correct proportion and the jam will set. 'Drop' test—if a spot of jam is dropped on to a cold surface, and a skin forms quickly which crinkles when pushed with the finger, then the jam will set. This should be combined with the thermometer test, for some fruits require a higher temperature, a few degrees making all the difference.

The last test is the weight test, and the student could try this with a small batch. It consists of boiling until a definite weight is reached, the requisite figure being when the weight of added sugar forms 60% of the finished jam. Here is an example. If the recipe contains 3 lb. of sugar, the setting point is reached when the weight of jam is:

$$\frac{3}{1} \times \frac{100}{60} = 5 \text{ lb.}$$

The weight does not, of course, include the boiling pan.

In commercial production, meticulous control is exercised throughout the process. Laboratory control ensures that the set, and the amount of invert sugar and soluble extracts are correct. There should be about 70% soluble solids in the finished jam.

The finished jam at 180–200° F. is run into sterile jars and a disc of moisture proof paper is put on top. Sterile parchment or metal closures are placed in position and the jam rapidly cooled.

Standards.—Some years ago the Food Manufacturers Federation and the Society of Public Analysts agreed that all commercial jams shall contain not less than 68·5% of total soluble solids as shown when cold by a refractometer. Standards have also been fixed for first and second quality jams on the basis of the weight of fruit in 100 lb. of the finished product.—'Full fruit standard' and 'Lower fruit standard' respectively. The minimum fruit content is 35–42% according to the variety of fruit in the first quality jam, and 20% in the second quality.

Here for the student, is a recipe for greengage or plum jam:

lb.	*oz.*	
3	0	Greengages or plums
3	0	Sugar
	10–20	Water

Stew the fruit in the water until it is tender. Stir in sugar and boil quickly, removing the stones as they come to the surface. The tests for setting already given can be tried. If the weight test is used, then 5 lb. of jam is required. When the boiling is finished, carefully remove the scum before filling the jars.

Fruit Jelly.—The making of fruit jelly is a process of preserving fruit juice. When finished the product should be clear and translucent, liquid when warm and setting to a jelly when cold. The colour and flavour should be that of the natural fruit.

In the preparation, the same principles should be observed as for jam-making, for it is important that the balance of pectin, acid and sugar is correct if good quality jelly is to be produced.

All fruits, except strawberries and cherries—both are deficient in pectin—can be used. Elderberries, sloes, crab apples and blackberries are among the wild fruits used for jellies. All fruits must be ripe, except apples and gooseberries, over-ripe, unsound or mouldy fruit must be rejected.

The fruit must be thoroughly washed and large fruit such as apples and plums may be cut up into small pieces before they are simmered gently in sufficient water until tender.

The necessary water content will vary according to the type of fruit being used. As a guide, loganberries, raspberries and redcurrants will need 10 lb. of water to about 21 lb. of fruit, while blackcurrants, plums, apples and gooseberries will need 10 lb. of water to only 11 lb. of fruit.

After simmering, the juice is strained through a sterile felt bag, taken to the boil and the sugar stirred in. The amount of sugar can be calculated by testing the pectin quantity and quality.

This is done by placing a little of the juice in a glass vessel or a test tube and mixing in about three times the quantity of methylated spirit, after which the spirit is carefully decanted off. As the pectin is insoluble in alcohol it will be thrown out of the solution and remain in the form of a jelly-like clot. If it is fairly firm then the juice is rich in pectin and will need 16 oz. of sugar to each 20 oz. of juice. If less firm then 14 oz. will be sufficient. If there is little pectin present, then another fruit juice, rich in pectin should be mixed with it, or commercial pectin added.

The juice with the sugar added and dissolved, is rapidly brought to the boil. Some jellies require only a few minutes boiling, others may take up to 15 min. The thermometer (217–220° F.) should be used together with the drop test. The jelly must not be stirred during the boiling or the clarity of the finished product will be affected. The jelly is carefully skimmed and poured into warm, dry, sterile jars and while still warm, wax paper discs are placed on the surface. When cool they are sealed in the same way as described in jam-making.

Here is a recipe for apple jelly which the student may like to try: Wash and cut up some cooking apples, paring and coring is unnecessary. Add enough water to cover them and simmer gently for an hour and strain. Weigh the juice and add an equal weight of sugar to it. Bring the juice to the boil and add the flavouring, which can be clove, ginger or cinnamon. Boil the mixture rapidly until the setting point is reached.

Cold-set Jelly.—With the knowledge that a correct balance of pectin and sugar when acidified will form a jelly, the quick process cold-set jelly was evolved. This high-grade product can be purchased for use in the bakery, being excellent for the quick finish of tartlets and flans. It consists of a sweetened pectin syrup with, in another container, a small quantity of what is known as 'complement' which is a solution of citric or tartaric acid.

The instructions for use are supplied and to each weighed amount of syrup a measured amount of acid is added and stirred in. The mixture is quickly poured over the fruit in the tartlets or flans where it sets within a few minutes. The mixture can be coloured and flavoured, but this must be done before the complement is added. Only clear jelly colours should be used or the finished jelly will be 'cloudy'.

For the student who would like to experiment, here is a recipe—given by Daniel in *Bakery Materials and Methods*, for making cold-set jelly:

lb.	*oz.*		*lb.*	*oz.*	
1	12	Water	2	4	Sugar
	¾	Pectin (acid free)		10	Glucose (low acidity)

Blend the dry pectin with some of the sugar and mix into the water which should be between 160–170° F. When the pectin is dissolved, heat the mixture to boiling-point. At this stage the warmed glucose is added. Finally the rest of the sugar is poured in and when dissolved the solution is boiled to 218° F. The solution is cooled and used as requires. The complement is made by dissolving 1 oz. of citric acid crystals in 1 oz. of hot water. The complement is used at the rate of 3–4 c.c. to each 1 lb. of syrup; the larger amount speeds up the setting time.

Piping Jelly.—The student will be familiar with piping jelly for it is used extensively in bakeries for the finish and decoration of cakes and pastries. Piping jellies of excellent quality can be bought from reputable firms, and it is available in many colours and flavours, such as raspberry, strawberry, apricot, greengage and a colourless, bland product known as neutral piping jelly. This last named can be coloured and flavoured as desired by the confectioner. If warmed it is useful also as a glaze.

Like all other decorative materials, piping jelly must be used with care and discretion. Its chief attraction is in its bright colours and translucent texture, especially if it is used in the right amount and on the right background. As the colours are bright, care must be taken to avoid colour clashes, particularly so with the red jellies, for they rarely harmonize with the red of cherries or pink creams and icings.

Red jellies look very attractive where there is a distinct contrast, such as on a 'flashed' meringue fancy or gateau, or on a Viennese tart after it is dusted with icing sugar. On the meringue the blend of the colour with the pale gold of the 'flashing' creates an attractive finish. This applies to jellies of other colours. On the Viennese tart, the bright stab of shiny translucent colour is enhanced against the broken textured white surface presented by the icing sugar.

The viscosity of piping jelly can be lowered by heating, when it can be used for dipping purposes or used to run on to franzipan or other fancies as part of an attractive finish.

If care, thought and discretion are used, the student will find that piping jellies are a valuable decorative media. If cakes and pastries look cheap through lack of such care, it is not the fault of the jelly but lack of good taste and craftsmanship in the user.

To understand this product more fully and to be able to answer possible questions, here are examples of formulae, any one of which the student may like to try.

Piping Jelly (1)

	lb.	*oz.*	
(*a*)	1	1½	Water
		½	Agar-agar
	Soak together for 10 hr.		
	2	8	Sugar
(*b*)		12½	Water
		2½	Glycerine
	Boil to 240° F.		
(*c*)	1	8	Apricot purée
		½	Tartaric acid

When ready add (*a*) to (*b*) and mix well. Then add (*c*). Replace on heat and boil to 228° F. Colour and flavour as desired.

To make apricot purée, boil 1 lb. of strained apricot pulp and 1 lb. of sugar for eight minutes.

Piping Jelly (2)

	lb.	*oz.*	
(*a*)	1	1½	Water
		½	Agar-agar
	Soak together for 10 hr.		
	2	8	Sugar
(*b*)	2	0	Apple juice
		¼	Pectin
	Boil to 240° F.		
(*c*)		2½	Glycerine
		½	Tartaric acid

Add (*a*) to (*b*) then add (*c*). Boil the whole to 220° F. Colour and flavour as desired.

Piping Jelly (3)

lb.	*oz.*	
3	8	Sugar
	1½	Glycerine
3	11	Water
	1¼	Powdered agar-agar
	Bring to the boil	
	1½	Glucose (stir in)
	¼	citric acid (add when cool)

Lemon and Orange Curd.—Lemon and orange curds are valuable additions to the range of bakery raw materials.

They are essentially a cooked mixture of sugar, eggs, butter and the juice of lemons or oranges. There are well known firms who specialize in them and guarantee them to contain only butter, shell eggs and fresh juice from the appropriate fruit.

Curds can be used to add variety to short pastry tarts and used also to fill puff pastry tartlets. An attractive colour contrast can be produced if the puff pastry cases are dusted with icing sugar before they are filled. Curds can be used also to impart their colour and flavour to creams, icings and fondant. They can be used for the same purpose in cake batters provided that due allowance is made when calculating the balance of materials.

Here is a first-class formula for the student who would like to experiment:

Squeeze the juice of four lemons or oranges over 12 oz. of sugar in an enamel saucepan. Add 3 oz. of butter and 8 oz. of well beaten egg. Place the saucepan in a water bath and stir the mixture until it thickens. Pour into jars and seal as for jam.

Here is another formula:

Boil together:

lb.	*oz.*	
1	8	Sugar
	10	Water
	10	Sieved lemon juice
	8	Unsalted butter

Mix together:

lb.	*oz.*	
	10	Egg
	2	Cornflour
	5	Egg yolks

The boiling mixture is poured over the egg/cornflour mix, after which it is cooked over a water bath until it thickens, stirring all the time.

33

Colours used in Confectionery: Natural and Synthetic Colours; Source and Processing

COLOURS USED IN CONFECTIONERY

FOOD colours come under two main headings, natural and artificial. Almost all the natural colours have been in use for centuries. Artificial colours are comparatively new to the food industry.

Natural Colours—Cochineal.—This is obtained from an insect known as the cocchina; it is from the female that the colour is extracted. The insect is a native of Central America and is found on the cactus plant. It is now chiefly cultivated in the Canary Islands on a special species of cactus. The insects are collected and either scalded in boiling water, gassed by sulphur fumes, or killed over a charcoal fire. The way in which they are killed will determine the grade of the product.

After drying in the sun or artificial heat, the colour is extracted by grinding down the insects in water. The liquid is boiled for a long period, resulting in a non-stable solution. By the addition of alum and lime, the liquid is stabilized and does not precipitate.

Cochineal can be processed to produce a brighter colour known as carmine which is available to the confectioner in liquid or powder form. Carmine powder is used to produce the deep red on marzipan roses, and for deepening the colour of royal icing for fine over-piping, where an excess of liquid colour would unduly soften the consistency of the icing.

Saffron.—One of the traditional regional products of this country is the saffron cake, popular in Cornwall and the West of England. Saffron imparts the vivid yellow colour and a particular flavour to the cakes and buns. Commercial saffron consists of the dried stigmas of the saffron crocus grown in France and Spain. It is estimated that to produce one pound of dried saffron, forty to fifty thousand blooms are required.

The deep orange-yellow colouring matter is extracted by making an infusion with boiling water. Dried saffron will keep in excellent condition for a long time if protected from the light and kept dry. The liquid infusion, however, will decompose after a few days.

Annato.—This yellow colouring matter is obtained from the seed of a South American plant of that name. It is used for colouring margarine.

Turmeric.—This is another source of natural yellow colouring matter. It is prepared as a fine powder from the roots of the turmeric plant. The yellow colour changes to brown in the presence of an alkali.

Egg Yolks.—There is no better source of yellow colour for cakes than egg yolks, quite apart from their food value and emulsifying properties.

Egg Colour.—This is a harmless vegetable dye, made up by the confectioner according to the manufacturer's instructions. It is usually 1 oz. of powder to 1 quart of boiling water.

It is unfortunate that in the past, egg colour has been used indiscriminately and without care, especially in cheaper mixings, until the idea is generally held that its primary purpose is the fraudulent one of inferring that there has been a high proportion of eggs used. Its primary purpose is as a colour adjustment on the occasions when the butter or margarine, or the egg yolks, are light in colour. In this way the colour of the crumb is brightened and made more appetizing.

Green.—This is obtained from chlorophyll, the green colouring matter in plants. It is extracted with solvents from spinach, nettles and other green plants. For bakery use it used to be imported in little china pots from Grasse in Southern France.

Indigo.—The product of the indigo plant, which is a shrub with rounded leaves and pale red flowers. The stems, leaves and flowers are crushed and soaked in water for about 12 hr. The extract, which is yellow-green in colour, is separated and run into fresh vats where it ferments. It is stirred vigorously to introduce atmospheric oxgyen when indigo forms and is precipitated. It is filtered through linen and pressed into small cakes.

Indigo is now made synthetically.

Blue.—Blue is used to make icing look whiter. This is an optical illusion, for a pale blue looks to the human eye, 'whiter than white'. This is borne out by the use of blue in laundry work.

Coffee.—A strong infusion of roasted coffee beans, or ready made coffee extract, will impart the characteristic coffee colour and flavour to icings, creams and cake batters. Roasted chicory is also used to fortify the colour and flavour of coffee.

Raw Sugar.—Nothing is better than raw sugar for giving an attractive rich brown colour to bride, Christmas and birthday cakes. The colour is mainly due to the film of molasses surrounding the sugar crystals. Black treacle can also be used to impart a rich brown colour to the crumb of cakes.

Caramel.—This colouring is better known as 'Black Jack' and is simply caramelized sugar. The student will know that sugar is composed of carbon, hydrogen and oxygen, the last two in the same proportion as in water. If on heating, most of the hydrogen and oxygen is removed, carbon remains and this is the source of the colour.

Chocolate Colour.—This is imparted by the addition to creams, icings and cake batters of cocoa or chocolate in its several forms. Chocolate colours may be used to enhance the colour and often the flavour. Chocolate colours generally have a caramel and glycerine base; the flavouring agent, if used, is a chocolate extract.

Bicarbonate of Soda.—Although a chemical and not a natural colour it is included here. Quite apart from its use as an aerating agent in ginger goods, bicarbonate of soda imparts an additional depth of colour.

Used judiciously it will improve the crumb colour of chocolate cakes.

ARTIFICIAL COLOURS

These are produced almost entirely from coal tar. When coal is subjected to intense heat in the absence of air, it will break down and produce gas, ammonia liquid, coke and tar. When tar is distilled at various temperatures it breaks up into the following parts:

(1) Water and light oils at 170° C.
(2) Middle oils at 230° C.
(3) Heavy oils at 270° C.
(4) Anthracine oils at 270–360° C.
(5) Residual pitch at over 360° C.

Further distillation of Nos. 1 and 2 produce substances called intermediates—they are benzol, benzine, toluene, naphtha, phenol and naphthaline. These are mixed in various ways and in different proportions to produce synthetic colours.

All artificial colours used in foodstuffs should:

(1) Be acid fast.
(2) Be soluble in water or oil.
(3) Not fade on exposure to light.
(4) Not fade with alkalis.
(5) Possess good taste and odour and not precipitate.

(6) Be harmless and not affected by preservatives.
(7) Be on the permitted list of food colours. (Items on this list may differ in other countries.)

The most difficult qualities to obtain are, fastness to high temperatures and fastness to sulphur dioxide, which is present in many foodstuffs as a preservative. Sulphur dioxide will rapidly change a colour, sometimes almost completely decolorizing a coal tar colour. Most students will know that there are many colours used in the laboratory as indicators so that the degree of acidity or alkalinity of a substance may be established.

In the same way, colours may change in foodstuffs according to the degree of acidity or alkalinity, or they may be affected by other chemicals present in foodstuffs, for example, the balance of the constituent parts of baking powder in a mixing.

The student should note also that while most of the coal tar colours are 'acid' there are a few that are 'basic' and they will be adversely affected if mixed. As an example of this it is not advisable to mix lemon yellow which is 'acid' with rose pink which is 'basic'. Great care, therefore, is always necessary when colours are used in the bakery for different purposes.

Three colours which do not originate from coal tar are, the red and brown oxides of iron, which are purified forms of iron rust, and ultramarine which apart from producing blue, can be prepared in other colours including violet. Ultramarine was at one time obtained from Persia and Turkestan as lapis lazuli. It is now manufactured by heating kaolin, sodium carbonate, sulphur and charcoal to a very high temperature.

While by far the greater percentage of colours used in the bakery are water soluble, oil soluble colours can be obtained from well known manufacturers.

In 1947, a Food Standards Committee was set up by the Ministry of Food to advise the ministers concerned on measures for preventing danger to health, loss of nutritional value, and other measures for protecting the consumer. A sub-committee of this body recommended that the existing regulation should be amended to permit only the use of specified colours in food.

The list recommended includes 13 natural colours and 32 synthetic colours. These colours are adjudged on present evidence unlikely to be harmful when consumed in foods in the customary amounts. A further recommendation is that colours, in the light of any further investigation, may be added to or deleted from the permitted list, also that the list be reviewed after a period of five years. The recommendations have been implemented and are now in force and only colours from a single permitted list may now be used in foodstuffs. The onus for supplying only permitted colours is on the supplier, and a declaration to this effect must be attached to every colour supplied.

In addition to natural and artificial colours, the student must not forget that edible decorative materials have colour, which if used with taste and discretion will fit into colour schemes that will add to the attraction of confectionery products. It is in this connection perhaps that we can take as an example the Continental craftsman who is not slow in taking advantage of decorative materials both as regards colour and form. For instance, the colour and form of a pineapple slice, used either whole or cut into segments, has many possibilities in the making of colourful patterns. Pistachio nuts, cherries, crystallized fruits and flowers, angelica and jellies, all have a place in tasteful decorative work. In addition the Continental craftsman is alive to the pleasing effects obtained by toasting or 'flashing' marzipan, sugar paste, meringues, etc.

Plate No. XLI shows the traditional English Simnel cake which depends for part of its decoration on the 'flashing' of the almond paste border.

34

Making and Icing a Cake: Preparation of Hoop; Formula; Almond Pasting; Coating; The Bride Cake: Formula; Proportions; Added Decorations; Balance of the Design; Styles in Cake Decoration; History; Modern Trends; Danish Pastries; Formula; Method of Manufacture and Finish; Pork Pies: Formula and Method of Manufacture; Vol-au-vents: Method of Manufacture; Roux: Its use and Preparation

MAKING AND ICING A CAKE

WITH a knowledge of cakemaking methods and the purposes of cake decoration, together with continuous practice with the icing pipe, the student by now should have attained sufficient skill and knowledge to make and to decorate a cake himself.

The first requirement is a properly prepared cake hoop. This is achieved by placing a square of greaseproof paper and one or two squares of brown paper on the hoop, turning the edges down neatly and folding tightly under the rim, in a similar manner in which a temporary cover is made for a jam jar. This operation is known as 'drumming' a hoop.

The hoop is placed, paper downward, on to a baking-sheet covered with several thicknesses of newspaper or a sheet of thin cardboard for protection. A paper band cut from several thicknesses of paper two or three inches deeper than the hoop is placed inside, followed by a band of greaseproof paper, the depth of which should be a little over that of the baked cake. All this protection is necessary, for as the student will know, the cake will be rich in sugar, fat and eggs; it will be thick and dense in nature, so that adequate protection is necessary while the heat slowly penetrates to the centre of the cake until it is baked. A formula for a cake of good quality appears at the top of the next page.

The cake is made on the sugar batter method and an 11-in. hoop will be necessary. The cake will be baked in approximately 3 hr. and

lb.	*oz.*		*lb.*	*oz.*	
	2	Compound fat	1	0	Sultanas
	6	Butter		12	Currants
	8	Barbados sugar		4	Chopped peel
	10	Eggs		$\frac{3}{4}$	Rum
	10	Soft flour		2	Marzipan
	$\frac{1}{16}$	Baking-powder			Caramel colour

will be about 4 lb. in weight when baked. It will be suitable for either a birthday or a Christmas cake.

It is usual in commercial practice to make cakes of this type several weeks before they are wanted so that they may mature. They are wrapped and carefully stored, each batch being dated so that they can be used in rotation.

If the student's cake has been carefully made and baked, it should, when the next stage is reached, and the paper removed, be soft to the touch, have a pleasing odour and have no hard or burnt crust.

Almond paste is next required and if the student wishes to make it for himself here is the formula and the method:

10 oz. Ground almonds
10 oz. Icing sugar
10 oz. Castor sugar
2 oz. Egg yolk
Colour

The egg yolks, colour and castor sugar are mixed together over a water bath and taken to a temperature of 180° F. It is then mixed with the other ingredients to a pliable paste. It is good practice to cook the eggs in this way when using them in almond paste. Care must be taken when the mixing is finished on the bakery table, for if yeast spores are taken up from tiny pieces of dry dough in crevices, fermentation may be set up.

An alternative almond paste can be made by working into 1 lb. of first quality marzipan, 8 oz. each of castor and icing sugar, together with a little egg colour. This should be mixed with the same care as before. Either of these formulae will produce about 2 lb. of almond paste and this will be approximately correct for a 4 lb. cake, for it is usual to calculate the weight of almond paste at 50% of the weight of cake.

The student must then prepare some apricot jam by boiling it for a sufficient time in order that most of the water is evaporated from it. Failure to do this may result in fermentation or mould formation between the cake and the almond paste.

A little of the almond paste is rolled out into a rope, then pinned out and trimmed to a thin ribbon as near as possible to the depth and circumference of the cake, sugar being used on the table to prevent sticking. This ribbon of paste is brushed with the hot apricot pureé and the cake is placed on its side at one end of it. If the cake is then carefully rolled on to it, the paste will be picked up without trouble and the side of the cake will be neatly covered. The remainder of the almond paste is moulded to a round shape, approximately the size of the cake top which has previously been brushed with the hot apricot purée. With the almond paste disc in position and firmly fixed, the cake is turned over on to the sugared table top, careful pressure is put on the cake while it is slowly rotated. As this is being done, a metal scraper—known as an elbow scraper—is used to ensure that the side of the cake is straight and the top edge clearly defined. Some craftsmen reverse this procedure by finishing the top of the cake first before completing the side (Plate XLII).

It will be seen that a combination of pressure on the cake, the flat table top and the use of the scraper has resulted in the cake being covered neatly and symmetrically, with a smooth surface ready for coating with icing. The cake can then be fixed, by means of a little icing, on to a cake board that is at least 3 to 4 in. larger in diameter than the almond pasted cake.

At this stage some royal icing is necessary, and the student will know how to prepare this. About 2 lb. of icing sugar and 5 oz. of egg whites will make enough icing to coat and decorate a cake of this size.

For coating, a good turntable, a small palette knife—not too flexible—and a plastic bowl scraper will be necessary. Coating a cake is not easy for the beginner; continual practice is essential if the student is to become skilled. Nevertheless if he will study some simple principals the way will be easier.

When the cake, fixed to the board, is placed centrally on the turntable, a quantity of icing is spread on to the top, then with the tip of the palette knife to the centre of the cake and while rotating the turntable slowly, the icing is fairly evenly spread. The cake is then spun rapidly against the palette knife which is drawn off quickly as a smooth surface appears.

To do this reasonably successfully, it is necessary to stand firmly and comfortably, with the elbow pressed to the side of the body and with the arm rigid, the blade of the knife being at a slight angle to the surface of the cake. With the body firm and the knife still, the student will understand the principle involved, for the smooth surface is effected by the rapidly moving cake against a rigid blade, not a moving blade on a slowly revolving cake.

The sides are then coated with icing, the cake being rotated all the time and the icing well spread to eliminate any air bubbles. With the scraper in a vertical position and at a very slight angle from the side of the cake, the turntable is turned slowly. When the surface is smooth, and with the cake still rotating, the scraper is carefully withdrawn from the side of the cake.

To tidy up the top edge of the cake, the blade of the palette knife close to the handle is placed lightly on the edge and the cake rotated until a line of surplus icing is taken on the surface of the blade; this is repeated until the edge is cleared.

It is during the coating of a cake that the student will understand that evenness is impossible, if in the first place the almond paste has been put on carelessly.

With the cake almond pasted and coated and with the icing dry, the time has come for the second coating. Before this is put on, the first coat should be examined for ridges or projections, which if found, should be trimmed level with a sharp knife. In this way the surface of the cake will be smooth and level for the next coating, which is applied in exactly the same way, except that the icing should be softer in consistency.

An additional decorative effect can be given when coating the side of the cake by using a cut scraper. This type of scraper, according to the cuts, raises lines in relief on the smooth surface which are not only a decoration in themselves, but provide excellent guide lines for piping, for ribbon, or for gold or silver bands.

For some cake designs, it is usual to cover the board with icing between the side of the cake and the edge of the board. This is done by first covering the space roughly with icing, and then smoothing it off by placing the palette knife at a slight angle, with the tip close to the side of the cake and with the blade resting lightly on the edge of the board. With the table rotating and the knife held firm, the board is soon neatly and smoothly covered. When dry the cake is ready for piping.

THE BRIDE CAKE

All bakery students at one time or another will gaze on a beautifully decorated bride cake and look forward to the time when they can step back and survey their own work with a degree of pride and satisfaction.

This type of cake, of course, is not the be all and end all of the baker's craft. Equal skill, with technical knowledge in addition, is necessary for the creation of many other products of the bakery. Nevertheless, to create a thing of beauty can be satisfying and a stimulant to further effort.

XLII Almond-pasting a cake

XLIII An example of fine accurate work

XLIV The earlier style of bride cake decoration

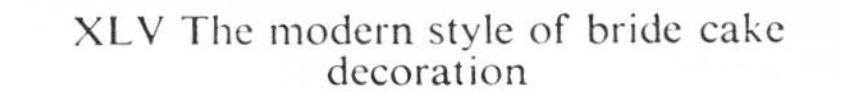

XLV The modern style of bride cake decoration

XLVI The impeccable work of R. Rock

XLVII A single-tier bride cake in the modern style

XLVIII A beautiful birthday cake

To be successful, mastery of the essential skills necessary in piping is a priority; they are controlled flexibility of the wrist and pressure control. With these skills there must be present that almost undefinable quality of good taste, which is inherent in some persons and to a certain extent can be learned by others.

Success, however, is the result of patience and the determination to practise continually. The student will do well to attend cake decoration classes regularly, not only to learn manipulative skill but also the principles of art and design.

The bride cake is traditionally British and, without doubt, British craftsmen are supreme in this type of cake decoration. This is as it should be, although in the field of exhibition work, there is a tendency to move away from the first principle of design—that is, fitness for purpose. The modern exhibition bride cake can, without doubt, grace a wedding breakfast table, for it is sugar artistry of the highest order. To grace the table, however, is not the sole purpose of a bride cake, for it must be not only the centre of attraction on the table, it has also to be cut and eaten.

Firstly then, it has to be attractive, secondly it must look like a cake and thirdly it must be of the highest possible quality. These essentials fulfilled, the craftsman can take pride in the fact that his work has given supreme pleasure to two people on an important occasion in their lives.

When it is considered also that on these same occasions there are many young people present who hope to attain the married state in due course, it will be seen that if the first glances of admiration are attended later by complete satisfaction, then it may be translated on future occasions to many more orders.

It must not be thought that the decorative standards of the past must be the standards of the present and the future, for while the basic principles of design do not change, the application of them moves with the times. It is the creative artist who is ahead, for he is the pioneer and the leader. We live in a streamlined age and this is reflected in modern design. No longer, as in the past, the quizzical glance followed later by unhurried study.

Now we must seek to attract and satisfy at a glance by brightness and a relative minimum of piping on the cake which, however, must be fine and accurate. As one well-known prize-winner has said, 'It is not so much what is put on a cake today, that matters, it is what is left off. What *is* put on must be done with thought and skill. Plate XLIII shows an example of this.

Overleaf is a formula for a first quality three-tier bride cake that will be approximately 20 lb. in weight when completed.

lb.	*oz.*		*lb.*	*oz.*	
1	0	Butter	3	0	Currants
	4	Compound fat	2	0	Sultanas
1	4	Barbados sugar		12	Peel
1	9	(1¼ pts.) Egg		3	Strip almonds (lightly roasted)
1	6	Flour		3	Ground almonds (lightly roasted)
	¼	Ground cinnamon		1½	Rum
		Ground nutmeg			

Zest and juice of one orange and one lemon. Bride cake colour.

The cake is made on the sugar batter method with a mixing temperature of 70° F. Baking temperature, 330° F. The bottom tier will need an 11-in. hoop and be weighed at 7 lb. 8 oz. The middle tier a 7-in. hoop and be weighed at 2 lb. 12 oz. and the top tier a 5-in. hoop and be weighed at 1 lb. 6 oz.

Baking times (approximately); bottom tier 4½ hr.; middle tier 3 hr.; top tier, 1½ hr. Baking losses, approximately 8%.

When baked and cool, the cakes are carefully wrapped in grease proof paper, and the date and weights carefully recorded on the wrappers before the cakes are stored. During storage, the cakes mature and mellow which has a marked improving effect on the flavour and the cutting and eating qualities.

Some craftsmen prefer to use rum or brandy on the cakes after they have been baked instead of in the cake before baking. To do this, they are unwrapped a few days before they are required for finishing and the spirit sprinkled over them so that it permeates, and is absorbed by the cakes.

For the three tiers, approximately 6 lb. of almond paste will be required, 4 lb. for the bottom tier and 1¼ lb. and 12 oz. respectively for the other two. The making of almond paste and its application to the cake, the preparation of royal icing and the methods of coating have already been described in detail. It is assumed by now that the student is fairly proficient and able to pipe and has a simple and pleasing design worked out.

When the cake has been piped, there are other important points to be considered, one of which is the choice and placing of such additions as sprays, slippers, silver leaves and horseshoes, etc. These should be placed with thought, not just where there is space and where they will stick. They must always be part of the decorative scheme; for this reason they must be chosen and placed carefully, never overloading the cake.

If the finished cake is to please, then it should be well proportioned and there is no better way to attain this, than to imagine the finished cake in an isosceles triangle as illustrated in Fig. 61.

If the imaginary lines run along the edges of the boards and the top edges of the cakes, to meet at the top of the ornament, then there is good proportion. The student will now see the importance of the height of the pillars and of the top ornament, for both are part of the total height of the cake. Lastly it is important that the col-

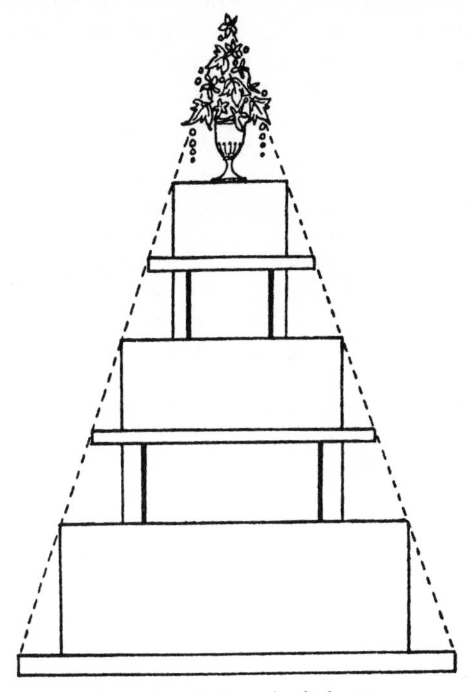

FIG. 61.—Bride cake balance.

our of the gum paste pillars and the ornament should match the colour of the royal icing.

STYLES IN CAKE DECORATION

If the student can get some old bakery books and journals, and study prints of the decorated cakes of the past and compare them with those of the present day, he will not fail to notice the tremendous change that has taken place in the pattern and style of cake decoration.

The bridal cake, as we know it today, seems to have developed towards the end of the last century. Prints of 1885 show cakes with a style of decoration that was heavy and clumsy, having little artistic merit, either in pattern or in form. All the available space on the cakes of this time was crammed with scroll work and artificial flowers.

The best known exponent of cake decoration at this time was Herr Willy, who had a school for icing and piping in London. The work, crude though it was by present-day standards, did at least lay the foundation for the evolution of the bride cake as we know it today. It was not long before it was realized that in cake decoration there was a new type of artistic creative work, with sugar as the medium.

Within the next few years, three names became prominent in the sphere of cake decoration, Schulbe, Adkins and Schur, all of them making a particular contribution to this new art. It was Schulbe who developed lace work and pioneered modelling in sugar. Adkins applied himself to design, balance and proportion while Schur was acclaimed for his scroll work.

It was Schur who introduced what the celebrated craftsman and critic H. G. Harris described as the curious moulded, hollowed border; afterwards known as the gutter border. His style became, for many years, the basis for the work of other cake decorators. It was then that Harris's friend and partner, S. P. Borella, brought cake decoration to such an apex of daintiness and beauty that work in this style has rarely been bettered.

Up to about 1912, the work of these four craftsmen was continuously copied, until the style began to change and less work was put on a cake when it began to be realized that space was the perfect background for the meticulous work that was still being maintained. The change from the daintiness of Borella to the new style, immediately after the first world war, was at the sacrifice of lightness, although the application of design and balance to cake decoration was taken a good deal further by A. C. Skeats.

All this time, the same changes in style took place in other cakes, such as Christmas and birthday cakes. The early prints, of course, give no indication of colour treatment by the older craftsmen. The same care, however, does not seem to have been taken in the application of colour to cake decoration as is the case today.

Changes took place also in the style of gateaux decoration although much more slowly. The meticulously over-piped gateau was the standard for many years, fondant and royal icing being the media for decoration. Royal icing was discontinued later in favour of fondant and butter cream, the familiar square, diamond, round and heart shapes being the most popular. Later came a period when gateaux were produced in the most incongruous shapes such as footballs, plants in flower-pots, wedges of cheese with marzipan mice nibbling at them, bags of gold and the like.

In the years between 1925–35 the painted plaque on exhibition Christmas and birthday cakes made its debut, enjoying a certain popularity and then suddenly going out of favour. It was then that the elongated cake, something like an enlarged cotton reel standing on end, came into fashion, the top and bottom borders of which were large circular run-in pieces, pierced with geometrical shapes to give a measure of lightness.

It was during this time that an attempt was made to make popular the coloured bridal cake, the idea being to have the cake the same colour as the bridesmaids' dresses, provided, of course, that the colour was suitable. The London Exhibition at that time staged cakes in the most beautiful pastel tints. The popularity of the traditional white wedding cake, however, was not seriously diminished and the coloured cake lost its brief appeal.

Up to the last war, cake decoration was further perfected in the hands of many fine craftsmen, among whom was J. G. Hampson, whose style is still the pattern for high class commercial work. It was during this period also that the first square cake was shown at the London Exhibition. The present style of exhibition bride cake decoration is a legacy left to us by the late R. Rock, whose work was beautiful in the extreme and admired all over the world. Plates XLIV, XLV and XLVI show three distinct styles in bride cake decoration. The first illustrates a beautiful three-tier cake finished in the earlier style. The two-tier cake is a fine example of meticulous work in the modern manner. Plate XLVI shows an example of the impeccable work of the late R. Rock; it is work of incredible beauty. Plate XLVII illustrates a single-tier bride cake decorated in the modern style.

Christmas and birthday cakes are staged at exhibitions in all parts of the country, showing a generous use of colour in perfect harmony, together with very fine, accurate line work. Plates XLVIII, XLIX, L, LI, and LII illustrate examples of modern exhibition Christmas and birthday cakes. Piping and design on commercial cakes are still largely based on that of the older masters, with due regard for the value of space.

Gateaux have been replaced by the 'week-end special' type of cake, the decoration of which is quickly and easily accomplished with fondant and the fudge type of cream, with the minimum of added decoration. This type of decorative work is pleasing if neatly done, for it lends itself to the use of the imagination.

There are signs that torten and the Continental type of gateaux are finding favour in this country. This is excellent, for it will give the opportunity for freehand work, and in this connection the student will be wise to perfect his skill by constant practice together with attendance at classes for cake decoration, in order to study art and design and the application of them to decorative work.

DANISH PASTRIES

Provided that they are properly made, Danish pastries are delightful not only in appearance and in the eating, but because of the many ways in which they can be shaped and finished. They are one of the items that may appear on a final practical examination paper.

Danish pastries are aerated by a combination of two methods, panary, that is by yeast, and by rolling and folding in butter or pastry fat, which process is known as lamination. Here is a formula:

lb.	*oz.*		*lb.*	*oz.*	
1	4	Flour		10	Milk (cold)
	1	Compound fat		1	Yeast
	2	Sugar		1½	Egg
		Salt			Colour
	14	Firm butter or pastry fat			Cardamon spice

The 1 oz. fat is rubbed into the sieved flour. The rest of the ingredients, except butter, are placed in a bay after the yeast has been dispersed in the milk. The whole is just mixed together, without developing or toughening the dough. The butter or pastry fat is rolled in as for the French method of making puff pastry, and given three half-turns.

Immediately on recovery from rolling, take a third of the paste and pin out to a rectangular shape about 20 in. by 12 in. Spread thinly with almond mixture over half the surface and fold over so that the piece is 10 in. by 12 in. Cut into strips about three-eighths of an inch wide.

The strips are then twisted by placing the palm of each hand at the ends, when one hand is brought forward and the other pushed away resulting in a twist as illustrated (Fig. 62*a*). They are then shaped as in illustrations *b* to *h*. All are then egg-washed and *b*, *c* and *d* given a dressing of a mixture of ground or nib almonds and sugar nibs. The spaces in *e*, *f*, *g* and *h* are filled by means of a savoy bag with custard. Here are formulae for the almond mixture and the custard:

Almond mixture

lb.	*oz.*	
1	0	Marzipan
2	0	Castor sugar
2	0	Butter

Beat well together

Custard

lb.	*oz.*	
1	4	(1 pt.) Milk
	2	Egg
	1¾	Cornflour
	2½	Sugar

Colour and flavour

To make the custard, mix the cornflour with sufficient milk and add the eggs. Add flavour, colour and sugar to the rest of the milk and bring to the boil. Add the boiling milk slowly to the egg/cornflour mix and stir carefully over a lowered gas until it thickens. Allow to cool before use.

Take another third of the pastry and pin out to a rectangle about 14 in. by 8 in. Spread thinly with almond mixture and sprinkle with

FIG. 62.—Danish pastry production.

currants, then roll up as for Chelsea buns and cut into pieces about 1¼ in. wide. Cut and shape as illustrated in Figs. 63, 64, 65 and 66, the last of which is firmly pressed in the centre with a wooden skewer. All are egg-washed.

The last piece is pinned out and cut into elongated triangles. They are washed lightly, and on each, a piece of marzipan is placed as illustrated (Fig. 67). If they are held in the hands by the top corners, and given a smart twist, they will quickly take the shape as illustrated. These are also egg-washed.

The pastries are allowed to prove in very little heat and humidity and baked carefully at 410–420° F. When baked they are immediately brushed with hot apricot purée, followed by water icing flavoured with vanilla and fresh lemon juice. After shaping, Danish pastries can be placed in the refrigerator and removed for baking at any time.

The shapes given by no means exhaust the variety. The student is advised to add to his repertoire by studying English and Continental recipe books and attending demonstrations on the subject.

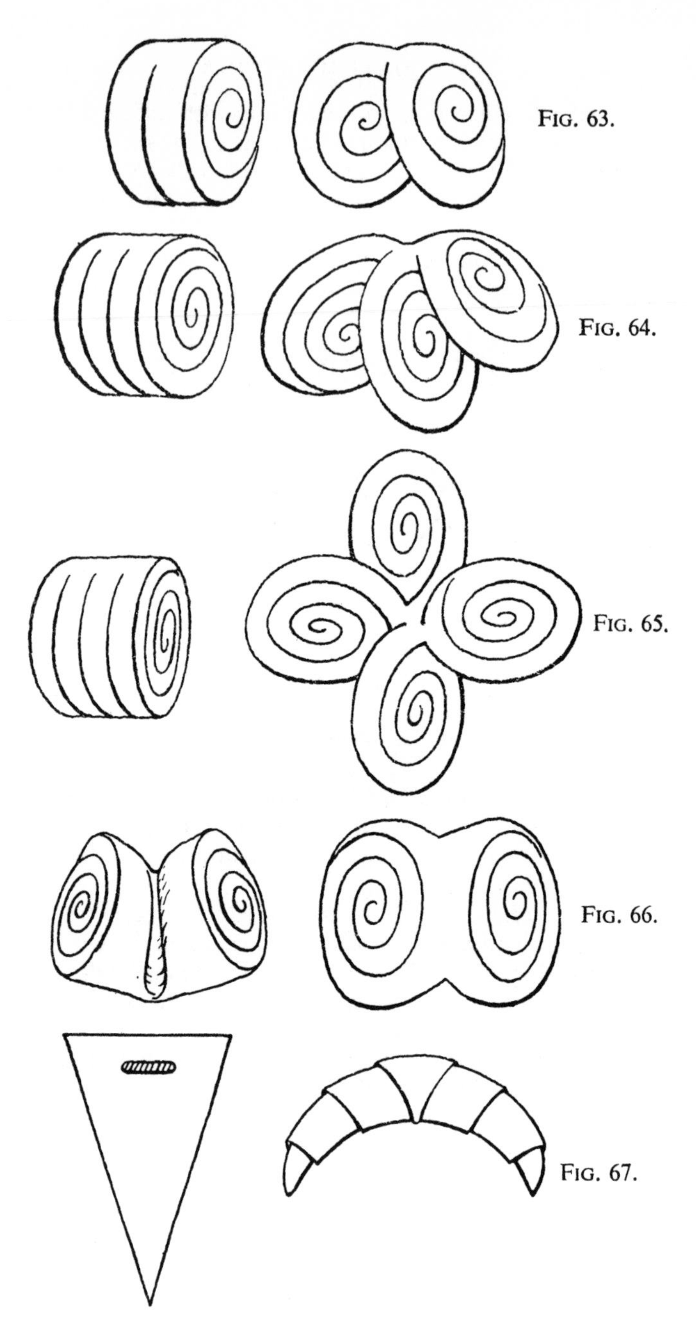

FIGS. 63-67.—Danish pastry production.

PORK-PIES

The pork pie finds itself on the 4th year syllabus, and so it may be an item with which the student has to deal with either on a written or a practical examination paper.

Here are the details of manufacture:

Paste			*Filling*			*Stock Seasoning*		
lb.	*oz.*		*lb.*	*oz.*		*lb.*	*oz.*	
3	0	Flour	3	0	Pork	1	0	Salt
1	4	Lard		1½	Seasoning		3	Pepper
	¼	Salt		6	Water		½	Sage
1	8	Water					½	Nutmeg

The water, lard and salt are placed in a pan, brought to the boil and poured into a bay made in the flour. The whole is then mixed together with a scraper until it is cool enough to use the hands.

After the bone and gristle have been removed from the pork it is put through a mincer with a $\frac{3}{16}$-in. plate. The seasoning and water are added and the whole well mixed. A proportion of fat pork can be used according to local taste.

If it is desired to have the pork a pinkish colour, it can be dipped into mature brine and allowed to drain before mincing, or 10% cured pork or bacon trimmings can be used in the filling. With either method the salt content in the seasoning must be adjusted.

Here are proportionate weights of paste and filling according to the finished weight of the pie:

¼ lb. pies	2 oz. paste	1½ oz. filling
½ ,, ,,	4 ,, ,,	3 ,, ,,
1 ,, ,,	7 ,, ,,	7½ ,, ,,
1½ ,, ,,	11 ,, ,,	12 ,, ,,
2 ,, ,,	14 ,, ,,	16 ,, ,,

The weight of the lids and the jelly will bring the pies to the approximate weight, taking baking losses into consideration.

As soon as the paste is made it is scaled to the desired weights, moulded round and left in a cool place until thoroughly cold. There are several methods of raising pies.

(1) By machine.
(2) Flatten balls, then press a well dusted pie block into each in turn. The edges will turn up as pressure is maintained. While rotating the block, the paste can be still further raised by the fingers.
(3) Pin out the pastry pieces a little, place the block in the centre of each disc and draw up the paste with the fingers.

(4) The pies can be partially raised with the fingers and thumbs before completing with the block.

(5) As for No. 2. Draw the paste downwards over an inverted block.

The pie cases can be placed into well-greased rings, but the craftsman's pride is the hand-raised pie baked without rings for support.

The lids are cut from the same paste with the appropriate size cutter. They are damped and placed into position on the top of the filling. The edges are trimmed neatly, and decoratively pinched with the fingers or with nippers. The pies are egg-washed and the tops are decorated with diamond shaped pastry leaves. Some craftsmen use a different shaped leaf for each day so that the pies are sold in strict rotation. After making two holes in the top with a skewer, they are baked as follows

¼ lb. pies	410° F.	45 min.
½ ,, ,,	,,	50 ,,
1 ,, ,,	400° F.	60 ,,
1½ ,, ,,	,,	80 ,,
2 ,, ,,	,,	100 ,,

When the pies are cool, the holes in the lid are cleared and the pies are filled with jelly. After a short time it will be found that more jelly can be added.

The jelly is made from good strained stock, made from well simmered rinds and feet. Gelatine can be used, either jelly being well seasoned.

If the stock does not set when spot tested, then gelatine may be added.

The correct baking of pies is of the greatest importance. The maximum baking time at the right temperature should always be given. *Never* 'rush bake' at higher temperatures or there may be a danger of food poisoning.

VOL-AU-VENTS

This is another item that will be found on the 4th year syllabus and may have to be made in a practical examination, or be expected as a question on the written paper.

Vol-au-vents are puff pastry cases that can be filled with either a sweet or a savoury filling. They can be large enough for six or eight persons, or made smaller to serve individually. Very small vol-au-vents or bouchées, can be made for the buffet table.

Puff pastry carefully made and turned should be used. This should be pinned out to a thickness of between $\frac{1}{2}$ in. and $\frac{3}{4}$ in. Have ready a cardboard template of any shape, although the oval form is unquestionably the most effective. Lay this on the paste and with a thin sharp knife cut out the pastry the same shape. It is as well to hold the knife slanting inwards a little, so that the bottom edge is a little larger than the top. Turn the piece upside down, which will bring the larger diameter on top, place on to a clean baking-sheet and carefully wash with egg.

With a sharp knife cut another oval about half-way through the pastry piece, about 1 in. from the edge. It is a good plan to do this with a hot knife, which prevents the cut surfaces knitting together.

The inner oval is next carefully scored in a fancy pattern using the point of a knife; this part is intended as the cover for the finished vol-au-vent.

The large vol-au-vents need protection during baking and to effect this, it is usual to take a strip of stout paper about 4 in. wide, and long enough to be folded and pinned together into an oval shape, and stood as a ring around the pastry case. The paper protection will prevent the pastry setting too quickly thus ensuring the maximum lift and a delicate golden colour.

Immediately on removal from the oven, the inner oval top is carefully removed and the pulpy interior of the case taken out with a spoon, care being taken not to damage the wall of the shell.

Before filling and sending to the table the cases are made hot gradually, so that the pastry is crisp and not tough.

Another method of making is similar to the two-piece puff pastry tart; with this method, however, it will be necessary to cut out and bake separately, a thin shape suitably decorated for the top.

Small vol-au-vent cases are made exactly as for two-piece puff pastry tarts, using either a plain or fluted cutter. The small discs cut from the top piece are egg-washed and baked separately, to be placed on top immediately after filling.

Large vol-au-vents are baked at approximately 380° F.; the smaller at 400–440° F., according to size.

Before filling the vol-au-vents, the student must be introduced to roux.

Roux is the binding element in most starch-thickened sauces. There are three: brown roux used for brown sauces and meat fillings, pale roux for cream sauces and veloutés, and white roux for white sauces.

To make a roux, equal amounts of clarified butter and flour (or cornflour) are mixed together free from lumps or the flour may be stirred into the melted butter. The mixture is stirred continuously in a pan over the gas until it is thoroughly cooked, during which time the starch cells burst, so releasing the soluble starch.

The differences in the three types is in the degree of cooking. For white roux it is cooked until the taste of raw flour is no longer evident but without allowing it to colour; pale roux is allowed to colour slightly, and brown roux still more.

To make the sauce, stock—which, if possible, should be the liquid savour of the main ingredient of the filling—is added to the roux. The stock must be added carefully if the sauce is to be free from lumps; it is then cooked until it thickens. When cold it will set as a gel. Instead of stock, milk may be used, but it will need to be seasoned.

Here is a recipe for a seasoned white sauce using milk:

Stage 1. Milk (1 pint)
Mace (small blade)
Peppercorns (6)
Cloves (6)
Small onion
Pieces of carrot
Pieces of celery
Salt (to taste)
Bay leaf (half)

Stage 2. Butter (2 oz.)
Flour (2 oz.)

Bring to the boil slowly and infuse for 10 min. Melt the butter, add flour and cook well without allowing it to colour.

Add the strained liquid slowly and carefully, stirring all the while and cook for three minutes over a low gas.

There are many ingredients that can be mixed in, or bound by, the white sauce and used as fillings, such as—meat, mushrooms, crab, lobster, eggs, cheese, chicken, oysters, ham, etc. The finished vol-au-vents may be garnished—according to the filling used—with either prawns, tomato, cheese, endive, parsley, etc.

35

Sugar-boiling: Saturated and Unsaturated Solutions; Methods of Recrystallization; Degrees of Boiling; Croquant; Praline; Modelling Pastes; Pulled Sugar; High-Ratio Cakes.

SUGAR-BOILING

In the past, sugar-boiling was an essential part of the confectioner's art. Caramels, fondants, bon-bons and pralines, pulled and grained sugar work for show-pieces, were all part of the daily routine; it was therefore necessary for the confectioner to attain a high degree of skill, generally born of application to the job and consequent experience.

Today the Continental apprentice is not only trained in the schools to this work, but has examples of this work always before him and has the opportunity of practising it in his daily work.

In this country, sweetmaking by the baker is almost non-existent, almost all being mass produced. Fondant, which is a product of sugar-boiling, was part of the routine work of the confectioner in the past; it is now bought in bulk from the manufacturer at a price and quality which makes it economically unsound for the small baker to give time and trouble to the making of his own.

The bakery schools and highly skilled specialists still carry on with this interesting craft work. The student is advised to practise it at every possible opportunity and to attend demonstrations given by the very fine craftsmen in this field.

Sugar, like many other crystals, can be dissolved in water. The substance dissolved becomes the solute and the liquid in which it is dissolved is known as the solvent. A given amount of solvent at a stated temperature can only dissolve a certain amount of solute, and when this has been dissolved the solution is saturated.

The student can prove this for himself if he takes a glass boiling tube containing cold water. By adding sugar slowly and stirring, it will be noted that the sugar will dissolve. This will go on until a point is reached when sugar crystals are discerned which will not dissolve.

Saturation point has been reached. If the student will heat the solution, the excess crystals will dissolve and the warm solution becomes saturated. As the solution is heated still further, more sugar can be added and this will also dissolve until again, a point is reached when crystals can be seen. The experiment can be repeated, showing saturation point at different temperatures. This can be continued until the water at boiling-point will dissolve almost five times its weight of sugar, although in practical work it is better to calculate that at boiling-point, 20 oz. (1 pint) of water will dissolve 4 lb. of sugar which is a water/sugar ratio of 1 : 3·2, and to consider this a saturated solution.

If a saturated solution has been properly prepared, and is allowed to cool, the 'excess' of sugar does not precipitate or 'fall out' of solution; it will remain perfectly clear and translucent until induced by one of several methods to re-crystallize. These solutions are known as super-saturated and according to the degree of super-saturation become progressively more unstable. Here is a table given by Lyle in *Technology for Sugar Refining Workers* showing the solubility of sugar:

Temperature ° C.	*Sucrose/100 parts of water*	*Water/100 parts of sucrose*
0	176	56·9
30	218	45·9
50	263	38·0
80	381	26·2

It will be seen that a saturated solution at the higher temperature will contain a progressively greater proportion of sugar as the water is boiled off. The student will know, of course, that water boils at 100° C. (212° F.) at which temperature it evaporates. It follows then that in the prolonged boiling of a sugar solution the water is driven off and the sugar remains. As this brake on temperature is eliminated, so the sugar remaining rises rapidly in temperature until at last it is caramelized.

As has already been mentioned, re-crystallization can be effected by several methods. Here they are:

(1) Seeding. Adding a crystal or crystals of sugar.
(2) Agitation or beating. This operation is known as graining. This is often done in conjunction with seeding.
(3) Highly super-saturated solutions can be crystallized by merely disturbing them, e.g. by moving the container or by tapping, or even by allowing them to stand, when the condition is so unstable that crystals form on their own account. Dust particles have been known to induce crystallization.

The quicker a solution crystallizes during agitation, the smaller will be the crystals, thus the last mentioned method produces the biggest crystal. It is, however, dependent on temperature and the degree of super-saturation.

If the student has two sugar solutions boiled to say, 115° C. which are both allowed to cool-in case A, to 50° C. and B to 20° C., in both cases they will be super-saturated solutions, that is, they will be unstable. A, however, will not be as unstable as B and will therefore crystallize out more slowly and produce bigger crystals. Case B will be very unstable and will therefore produce smaller crystals. The student will see this quite clearly if he compares a piece of coconut ice with a piece of fondant.

Sugar for coconut ice is boiled to a slightly lower figure than sugar for fondant. Graining is effected without cooling, so that the solution is only slightly super-saturated. Graining is by seeding with a small piece of fondant supplemented by agitation with a spatula. The crystals in the dispersed fondant act as nuclei on which other crystals form until the whole mass is crystallized.

It is interesting to note that seeding can effect crystal size, for the addition of fine fondant crystals will result in a smaller crystallization than would be the case if agitation alone was used, or if the addition was in the form of larger crystals.

Fondant is made from a sugar solution taken to a higher temperature than for coconut-ice, but which is allowed to cool considerably, making it highly super-saturated. Agitation or beating is used to induce re-crystallization which, after sufficient working, quickly forms minute crystals, the aggregate reflection of light from which gives such an excellent gloss on properly prepared fondant. The student cannot fail to note that coconut ice with a larger crystal is dull as compared with fondant.

If properly prepared, highly super-saturated solutions are allowed to cool without being disturbed, they will remain as clear, translucent, viscous fluids or as solids according to the degree of boiling, the highly boiled solutions setting as a hard, brittle mass. Highly boiled sugar solutions are used for dipping fruits and marzipan for petits-fours, and for dipping the small petit-choux used in the building of gateaux St. Honoré.

Degrees of Boiling.—With a knowledge of saturated and super-saturated solutions, the student will, no doubt, like to experiment with sugar boiling.

Take a heavy saucepan, one of tinned copper or aluminium. Into this put 4 lb. of preserving or mineral water sugar and 1 pint of water and place on the gas. The mixture may be stirred until it begins to boil to make sure that the sugar crystals are all dissolved. At boiling-point stirring must cease. Remove any scum from the surface, and keep the sides of the pan washed down, using a brush dipped into clean water.

The washing is absolutely necessary, for if any sugar is splashed up on to the sides of the pan it will crystallize and fall back into the boiling solution and act as nuclei and bring about premature graining.

At 225° F., 10 oz. of warmed glucose is added, or a small quantity of weak acid such as lemon juice or cream of tartar, dispersed in a little water. Dispersion of the glucose or the acid is effected by convection currents in the boiling solution. On no account must either be stirred in or graining will occur.

Glucose is added to prevent premature graining, for it is an uncrystallizable sugar. When an acid is used, glucose is actually manufactured in the boiling solution by chemical change.

The acid acts as a catalyst and hydrolysis takes place; a molecule of sucrose takes up a molecule of water and splits into separate molecules of dextrose and levulose, which are monosaccharides or invert sugars.

It is levulose that will not crystallize and will help in preventing premature graining. After this chemical reaction, which is known as inversion, the pan will contain sucrose, dextrose, levulose, water and the acid which will remain unchanged. Only a very small amount of acid will be necessary—one sixteenth of an ounce to 4 lb. of sugar is sufficient. Even so, the extent of chemical change will depend not only on the amount of acid, but on the type used. The period of boiling and the final temperature also have a bearing on the degree of change.

In the making of toffees and caramels, it is necessary to stir the mixture, but because butter or fat is used in addition to glucose, stirring is effected without the mixture graining.

When the student has added the glucose or acid, the solution is boiled to the required degree as rapidly as possible. Slow cooking will increase the rate of inversion, and as the invert sugars caramelize at a lower temperature than sucrose, discoloration may occur.

It the student is able to attend a demonstration given by a skilled craftsman, he will be struck by the fact that more often than not, the hand is used for testing the boiling sugar, for many craftsmen dispense with the thermometer altogether. Others will supplement the hand test with a thermometer reading.

There is a reason for the hand testing, for it will give the experienced craftsman exact knowledge of the degree of cooking which may, under certain circumstances, differ from the thermal figure. Two separate boilings may both show the same degree of temperature, but

XLIX A Christmas cake

L Another very fine birthday cake

LI A birthday cake for a child

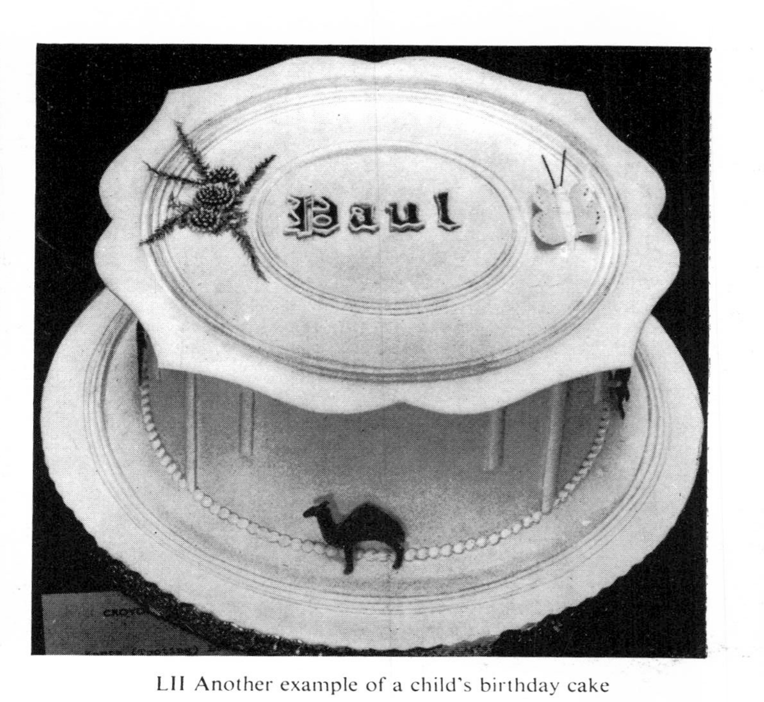

LII Another example of a child's birthday cake

LIII A fine example of flower modelling

LIV A group of marzipan vegetables

LV A presentation casket made with sugar paste

because of the differing glucose contents, neither will be the same in the degree of cooking. Here are the hand tests with the approximate temperatures.

Thread.—225° F. If the student will touch the surface of the boiling sugar lightly with the tip of his fingers, then press the finger and thumb together and slowly open them again, a thread of sugar will be seen. There will be no danger of a burn if the finger is perfectly dry.

Pearl—230° F. If the test is repeated, it will be noticed that the thread is thicker and as the finger and thumb are pressed together and separated repeatedly, the thread is seen to break and shape up into a pearl-like ball.

Blow.—235° F. If a piece of looped wire is dipped into the solution, a window of sugar will form within the loop. If this is blown gently it will be seen to stretch before it bursts.

Feather.—240° F. The test is repeated. Gentle blowing will result in the sugar flying off the loop like a string of feathers.

Soft Ball—245° F. This is a dual test—of the sugar and the student. The hand is dipped into cold water, then quickly some boiling sugar is hooked out with the forefinger and hand and sugar placed back immediately into cold water. If the sugar is in the correct condition, it can be moulded into a soft ball, which will drop with a dull thud on a marble slab.

Hard Ball.—250° F. The test is repeated. This time the moulded ball will be harder and fall with a sharp crack. The blowing test with the looped wire will result in a string of long bubbles coming off the wire.

Soft Crack.—270° F. Again a small amount of sugar is hooked out with the finger. This time the surface of the sugar sets at once under water while the centre remains soft. This is more apparent if the sugar piece is bitten between the teeth. A word of warning to those who wear dentures, for the removal of the sugar may bring the dentures with it!

Hard Crack.—280–310° F. Again the same test. The sugar now is quite brittle and hard. After this temperature is reached the sugar quickly changes to a pale amber in colour, then to a dark brown, until at last it is caramelized.

Croquant and Praline.—If some sugar is put into a heavy pan—a copper pan for preference—and then heated, it will slowly change to a viscous amber coloured liquid very similar in appearance to golden syrup; the sugar has melted.

If a squeeze of lemon juice is added before melting, some of the sugar is inverted and the mass does not set hard immediately, remaining in a malleable condition if put on a warm oiled slab. The addition of some lightly roasted almond nibs or chopped hazelnuts before it is poured out, results in a confection known as croquant or nougat. Croquant is a French word meaning crisp; crackling; crunchy, and it is suggested, therefore, that croquant is the correct term.

Croquant can be rolled out with an oiled roller and cut out into various shapes which can be used for decorating petits-fours, fancies and gateaux. It can also be used for chocolate centres or made up into ornamental confectionery pieces which are cut out with the help of templates, assembled and decorated. These are used for table decoration, usually holding petits-fours, bon-bons, rout biscuits, etc. Powdered croquant can be used for decorative work.

If the croquant is pounded in a mortar or passed through granite rollers, praline paste is formed. This can be used in creams, imparting the delicate flavour of roasted almonds or hazelnuts. It can be mixed with chocolate, and as chocolate praline paste, it can be rolled out and when set, cut up into various shapes for chocolate centres.

MODELLING PASTES

All decorative work is creative, and nothing gives the craftsman greater satisfaction than to use his hands and mind in the creation of beautiful things. Cake decoration gives the baker this opportunity, whether it be in the simple arrangement of nuts or fruit on the top of a cake, or in sugar artistry of the highest quality.

Modelling is one of many facets that gives pleasure to the craftsman. Models can be fashioned out of a wide range of products and applied to many types of cakes. The objects modelled can be simple or more ambitious, according to the wish and skill of the craftsman, the type of product on which they are to be used, the occasion and lastly the age of the recipient of the finished product.

Fashions change in all things; cake decoration is no exception. In spite of this, some kinds of cake decoration have endured through the years; examples of these are marzipan flowers and fruits, and the gum paste ornaments used on the top of the traditional bride cake, although the manufacture of the last is now in the hands of large specialist manufacturers.

Modelling Marzipan.—For modelling marzipan flowers take the following:

lb.	*oz.*	
1	0	Marzipan
	12	Gum paste
	12	Icing sugar

The marzipan should be of the finest possible quality. It is mixed with the sugar carefully, using the tips of the fingers as far as possible to prevent the possible 'oiling' which is caused by the heat of the hand inducing a separation of the almond oil. When the sugar is mixed in, blend in the gum paste. This modelling paste can be coloured to any pleasing pastel tint and at all times it must be kept covered when not in use.

From this paste many kinds of flowers and vegetables can be modelled, including the ever popular marzipan rose (Plates LIII and LIV). Fidelity to nature can only come from long practice, using the natural flower as a model. From this paste animals can be modelled, and the student will find endless satisfaction from this type of work. All animal shapes are simplified, detail being eliminated; nevertheless if neatly done, the essential quality is there and is immediately recognized, especially if it is enhanced by the imaginative deft touch here and there that is the hallmark of the creative craftsman. This medium lends itself admirably to the moulding of figures using plaster or sulphur moulds.

For marzipan fruits make up the following:

lb.	*oz.*	
1	0	Marzipan
1	0	Icing sugar

Mix well, observing the same precautions against 'oiling' as before It can be coloured as desired. Again, fidelity to nature can be best ensured by copying the natural fruit. After sufficient practice, very fine work can be executed in this field. The modelled shape can be coloured by brush or by aerograph.

Gum Paste.—The use of this type of paste by the baker is now largely discontinued, due to the fact that it dries so hard and is scarcely edible. It is used mainly in the manufacture of cake ornaments, and to a much lesser degree by individual craftsmen for adding stability to modelling marzipan, and for special decorative motifs to be used on presentation and similar cakes. Here is a formula:

lb.	*oz.*	
2	0	Royal icing (without acid)
	½	Powdered gum tragacanth
1	0	Icing sugar

Blue is added to white gum paste.

The powdered gum is stirred into the royal icing and allowed to stand for 24 hr. Icing sugar is then added until the desired consistency is reached. Gum paste dries very quickly so that it must be carefully covered with a damp cloth at all times. It can be coloured to any pleasing pastel tint, and pinned out and cut to any shape. It is particularly useful for making easily applied Christmas cake decorations. These can be made and stored long before the Christmas rush.

Sugar Paste.—This pleasing edible material can be bought from several reputable firms, or can be prepared as follows:

lb.	*oz.*		*lb.*	*oz.*	
3	0	Gum paste		11	Cocoa butter
	9	Glucose		12	Royal icing (no acid)
	14	Icing sugar			Colour as desired

Melt the glucose and the cocoa butter and blend them into the royal icing. Add this mixture to the gum paste, then add the icing sugar and mix well. Store in polythene bags in boxes or tins.

Sugar paste has many uses in decorative work. It can be used almost exclusively to decorate cakes and gateaux. The use of special rolling pins and marzipan nippers is an advantage in this work. Flowers and animals can also be modelled in this medium; roses being particularly beautiful because of the thinness of the petals that can be attained together with a clarity of colour. White roses made with a good sugar paste are particularly fine.

Sugar paste lends itself admirably also to another quickly made and attractive type of cut out flower. For these the paste is pinned out and shapes cut with a very small fluted cutter. The petals are then marked out with the back of a knife; the pieces are 'cupped' by placing in the palm of the hand and carefully shaping with the tip of the finger. When dry, a spot of chocolate, royal icing, fondant or jelly is piped in the centre to give a colour contrast. Plate LV shows a presentation casket made with sugar paste.

While cleanliness is essential at all times, it is particularly so when handling modelling pastes, for even the tiniest spot of dirt is immediately discernible against the pale tint of the paste, and craftsmanship is at once in question.

Pulled Sugar.—This highly specialized art results in some pleasing decorative effects. Ribbons with a wonderful satin-like sheen, and flowers with a lovely shimmering surface texture, bear obvious evidence of highly skilled craftsmanship. The sugar is prepared as follows:

lb.	*oz.*	
2	0	Lump sugar
	10	Water
		Glucose (one tablespoon)

Enough cream of tartar to cover a sixpence.

The sugar is carefully dissolved in the water. The acid and glucose is added at 225° F. and the solution is boiled to 290° F., the pan being washed down continuously. The sugar is coloured and pulled on an oiled marble slab, after which it is kept warm so that its malleable condition is maintained while it is being fashioned.

Ice and Chocolate.—Ice and chocolate are two other materials that will offer pleasure to those with a taste for sculpture. Exquisite show pieces for the table can be executed from blocks of ice, and for the shop window from a slab of chocolate.

The student who attends a bakery school will be well advised to watch carefully the demonstrations given by the teachers. Every student is advised to study the many textbooks, both British and Continental, and seek at all times to attend the demonstrations so willingly given by the very fine craftsmen who specialize in various skills. In this way he may find that he has an aptitude for one or more of them himself.

A love of creative work, the capacity for hard work, together with continuous practice will eventually bring him to the top, when he will find complete satisfaction in exercising his skill and delighting others in the process. He will be a craftsman and there is no finer ambition, particularly in the baking industry.

HIGH-RATIO CAKES

This type of cake was introduced into this country from the U.S.A. in the 1930's and at that time created a great deal of interest in the baking industry. Now high-ratio cakes are made in almost every bakery.

They are so called because of the high proportion of sugar and milk to the weight of flour that can be incorporated in the mix.

Formula balance teaches us that sugar and milk must never exceed the weight of flour in a normal cake. An excess of sugar will cause the cake to sink—this is known as the 'M' fault—and excess of milk will cause the cake to collapse at the sides—the 'X' fault. Since the sugar content in the new type of cake is so high, some compensatory balance adjustment must be made to prevent the cake from sinking; extra egg and/or milk then becomes necessary. This is only possible with the help of special flour and special shortenings (Chapters 23 & 26).

With the increased power of absorption and adsorption conferred on the flour by special milling and subsequent treatment, and the high emulsifying powers of the special fat, an average moisture ratio to flour of as much as 150 : 100 is possible against an average of 80 : 100, and a maximum of 100 : 100 in normal cakes. The average sugar/

flour ratio is as much as 120 : 100, whereas in the normal cake it is about 60 : 100 with a maximum of 100 : 100.

The method of manufacture is different also. High-ratio cakes are made on a three-stage process. The dry ingredients and fat are placed in the machine bowl and brought to a fine crumbly consistency on low speed. On the same speed, the water is added gradually over four minutes. The bowl and beater is scraped down twice during that time.

Finally the egg is added gradually over one to two minutes, the bowl and beater scraped down, and the mixture blended for a further three minutes on low speed. High-ratio cake mixtures are never beaten, they are always blended. Beating will always cause shrinkage of the cake during baking. Here are examples of two kinds of high-ratio cake:

Angel			*Golden*		
lb.	*oz.*		*lb.*	*oz.*	
5	0	Special cake flour	5	0	Special cake flour
2	8	Special shortening	2	8	Special shortening
6	0	Castor sugar	6	4	Castor sugar
	8	Milk powder		8	Milk powder
	1	Salt		1	Salt
	4¼	Baking powder		3	Baking powder
	¾	Cream powder	2	8	Water
3	7	Water	3	12	Eggs
3	2	Egg whites			
120 : 100 sugar/flour ratio			125 : 100 sugar/flour ratio		
130 : 100 Moisture/ flour ratio			125 : 100 moisture/flour ratio		

Mixing temperatures 70° F. Baking temperatures: 15 oz. in 1-lb. bread tins 370–380° F.: 8 oz. in 7-in. sandwich plates 390–400° F.

36

Emulsions and Homogenization: Emulsifying Agents; Costings; Examinations

EMULSIONS AND HOMOGENIZERS

An emulsion as used in the bakery industry is an intimate mixture of oil and water. If the student will take a glass container with a screw lid and partly fill it with a mixture of oil and water and then shake it vigorously, an emulsion will be formed. It will be very unstable, however, for it will soon separate out and the oil will form a layer on the surface of the water. The greater the agitation the longer will it take to separate. This is because the mixture is broken up into smaller droplets, which take longer to run together and coalesce.

It follows then, that if the mixture can be broken up into extremely tiny droplets, then a greater stability can be maintained. This is the principle of mechanical emulsification. There are natural emulsions of which milk is an outstanding example. It is, however, not completely stable, for the cream will rise to the top, unless the milk has been previously homogenized.

There are two kinds of emulsion, an oil in water and water in oil. In the first, the tiny droplets of oil are dispersed in water. The oil is known as the disperse phase and the water the continuous phase. The opposite is the case in a water in oil emulsion for the tiny droplets of water are dispersed through the continuous phase of the oil.

To give greater permanence to an emulsion, stabilizers are used, which increase the viscosity of the mixture, that is, the rate of flow is decreased. At the same time the stabilizer appears to form a film round the droplets of the disperse phase, so acting as an insulator, thus maintaining a more permanent dispersion. Milk is an example of an oil in water emulsion and in this instance, casein is the stabilizer.

Butter creams are an example of water in oil emulsions. Butter and margarine are further examples. Dairy cream is an oil in water emulsion, but in this case, the proportion of oil—as butter fat—is much greater than in milk. The only water present in butter cream is the comparatively small amounts in butter and in fondant (if used), and in additions such as egg, egg albumen or milk. Butter creams, of course, need beating only and are not mechanically emulsified. Butter and margarine contain only small amounts of water.

Emulsifying Agents.—These stabilizing agents are substances that confer a measure of permanence on an emulsion. There are many stabilizers contained in the raw materials used in the bakery, among which are the yolks and the whites of egg, the protein of milk (casein) and flour (gluten). Gelatine and agar-agar are also excellent stabilizers.

Yolk of egg contains the powerful emulsifying agent, lecithin which is a phosphorized fatty protein. It is the lecithin of the yolk and the albumen of egg, together with a protein in the butter or margarine, that is responsible for a measure of permanence in the emulsification of a properly beaten mixture of butter, sugar and egg, in the sugar batter method of cake making.

Lecithin is also produced commercially from the soya bean.

Homogenizers.—The mechanical emulsification of a mixture is probably better known now as homogenization. This is a process of breaking up the constituents of a liquid mixture, so that they are converted into minute droplets. In this form they are so small that they remain in suspension. As explained, greater permanence is given by the use of stabilizers.

The principle, which only varies in detail, is to force the mixture at high pressure through a small aperture at a known rate, thus reducing the globules and particles of the mixture. Pressures may vary be-bween 100 and 4,000 lb. per square inch. The use of high pressures does not necessarily result in better emulsions.

More pressure means more power and greater expense. Economically, the type of machine, the nature of the mixture, with subsequent laboratory tests, are of first importance. Advice and guidance will always be given by manufacturing firms.

The jets are made from a hard wearing alloy which will withstand the high pressures. The size of the apertures will vary according to the nature of the mixture, but all are extremely small. An average would be about 0·005 of an inch. These machines are constructed so that they can be readily dismantled for cleaning and, what is of equal importance, all metal parts in contact with food-stuffs are made from stainless steel.

SIMPLE COSTINGS

The object of making bread and confectionery, apart from service to the community, is to make a profit so that the business is maintained. One cannot be certain of this, unless an accurate, well-organized system of costing is used. This is effected by books and files in which information on every stage of production, delivery and selling is recorded. The information can thus be found without delay.

The number and types of books that are kept depends to a large extent on the size of the business and the volume of production. In a small business one or two books may be all that is necessary. As the business grows these can be increased in number by sub-divisions. For instance, the stock book can become two books dealing with breadmaking and confectionery raw materials respectively, or the wages book can be divided to deal with wages for breadmaking and those for confectionery. This will go on, until in a large business the office system is such that every phase of business activity is recorded and filed and kept up-to-date, so that information is forthcoming at any time.

Here are the essentials of a costing system:

Stock Book.—This will contain all the items of stock at the beginning of a week, additions to stock during the week, and the stock at the end of the week. The difference will be the stock used. There will be a column to record the market price of each item of stock, so that the total cost of materials used can easily be calculated.

If this is done systematically and accurately, then the basis for efficient costing is established.

Formula Costing.—This is to give information on every type of product manufactured. It is generally done by means of a card index filing system. Each card contains the name of the product, the formula and cash value of each of the materials used (this will include such items as fat for greasing, paper for lining and any decorative additions, etc.), together with the yield of the formula and the calculated material cost of each unit produced. To cover fluctuations in material costs, these cards should be constantly revised.

Wages Book.—This is compulsory, and must be made up and be available for inspection if requested. It will record wages paid, including any overtime and bonus; it will show also all legal deductions such as insurance contributions, and P.A.Y.E.

Delivery Costs.—This will itemize the cost of petrol, oil, tyres, repairs and depreciation, maintenance, etc. These costs can then be estimated in relation to the value of the goods produced.

Machinery, Tools and Equipment.—Information will be necessary on existing plant, new equipment, replacements, repairs, depreciation and the recovery on the sale of old equipment.

Selling Costs.—If there are branch shops it will be necessary to have details of rates and rent, heating, lighting, wages, cleaning and wrapping, etc.

Production Records.—These will show an analysis of overhead costs, so that percentages in relation to the value of goods produced can be determined. Generally this is done under two headings:

(1) Bread production costs, which are calculated in relation to sacks of flour used.

(2) Confectionery, where the costs are generally based on each £1 of confectionery produced.

It is from the information contained in these books and records that the selling prices of bakery products can be assessed and from which a profit and loss account and a balance sheet can be compiled.

In bakery schools the student will have the opportunity of buying some of the products made, generally at a price assessed on the cost of raw materisls used, plus an additional percentage to cover the cost of fuel and possible wastage.

Madeira Cakes

Weight		*Ingredients*	*Cost*		*date* 5/8/58 *Value*		*date*	*date*
			per lb.					
lb.	*oz.*		*s.*	*d.*	*s.*	*d.*		
2	0	Compound	1	6	3	0		
6	0	Butter	2	6	15	0		
8	0	Sugar		9	6	0		
10	0	Eggs	2	6	25	0		
12	0	Flour		6	6	0		
	2	Powder		8		1		
1	12	Milk		4		7		
		Colour				1		
		Essence (Vanilla)				3		
		Paper linings				3		
39	14				56	3		

Weight 15½ oz. Yield 40. Material cost per unit 1*s.* 5*d.* (16·87*d.*).

It becomes necessary, therefore, for the student to have some knowledge of simple costing, so that he may be able to calculate the approximate cost of a loaf or a cake, or answer a question on the subject in a written examination. To facilitate costing, the school will have a list, easy of access, showing the current cost of bakery raw materials, the list being constantly revised because of price fluctuations. An example of a material costing card appears opposite.

The two extra date columns provide for re-costing in the event of price fluctuations. This type of filing card can be elaborated to include, for example, baking temperature, baking losses and the method of manufacture. Still further, the percentage of production and overhead costs, calculated on each £1's worth of materials used can be added. In this way the selling price may be calculated and recorded.

EXAMINATIONS

Amongst the certificates to which the bakery student may aspire are those of the City and Guilds of London Institute. Each year many students take examinations at various levels. For many of them this is their first major examination.

The purpose of the examination is to give the student the opportunity of showing, through the written paper and the practical work, that he is worthy to hold the City and Guilds certificate, which will mean that he has applied himself to his studies, attended the lectures and demonstrations and taken a keen interest in the practical work over each session.

His knowledge of the subjects will be assessed by examiners. With the written work, the examination is impersonal, for the papers are sent away for marking. In the practical examinations the examiners will be present in person to watch the candidate at work, so that marks can be awarded for the workmanship displayed during the examination and for the quality of the finished products at the end.

It will be seen that, in competent hands, marks can be earned which can add up to a high percentage. On the other hand, marks can be lost for avoidable faults, which may mean that the student may only just pass, or most disappointingly just fail. It will not be out of place, therefore, to study the points which, if neglected, can well mean the difference between success and failure.

Written.—The student will find that the written examination comes first, the date being synchronized throughout the country. He will be notified in good time of the day, time and place of the examination;

he should take note of the details and present himself in good time, so that he may feel composed. He will take with him his favourite pen, and the receipt for his examination fee.

It is a first-rate philosophy to determine to do one's best, for nobody could possibly do more; out of this philosophy will come a certain amount of composure and a clarity of mind that will enable the candidate to avoid many mistakes in attempting the written paper.

The first requirement will be to fill in details on a form attached to the ruled foolscap paper provided. This should be done neatly and legibly, and here the official receipt will be necessary for the number on it will be required.

When carefully reading the paper it will be seen that each question is not generally concerned with one aspect of a single subject, but rather posed so that the student may have the opportunity of showing his knowledge on the whole subject-matter of the question. Here is an example from a previous paper:

'Explain fully the difference between wheatmeals and germ meals. Why is it customary to make brown breads on a short process?'

It will be noted that in the answer the student will be expected not only to know the difference in the composition of the meals, but the effects of the constituent parts on the fermentation process. From this he will be able to finish the question by stating the reasons for the shorter process. This will not be difficult for those who have applied themselves to their studies.

It is well for the student to know that those who set the questions are kindly human beings who have no desire to set catch questions, but rather to give the conscientious student an opportunity of showing his knowledge on a particular subject. The examiners themselves are qualified people, and have been through many examinations, so that they have a fellow feeling for those who are just beginning.

The student, however, must read the questions carefully and understand them fully before starting to write. Nothing can be worse than to spend 30 min. on a brilliant little answer to a question only to find afterwards that the question has been completely misunderstood. The writer once remembers spending 30 min. on an examination question asking for the source, processing and description of three dried fruits used in the baking industry. It was after the examination that it was explained that peel is not a dried but a candied fruit, thus a third of the possible marks were lost.

Out of the questions from which to select, there is always one or more that is just to one's liking, and it is a good idea, after making sure that it is fully understood, to start on the favourite first. It will be found that after finishing it, the brain is attuned to the task in hand and that there is such a sense of satisfaction in completing one question, that the second is speedily commenced.

All writing should be neat and legible and care should be taken with spelling; never clip words, for example 'marge' for margarine, or use such abbreviations as b.p. for baking-powder. Punctuate sentences properly and do not be afraid of paragraphing, so that the paper looks neat and tidy rather than like a long monotonous screed covering line after line of the paper.

Time also must be carefully studied, or it will be found that questions in the first part of the paper may be over-answered at the expense of those that follow.

To sum up, try to put yourselves in the place of the person who will mark your paper, and imagine your own pleasure when out of many papers, a neat, legible, easy-to-read paper is before you. Like the people who set the paper, those who mark them are human too!

Practical.—For the practical examination the student should enter the bakery in good time, bringing with him his official receipt, class recipe book, a pencil and notebook and his white protective clothing, together with any articles that he may have been instructed to bring.

When the time draws near for the start of the examination, the candidate, in company with his fellows, will hear read out the conditions and rules under which the examination is to be held. The examiners will introduce themselves in a friendly way, showing themselves to be kindly and reasonable people provided that the students play the game and conform to the spirit of the conditions and rules laid down.

The student will receive the examination paper before the date set for the examination. He will be required to answer all the questions. Recipes, therefore, will have to be set out so that the work can be carried out efficiently.

The calculations will be necessary. If, for instance, the paper asks for four white loaves to be weighed in at 1 lb., this obviously will need 4 lb. of dough. The student's own recipe may be for three loaves; therefore he will need to adjust his own formula so that he will have enough dough for four loaves. Similarly, the confectionery paper may ask for three madeira cakes to be 1 lb. each when baked; his own recipe may have a yield of four cakes, and again he will need to make the necessary weight adjustments. Planning is also necessary in the order of making and baking. If the student decides, for instance, on a white bread dough with a fermentation time of 2 hr., then obviously it will need to be made before a wheatmeal dough with a bulk fermentation time of 1½ hours, which in turn will be made before germ bread that must be made up and put straight into tins.

When he is satisfied that his calculations are correct, and he has decided on the order of making, this should be recorded in his notebook so that it may be seen by the examiner.

When studying the paper, the student will notice that up to 20% of the marks can be awarded for manipulation, general skill, neatness of work and correct quantities of flour and other ingredients used, and 80% for the quality and finish of the goods produced.

Before the practical work begins, the student will do well to turn up his sleeves and wash his hands.

Weighing of raw materials should be done carefully and accurately; all materials should be weighed and assembled before mixing is begun. Dough-making, knocking back and scaling times should be carefully recorded in the notebook, so that any question from the examiners on these points can be promptly answered.

Do not take too much notice of what the other fellow is doing; always remember that he may be doing his job in a different but equally correct manner. On the other hand he may be completely wrong as you yourself will be if you copy him. Strive for systematic neatness and care in all that is done, and keep the mind on the task in hand.

When everything is baked and finished, the table-top scrubbed and clean, and all utensils washed, dried and put away, the bread or cakes produced are then carefully and neatly arranged on the table. The student's number is appended, so that the examiners will know whose work is being marked.

If the student has done his very best he can be sure that the examiners will be aware of it. If he has shown himself a clean and efficient workman, then up to 20% of the marks are already his; if in addition the quality and finish of the goods are of high standard, then up to 80% of the marks are his also.

As with the Basic Bakery examination, the papers for the two Advanced Craft practical examinations are sent to the candidate before the dates set. The papers have questions from which the candidate can select a stated number.

Requisition forms are also provided on which the student is required to fill in the calculated requirements of raw materials for the items that he has chosen to make.

This requirement underlines the necessity for the student at all times to make certain during class work, that *all* relevant information regarding items of bread and flour confectionery are recorded in the recipe books which are allowed to be used during the practical examinations.

The student should remember that if he passes, his teachers will be just as pleased as he is, for they have taken him step by step on the way.

BIBLIOGRAPHY

ALLINSON, T. R. *The Whole Wheat Story*.
BANFIELD, W. T. *Manna*. London: Maclaren, 1948.
BENNION, E. *Breadmaking*. Oxford: O.U.P., 1954.
——. *A Primer on Breadmaking*. Oxford: O.U.P., 1951.
BENNION, E., and STEWART, J. *Cakemaking*. London: Leonard Hill, 1943.
BLANDY, J. *The Baker's Guide*. London: Newton and Eskell, 1899.
CRANG, B. A. *Preserves for all Occasions*. London: Penguin, 1944.
DANIEL, A. *Bakery Materials and Methods*. London: Maclaren, 1953.
——. *Up-to-Date Confectionery*. London: Maclaren, 1953. (Revised 1965)
FANCE, W. J., and WRAGG. *Up-to-Date Breadmaking*. London: Maclaren, 1968.
HANNEMAN and MARSHALL. *Cake Design and Decoration*. London: Maclaren, 1954.
HARRIS, H. G., and BORELLA, S. P. *All About Pastries*. London: Maclaren, about 1907.
——, ——. *All about Genoese, Petits Fours and Bon-Bons*. London: Maclaren, about 1907.
IRONS, J. R. *Breadcraft*. London: Virtue, 1948.
JAGO, W. *Principles of Breadmaking*. London: Maclaren (Revised Edition), 1946.
KENT-JONES, D. W., and AMOS, A. J. *Modern Cereal Chemistry*. Liverpool: Northern Publishing Co. Ltd., 1947.
KENT-JONES, D. W., and PRICE, J. *The Practice and Science of Breadmaking*. Liverpool: Northern Publishing Co., 1934.
KIRKLAND, J. *Modern Baker, Confectioner and Caterer*. London: Gresham Publishing Co., 1924.
LYLE, O. *Technology for Sugar Refining Workers*. London: Chapman & Hall, 1941.
MINISTRY OF FOOD. *Manual of Nutrition*. London: H.M.S.O., 1955.
RANKIN, W. M., and HILDRETH, E. M. *Intermediate Domestic Science* (Part I). London: Allmann, 1952.
RENSHAW, JOHN. *Marzipan*. Mitcham: John Renshaw, Ltd., 1951.
RICHTER, V. *Vienna Bread*. London: Maclaren, 1951.
RUSSELL, J. *Creative Cake Decoration*. London: Leonard Hill, 1957.
SHEPPARD, R., and NEWTON, E. *The Story of Bread*. London: Routledge, 1957.
SIMMONS, O. *The Book of Bread*. London: Maclaren, 1903.

FLOUR CONFECTIONERY

URIE, A., and HULSE, J. H. *The Science, Raw Materials and Hygiene of Baking*. London: Macdonald & Evans, 1952.
VINE, F. T. *Practical Breadmaking*. London: 'Baker & Confectioner', 1897.
——. *Savoury Pastry*. London: 'Baker & Confectioner', 1900.
WHYMPER, R. *Staleness in Bread*.

JOURNALS, ETC.

Arkady Review.
Baker.
Baker & Confectioner.
Bakers' Review.
Baking and Confectionery Craft.
British Baker.
Bulletins of Messrs. Craigmillar and British Creameries Ltd.
Bulletins of Messrs. Hedley Ltd.
Newsletters of the Association of Bakery Teachers.
Reports of the British Baking Industries Research Association.

INDEX